The Last King of Paradise

Eugene Burns has also written

THEN THERE WAS ONE
The *U. S. S. Enterprise* and the First Year of War
(Harcourt, Brace & Co., 1944)

Eugene Burns

The
Last King of
Paradise

Pellegrini & Cudahy
New York

To Olga

Contents

Part One

Of Dark Hearts (*Na puuwai Eleele*) 1836–1857

Part Two

Part Three

Contents ix

Part **Four**

Alas! Broken Are My Hands *(Auwe! Mo ' ku'u Lima!)*
1887–1891

Author's Note

I went to Hawaii as a park ranger. Due to the Islands' isolation I found the plant and animal life strange and unrelated to anything I knew in our mainland parks. Discovering the many new species was exciting—but not nearly so exciting as finding the new culture of the remnant native Polynesians, rapidly dying out. An urge to record that fast disappearing culture and, in a slight measure to do what I could to preserve it, prompted me to put together *The Last King of Paradise,* as a biography of Hawaii.

Almost immediately in my reading I found that very little of Hawaii's current literature was based upon fact—writer after writer had skimmed the surface and added a frill here and dropped an essential fact there, and "under azure skies" Honolulu became a romantic goody-goody city while actually it was one of the toughest ports in the world, what with a foreign male population outnumbering the native two to one when the whaling fleet was in! So I went to the original sources and for four years did nothing but read the old manuscripts—many of them faded handpress copies. Gradually the true story of old Hawaii emerged.

In collecting my material, I soon found that fact is seldom objective, uncolored, in the minds of the living. Each person

adds or subtracts from the true event to suit his own ego.
Besides, the Polynesian, in his effort to be a good host, agrees
with his guest on any subject. Admire his calabash bowl and
say: "This is a beautiful bowl; it must be an heirloom, perhaps a hundred years old," and the host, although he carved
it the previous week, will agree: "Indeed, it is just one hundred years old," and, more than likely, the guest will find
the bowl among his belongings when he arrives home.

As Hawaii's dim past came into sharper focus with my
reading, the outline of *The Last King of Paradise* emerged.
Almost unconsciously I knew that I must describe the culture
which grew naturally out of land and sea and sky, and how
it met the white man's civilization head on, and lost; and
that I would find a native leader who tried to hold off the
inevitable as best he could and lead his people back. I found
him in David Kalakaua, the last king of the Hawaiian Islands.

So, *The Last King of Paradise* is a product of original
sources. In not one instance did I trust to rewritten material
or belated interviews, easier though that might have been.
Instead I read the faded letters, journals, early newspapers,
books, pamphlets, documents, and consulate records of the
very date that the event happened. As a result, I can vouch
for every character in *The Last King of Paradise*, and there
are more than a hundred, and every incident—strange and
fantastic as some may seem—and support all this with historical records.

To present the whole picture of the Polynesian way of
life in *The Last King of Paradise*, I found myself recording
events though I knew they would shock and offend some
readers—such as brother-sister mating; David Kalakaua's pray-
to-death-ritual of his own sister; Chieftess Liliha's prophetic
curse on the Kamehamehas; and David's sex education in
adolescence, when he was taught the Polynesian art of inter-

course by his grandmother, even to the use of aphrodisiacs.

For the student who wishes to pursue further some of the fabulous events: The minute book of the Hale Naua society is in Public Archives in Iolani Palace grounds, within a dozen steps of the very spot where the males rolled the ball of twine in front of the naked females; the incidents at the Cookes' school may be gleaned from the records in the Mission House library (but do not trust the book of the Chiefs' Children's School, which was published privately for the descendants of Juliette and Amos Cooke, because that is expurgated). Monsarrat's seduction of the Princess Victoria is a matter of U. S. State Department record, painstakingly recorded almost to the last detail by the American consul in Hawaii. King Kalakaua's somewhat indiscreet offer of marriage between his little niece Kaiulani and the Japanese prince is a matter of record in the Public Archives; the king's fantastic trip around the world can be read in the newspaper clippings of the day, although all official accounts gently skirt the matter of the bibulous Baron Robert von Oehlhoffen as a member of the party. The hilarious coronation scene, which came ten years too late, can be read in the many private letters of that period. The impossible fertilizer-ship navy, with an admiral aboard who traded muskets and powder for gin, can be read in a comic operetta of the day together with the more serious diplomatic exchange of letters with foreign governments including Prince Bismarck's threat of war. The Edison phonograph record of King Kalakaua's voice, taken on his deathbed in the Palace Hotel, San Francisco, can be seen in the Bishop Museum, together with the restored crown which had been broken up after King Kalakaua's death by a group of pilfering soldiers and the largest diamond had been pried out and sent to a soldier's sweetheart in Oklahoma (the record of that trial can be read in the Territorial

Archives of Hawaii). But the student must not stop here, for
other letters and journals are in the Queen Emma Museum,
the Hilo Public Library, the University of Hawaii Library,
and Tice Phillips' collection of Hawaiian pamphlets. Here
will be found clues to new material.

With the wealth of material unearthed, it was a constant
temptation to digress in *The Last King of Paradise,* but the
book would have grown too far beyond reasonable limits. For
example, I might have told how Mark Twain was carried on
a stretcher to the Queen's hospital and there interviewed
survivors of the sailing ship *Hornet* which burned at sea off
Peru. They made an open-sea voyage to Hawaii which far
surpassed the exploits of Captain Bligh of *Bounty* fame.
(Bligh, incidentally, visited Hawaii much earlier on Captain
George Vancouver's ship). Or I could have told of a wonderful though abominably written heroic couplet of Robert
Louis Stevenson in which he proves to a drinking crony that
he cannot write in this style—and proves his point con-
clusively.

Throughout *The Last King of Paradise,* the spelling of
place names has been modernized—Owhyhee is Hawaii, Hido
is Hilo, Whytiti is Waikiki, and Hono-roo-roo is Honolulu.
However, I have kept such names as Grog Street (Nuuanu)
and Cape Horn, the whorehouse district, which got its name
from the saying that all sailors who came to Hawaii hung
their consciences on the Horn coming 'round, and then
picked them up again on the way back to staid New England.
Also, I used words in Hawaiian chants and conversation which
I felt closely reflected the Polynesian feeling. For example,
in Hawaii there is no such word or thought as adultery. It
was a common practice and such conjugal flirtations were
known as "mischievous sleepings." However, there was this
difference: the female usually selected her mate for the oc-

casion. And so, even the missionaries who translated the Bible into Hawaiian had to content themselves by saying: *"Thou shalt not commit mischievous sleeping!"*

The nicest thing about an *Author's Note* is that it provides an opportunity to make acknowledgments, and I have many. My first thanks go to the Hawaiian staff of the Public Archives of Hawaii under the able direction of Archivist Maude Jones, whose mother was an intimate of Queen Emma, and her assistant, Henrietta Robinson Holt, both island-born, who gave me needed help cheerfully for six years; the valued friendship and lore of the great Hawaiian scholar and teacher, Mary Kawena Pukui of the Bishop Museum, Honolulu, whose ancestors were Polynesian *kahunas* and chanters. Mary not only directed me to valuable source material in the Bishop Museum but also read manuscript for its Hawaiian content and history (and I shall always be grateful for the tears that came to her eyes when she read my chant of Kamehameha and said: "Gene, you are the first white man who has truly captured the feeling of the Polynesian"). I owe a great deal to the historical and anthropological authorities, Ralph S. Kuykendall of the University of Hawaii, author of the scholarly history, *The Hawaiian Kingdom, 1778–1854;* Sir Peter Buck of Yale University, Director of the Bishop Museum, who made suggestions and unknotted difficult problems; the ever-ready help of Mrs. Violet A. Silverman who never failed to answer such poisonous questions as: "When were mosquitoes brought into Hawaii?", "Was there Hennessy brandy in Hawaii in 1836?", "When was barbed wire introduced?"

My job as foreign correspondent with the Associated Press gave me an interesting living, although many anxious hours while carrying parts of this manuscript in the back of my shirt during bomb- and bullet-filled action aboard the USS Enterprise, with the first division of Marines on Guadalcanal, and with the Army and Navy in the Aleutians, Central Pacific and India. I want to thank Maxine Starks, Dorothy Fantasia, Ah Jook Leong, Dorothy Linehan, and Olga Mihailovna Frinsko, who labored heroically through "hurry up" hours; Florence Graves Strong who read the MS and made valuable suggestions; Sheila Cudahy, Nannine Joseph, and Helen Christine Bennett who helped edit and shape it for publication; my twin daughters Carol and Stephanie, seven, who in their eagerness to help occasionally got tangled up in their manuscript; and my wife, Olga, who knows how to mix old-fashioneds, arrange flowers, fry chicken, play the piano, make critical analyses and read proof, and who has put up with my unpredictable hours, day and night, for fourteen years.

Sausalito,   Eugene Burns.
California

List of Major Figures in The Last King of Paradise

DAVID KALAKAUA (*Kah-lah-kow-ah*), King of Hawaii, 1874–1891.

AIKANAKA (*Eye-kah-nah-kah*), high-born chief, seer, ancestor of DAVID KALAKAUA.

AKI, Chinese rice planter, who paid KING KALAKAUA a seventy-one-thousand dollar opium bribe.

WILLIAM NEVINS ARMSTRONG, missionary's son, lawyer, morale-keeper of KING KALAKAUA on the world-girdling cruise.

VOLNEY V. ASHFORD, Reform Party member and Royalist.

ROBERT HOAPILI BAKER, member of KING KALAKAUA's household troops.

PRINCESS BERNICE PAUAHI PAKI BISHOP (*Pow-ah-hee Pah-key*), wife of Customs Clerk CHARLES R. BISHOP.

JOHN W. BLOSSOM, Jamaica Negro, alleged father of DAVID KALAKAUA.

JOHN E. BUSH, gin-drinking friend of KING KALAKAUA, Minister Plenipotentiary to Samoa, who nearly provoked Germany to declare war on Hawaii.

ALEXANDER JOY CARTWRIGHT, one of the founders of American baseball and an organizer of the seditious Committee of Thirteen.

WILLIAM RICHARDS CASTLE, missionary's son and an organizer of the treasonable Citizens' League.

ARCHIBALD S. CLEGHORN, consort of PRINCESS LIKELIKE, brother-in-law of KING KALAKAUA.

AMOS STARR COOKE, missionary, founder of the Chiefs' Children's School, and businessman.

JULIETTE MONTAGUE COOKE, wife of AMOS, and teacher of kings.

JOHN CUMMINS, bon vivant, friend of KING KALAKAUA.

SANFORD BALLARD DOLE, lawyer and reformer.

JOHN DOMINIS, consort of PRINCESS LILIUOKALANI and Governor of Oahu.

COLONEL THOMAS DRYER, PRESIDENT LINCOLN'S Commissioner to Hawaii.

QUEEN EMMA, wife of KAMEHAMEHA IV, reared by DR. THOMAS C. B. ROOKE.

WALTER MURRAY GIBSON, adventurer, Premier of Hawaii, planner of the Empire of Oceania.

WILLIAM LOTHIAN GREEN, English-born businessman, statesman.

HAAHEO (Ha-ah-hay-oh), Chieftess, Governor of Maui, foster mother of DAVID KALAKAUA.

CURTIS P. IAUKEA (E-ow-kay-ah), KING KALAKAUA'S Grand Chamberlain.

COUNT KAORU INOUYE, Japanese Foreign Minister who tried to negotiate a treaty of federation with Hawaii.

GEORGE E. GRIDLEY JACKSON, reform school superintendent, Admiral of Hawaii's Navy.

CHARLES HASTINGS JUDD, Grand Chamberlain, who tried to keep KING KALAKAUA on the straight and narrow on his world cruise and fortunately failed.

GERRIT P. JUDD, missionary, statesman.

JUNIUS KAAE (Kah-ah-ay), sorcerer, bribe-promoter.

PRINCESS KAIULANI (*Ki-uh-lah-knee*), daughter of KING KALA-KAUA's sister and the only recognized child born to the KALAKAUA dynasty.

KALAMA (*Kah-lah-mah*), favorite among the five wives of KING KAMEHAMEHA III.

KAMEHAMEHA III (*Kay-may-hah-may-hah*), King of Hawaii, 1825–1854, son of KAMEHAMEHA THE GREAT.

KAMEHAMEHA IV (*Alexander*), King of Hawaii, 1854–1863. Hot-tempered son of GOVERNOR KEKUANAOA of Oahu and CHIEFTESS KINAU, Premier of Hawaii.

KAMEHAMEHA V (*Lot*), King of Hawaii, 1863–1872, son of GOVERNOR KEKUANAOA.

PRINCESS VICTORIA KAMAMALU (*Kah-mah-mah-lu*), Premier, pretty sister of kings and betrothed of DAVID KALAKAUA.

KAMANAWA (*Kah-mah-nah-wah*), grandfather of DAVID KALA-KAUA, first chief hanged in the Islands.

CAESAR KAPAAKEA (*Kah-pah-ah-kay-ah*), boy husband of ANE KEOHOKALOLE and possible father of DAVID KALAKAUA.

KAPIOLANI (*Kah-pee-oh-lah-knee*), Queen of Hawaii, wife of DAVID KALAKAUA.

MATTHEW KEKUANAOA (*Kay-kuh-ah-nah-oh-ah*), Governor of Oahu, keeper of the fort.

ANE KEOHOKALOLE (*Ah-nay Kay-oh-hoh-kay-loh-lay*), noble chieftess, mother of DAVID KALAKAUA.

KINAU (*Key-now*), one of KAMEHAMEHA II's wives, female co-ruler with KAMEHAMEHA III, wife of KEKUANAOA, mother of kings.

PRINCESS LIKELIKE (*Lee-kay-lee-kay*), prayed-to-death sister of KING KALAKAUA.

LILIHA (*Lee-lee-hah*), Governor of Oahu, owner of Hono-lulu's first commercialized bawdy house, protector of DAVID KALAKAUA.

PRINCESS LILIUOKALANI (*Lee-lee-uh-oh-kah-lah-knee*), sister of KING KALAKAUA, Queen Regent during his round-the-world trip. Last Queen of Hawaii.

WILLIAM LUNALILO *(Lew-nah-lee-loh)*, King of Hawaii, 1872–1874, heavy drinker.

MELE *(May-lay)*, a bedmate of KING KALAKAUA.

GENERAL WILLIAM MILLER, British Consul General to Hawaii.

MARCUS CUMMINS MONSARRAT, banished seducer of DAVID KALAKAUA's betrothed, PRINCESS VICTORIA.

CELSO CAESAR MORENO, Italian adventurer, promoter, flatterer and politician.

PRINCE MOSES, brother of KINGS ALEXANDER and LOT, unregenerate Governor of Kauai.

MUTSUHITO, Emperor of Japan, 1852–1912, who launched Japan on her first "Greater East Asia Co-prosperity Sphere" and treated the visiting KING KALAKAUA as an equal.

BARON ROBERT VON OEHLHOFFEN, bibulous companion of KING KALAKAUA, butler, food taster and "poet laureate."

ROBERT WAIPA PARKER *(Wy-pah)*, lieutenant in KING KALAKAUA's army.

LORD GEORGE PAULET, British naval officer who administered the Hawaiian islands for one hundred and fifty-five days.

PRINCESS RUTH, high-born chieftess, one of the last of the KAMEHAMEHA dynasty.

GEORGE RYAN, soldier of fortune, despoiler of Hawaii's crown.

CLAUS SPRECKELS, financier, sugar king of the Hawaiian Islands.

ADMIRAL RICHARD THOMAS, British Naval Officer, who restored the Hawaiian Islands to their native rulers.

LORRIN THURSTON, grandson of missionary ASA THURSTON,

king-hater, prime organizer of the treasonable Citizens' League.

TUTU *(Tew-tew)*, aged grandmother of DAVID KALAKAUA, who gave him his first lessons in sexual intercourse.

GINA WILCOX *(Princess Victoria Colonna di Stigliano)* Italian-born wife of Robert Wilcox.

ROBERT WILLIAM WILCOX, part-Hawaiian military student in Italy, Hawaiian patriot.

JAMES H. WODEHOUSE, British Commissioner, who tried to forestall American annexation of the Kingdom of Hawaii.

Prologue

The Polynesian civilization, which spread over ten million square miles of the Pacific, reached its apex in the Hawaiian Islands.

At least fourteen centuries before the white man arrived, the Polynesians discovered these isolated volcanic islands which are the summits of the greatest mountain range in the world, towering 32,000 feet above the deep ocean floor.

The ancestors of these copper-colored sons of the sea, earth and sky moved into the Pacific just about the time Christ was born in Bethlehem. Their language, legends, customs, and handicrafts show a close kinship with the East—Malaya, India, Arabia, and perhaps even the Mediterranean. The *Kon-tiki's* crew recently drifted on a balsa-raft into South Pacific islands from Peru to test a theory that the Polynesians, too, might have come from South America. It might be claimed as well that the Polynesians came from North America, China, or Africa. Seasonally, glass balls float in from Japan; fir logs from British Columbia, Canada; and giant cocoanuts from Madagascar. No one really knows where the Polynesians came from.

Their social structure was feudal—an upper class of deified chiefs, a lower of commoners. The priests, navigators, and expert craftsmen were close-grouped with the lesser chiefs. The chiefs owned the land and the commoners were the vassals. An ambitious chief, occasionally, tried to combine the islands under his rule; none, however, was successful until Kamehameha the Great (1758–1819), who got the help of white men.

Polynesians were great sailors and always lived by the sea or where they could see it. The men provided food; the women made bark-cloth clothing and took care of the children. Life was leisurely, in the main.

The hundreds of Polynesian gods were always near, and were asked for help in catching fish, building a house, or in making a chief's feather cloak. A *Kapu* system was part of this religion, keeping sacred things apart from the common. For example, commoners were forbidden to stand in the presence of a chief, who was part-god.

Polynesian legend says that the first white man to see Hawaii was a ship-wrecked sailor. However, the unmistakable imprint of the white man was left by the English navigator, James Cook, in 1778, two years after our Declaration of Independence. When he came ashore, the Polynesians fell to the ground and worshipped him as Lono, god of harvest. In turn, Cook and his men gave them gunpowder and syphilis which, within a few years, halved the population, then quartered it.

Other whites hastened the destruction of the yielding Polynesian civilization—a soft one compared to the white. Traders came from Russia, Spain, England, France and the United States to exploit them and exchange whiskey for pigs; carriages and silverware for sandalwood; gingham for fish; silk umbrellas for sex. A minor chief paid eight hundred dollars for a single mirror! Well-meaning missionaries, descendants of the Pilgrim Fathers, taught them to spell; to exchange shapeless Mother Hubbards for *tapa* wrap-arounds, prayer meetings for ceremonial dances, songs and chants; and took away their gods and tabus. What good the missionary might have done with his Christian doctrines was upset by tens of thousands of drinking, whoring whalers who wintered in these hospitable islands and took what they wanted.

The Hawaiian chiefs and rulers fought against these intrusions, and they might have prevailed except that the great sea-going powers fought for control of these islands which lay across their sea-lanes. At one time or another, British, Russian, French and American flags flew in Hawaii.

Part **One**

Of Dark Hearts (*Na Puuwai Eleele*) 1836–1857

1 A Royal Hawaiian Chief Is Born

The Royal Chieftess Ane of Hawaii was stretched out naked on her back, heels well apart, atop tier on tier of finely woven *Niihau* mats, awaiting the birth of a child who was, as events fell out, someday to rule the Polynesian kingdom. Grandmother Tutu, who had cared for Ane since she was six months gone with child, carefully ran her oiled palms over Ane's majestic belly to position the child for birth. Like others of Hawaiian nobility, Ane Keohokalole was large, nearly six feet tall, and heavy. She weighed two hundred and sixty-six pounds. Although her suffering was great, she balled her sweaty fists and not a sound escaped her. An outcry heard by those gathered in her courtyard would have disgraced her forever.

Near the white sand beach with its leaning coconut trees, Ane's house rose from a hill outside Honolulu. Tied with twine made of bark, its grass walls mounted loftily to hewn beams and rafters, thirty feet above so that the rooms might be cool during the hottest days. There were two others in Ane's room, Ane's boy husband, Caesar Kapaakea, and the powerful rich Chieftess Haaheo, Governor of the island of Maui. Huddled on *lauhala* mats, the fifteen-year-old Caesar was writhing in even greater agony than his wife. When

3

Ane's pains began, Tutu had sung chants to *Ku,* strongest of the medical gods, to transfer the major pains to the husband—even though he was not, according to Ane, the baby's father. The man who had sired the unborn, said Ane, was King Kamehameha III, ruler of the Islands, called *Akua*—god—by his subjects.

As Ane's labor advanced, the Maui Chieftess rubbed her nose against the woman's wet cheek. "Ane, the gods are attending you. From your fertile stomach our land lives anew."

Earlier that afternoon, when the water had broken from Ane's womb, Haaheo had sent runners to summon the Hawaiian populace and the high ranking chiefs to attend the birth: the more rank present, the more auspicious the infant's launching. Among those summoned were Liliha Boki, widow of the former governor of Oahu; Kinau, widow of the late King Kamehameha II and now Premier and co-ruler of the Islands with the present King; Queen Kalama, the young King's favorite among his five wives; Hoapili-wahine, revered widow of King Kamehameha I; and Governor Matthew Kekuanaoa of Oahu, Kinau's present husband and father of the King and Prince Alexander, King-designate.

As the shadows lengthened, Tutu and Haaheo made excuses to step out to the doorway—which was flanked by Ane's daylight-burning torches—to scan the sky for a portent from the god of light and life. But search as they might, the clear blue sky held no promise of thunder and lightning. The only hope of a sign was that the trade wind had gentled into a whisper caught in the tousled crowns of the palms, and the still air had become oppressively heavy.

Indoors, Ane's house remained cool. It was royally full of treasured mats, calabashes, *poi* pounders, feathered cloaks, *kahili** staffs, and serving-boards large enough to hold whole *imu*-cooked hogs.

To forestall questions about the hoped-for omen, Tutu spoke softly of the day's affairs, events of concern to the nobility—the schools of red fish in the harbor, the fencing matches of King Kamehameha and visiting naval officers, and the important conference between the King and his chiefs with Lord Edward Russell regarding the appalling but possible cession of the islands to England.

Before giving the order to extinguish Ane's daylight-burning torches, Chieftess Haaheo again studied the heavens. The sun had already walked its course down the slope of the Waianae mountains and disappeared into the bronzed sea. Haaheo lowered her eyes to the people gathered in the courtyard. They, too, were watching for a sign, and murmured among themselves. To escape their questioning glances, Haaheo hurried back into the house.

Night fell with tropical suddenness upon Honolulu's fort, palace, and the masts of three hundred whaling barques, arrived from the fog-girt Aleutians. The bell at the white coral-stone fort tolled. Before its vibrations ceased, the town crier's voice rose clearly: "Seven o'clock and all is well in Honolulu. Chieftess Ane Keohokalole is giving birth to a child. The Chiefs are in conference with Lord Edward Russell. Seven o'clock. All is well in Honolulu."

At the crier's call, a native lamplighter with a flaming torch started upon his route from Fair Haven harbor, along Grog Street, the main thoroughfare which reflected the varied life of the islands. The lower end of Grog Street—known as Cape Horn—matched the record of any seaport for disso-

---

* A *kahili* is a long ivory-handled pole decorated at one end with a cluster of feather plumes. The taller the *kahili*, the higher the chief's standing.

luteness, while the upper end held fine homes, owned by prosperous consuls, successful business men and missionaries. In between flourished the activities of a trading port catering to thousands of whalers: ships' chandlers, whorehouses, grog shops, dance halls, a bakery, bowling alleys, a barber shop, hotels, trading posts, coffee houses, a newspaper press, and a native Congregational church.

Along the way the lamplighter stopped at Butler's coffee house for his drink of Pere's applejack.

"Ane Keohokalole, you hear, going to have a baby tonight?" he asked eagerly of four Yankees who sat drinking brandy. No one replied, so he sat with ears open, listening. A brown girl with a pink parasol, stepping daintily past, aroused laughter. A pink parasol was the sign of the favor of a certain old, retired sea dog. Following her, a second brown girl met respectful nods. The lamplighter knew her, daughter of Captain Oliver Holmes, once Governor of Oahu and father of seven girls. [The American poet and novelist Oliver Wendell Holmes was named for this uncle.] Two men, clad in the black garb of Congregational missionaries went by in silence. The missionaries had abetted the King in driving two Catholic priests from the Island, and had approved Premier Kinau's order that all Catholic believers should be thrown into prison at hard labor, and those who persisted should be rolled in human dung until they renounced their Popish religion. As a result France had threatened to seize Hawaii, as she had Tahiti; and to forestall this, King Kamehameha III was now seeking a compact with England.

The talk at Butler's had veered to the expected baby.

"If it comes," chuckled an old sailor, "we'll see somethin'. Last time royalty here had a baby there was a parade. One of the princesses jumped off her litter and peeled off her clothes. That meant all females of the same rank or less had to do likewise. Must have been hundreds of them naked as radishes. Never saw so much meat in my life!"

A noisy gang of sailors staggered out of a grog shop and went storming down the street, laughing, cursing, singing. Holding a blanket like a drumhead, a group hurled a naked Hawaiian girl into the air. The lamp showed the girl struggling, arms and legs whirling as they tossed her and sang:

> "Oh Molly Ann is a brown Hawaiian
> Way, aye! Roll and go.
> She drinks rum and chews terbacker!
> Spend my money on Molly Ann!"

Finally the drunken men tumbled down in a heap.

The girl got up and one of the sailors offered her a drink from a square-faced gin bottle. She refused. When he slopped it over her, she grabbed the bottle, filled her mouth with gin and spat it out at him. The man struck her full in the mouth with his fist. Others yanked him off, and, again bouncing the naked, hysterical brown girl, now bleeding from the mouth, they continued on to Sea Street until they got to their ship, where the girl would be raped and tattooed to their liking, as others had been before her, and released the next morning, if she were fortunate.

Scarcely had the roistering mob left when a surrey imported from London drove through the street, followed by a company of thirty retainers and a swarm of naked children. It held Madame Liliha Boki, who had visited England a dozen years before, and had been the toast of British society. She was a tall, strikingly beautiful woman in her late twenties; her shining black hair had been stiffened with egg-whites and combed into a high pompadour. Her bare feet protruded from under the full skirt of an imported velvet dress which exposed her full breasts. A French poodle

nestled in her lap. The slender, regal Liliha, head of Oahu's
first house of prostitution, was about to become a mother—by
adoption. Ane Keohokalole had promised Liliha the unborn
descendant of Aikanaka, the man-eater.

As Liliha's retinue turned into Exchange Street, a runner came down Grog Street, shouting the coming of Queen
Kalama. Surrounded by a phalanx of fifty retainers robed in
rare cloaks* made of prized red and gold feathers, the young
Queen, the King's favorite, rode in an elegant barouche. An
attendant alongside carried a huge damask umbrella orna-
mented with gilding and golden tassels. On either side ran
two men, clad only in loincloths, who bore feathered kahili
staffs eight feet long. As the carriage passed, all natives hum-
bled themselves by removing an article of clothing. Those
wearing only a loincloth dropped that to their ankles and
stood naked.

Following the Queen came the King's runner, shouting
at the top of his lungs: *"A-ku-a! Akua. Noho, noho!"* Noisy
Grog Street suddenly hushed. Even the music in the bawdy
houses stopped. This was the King! Every native prostrated.
Should any Hawaiian's shadow fall athwart the King, the offender would be whipped to death on the spot. First came
four tall kahili-bearers. Flaming torches borne by a hundred
natives illumined the noble figure of the tall king, astride
a magnificent stallion. Running beside him were spittlebearers carrying dark, polished bowls filled with aromatic
crushed leaves. These spittle-bowls were closely guarded, for

---

* A few of these cloaks are still in existence; the best collection is locked
in a vault in the Bishop Museum, Honolulu. These cloaks are valued in
excess of one million dollars. It took fifty of the tiny red and gold feathers
to cover a thumbnail and but two such feathers came from each tiny bird,
now extinct. Most cloaks took more than four generations to make. The color
yellow was reserved for Hawaii's royalty.

if an enemy were to get possession of a chief's spittle, finger-nail parings, or hair, it might mean the chief's death.

The King and his retinue moved on and word spread along Grog Street that he had not taken the road to Ane's home, although Liliha Boki and Queen Kalama were mounting, by different ways, the rise that led to the scene of the child-birth.

By this time, several thousand had gathered about the driveway and in the courtyard. In the light of the candlenut torches the bodies of the nut-brown Hawaiians shone against the bright red of the feather cloaks and helmets. Ranking chiefs were newly arriving with their retinues, dancers, chanters, and singers. And the coming of many more was heralded by flickering torches converging from valley and hillside upon Ane's estate.

From the driveway a stentorian female voice trumpeted: "Excrement of grass-fed cows! Pull steady. Steady, you diseased dogs. I'll whip every last bitch's son of you!"

Through the open door Ane heard, forgot her pains and relaxed her sweating fists. That bellow could come from but one pair of female lungs, those of the profane Kinau, greatest political power in the Islands. When the three-hundred-pound Premier got off her cart, she raised her purple skirt, showing yellow cami-knickers continuing the blouse gathered with a puckering string above her melony bosom.

Hardly had the commotion of her arrival subsided when a runner proclaimed: "Queen Kalama! Kneel! Remove a piece of your clothing!"

Haaheo heard and came to the doorway. When she saw Kalama, resentment flared within her. The Queen's attendants carried feathered kahilis only eight feet long; the special ceremonial thirty-foot feathered staffs had remained at the palace. This was a studied insult to Ane.

Loud enough for Haaheo to hear, Premier Kinau called to the young Queen: "Ane claims the King sired the child in her stomach. What say you, Kalama? He's your husband."

The Queen replied abruptly: "Ane lies. She wants to get added rank for her *keiki*. I have it from him who saw them locked, that this child of hers belongs to the Negro, John Blossom."

Chieftess Premier Kinau was delighted at the reply. This would keep the soon-to-be-born baby in his place; Ane and Haaheo were getting much too lofty.

The King's sister also came quickly to Queen Kalama's defense. "When I heard that this Ane Keohokalole claimed that my brother lay locked with her on the mats at Waikiki in preference to me, I asked him point-blank: 'Is it true?' and he told me: 'I remember no connection with her.' "

The Queen continued: "Had the King sired the babe, he would have been here tonight."

Liliha Boki, who had been promised the child, shifted her French poodle in her lap and said gently, "Who among us can say she has not slept mischievously with white men or black? In Paris, Negroes are preferred above white men. Look to your own skin, Queen Kalama. It is lighter far than Ane's. Your mother, too, took her pleasures wherever she chanced upon them."

The Premier gave a contemptuous laugh. "Cheeky talk, Liliha." She lowered her voice. "Quiet, here comes Haaheo!"

"Well you say 'Quiet'!" stormed Haaheo as she stalked out of Ane's house. "When the King's son, Lot Kamehameha, was born, who was selected to be his foster mother—the most important post in the family? Was it you, Kinau, whom the king discarded to embrace Kalama here? Was it you, Kalama, barren of children and cursed with the white man's disease? No, it was this selfsame Ane Keohokalole, descendant of Aikanaka, this Ane, now ripe with child!"

A sudden peal of thunder drowned all voices. Jagged lightning forked the sky and flashed into Punchbowl Crater, legendary home of the fire goddess *Pele*. It was the first thunder and lightning in Honolulu for eight months.

Governor Matthew Kekuanaoa approached the angry Haaheo. With simple dignity he presented a bolt of royalty's yellow silk. "Here, Haaheo, take this to Ane. Has the descendant of Aikanaka been born yet?"

Haaheo shook her head.

Queen Kalama said coldly: "Come, where is the sign of a chief's birth?"

In desperation Haaheo again searched the heavens. Then, after another burst of thunder and lightning brighter than the first, she found the stars near the southern horizon. She cried, "There is Ane's sign from the god *Kane,* our god of light and life! It is the Southern Cross, alone visible. By the light of these stars our ancestors set their course over three thousand miles of trackless seas and found Hawaii fourteen centuries ago. Tonight, the gods of heaven are guiding the spirit of our new chief from our ancient home. From Ane Keohokalole's stomach the bones of our forefathers will again have life!"

She looked scornfully at her audience, hoping to humble these haughty aristocrats. As she spoke there grew within her a desire to possess the child, to take him away from the corruption of Honolulu so that he would grow into a great chief who would destroy the white man's influence and rise above the rivalry of the royal Aikanaka and Kamehameha clans to unite all Hawaiians. With this thought she turned from the crowd and went back into the house to Ane.

Following the great Chieftess Haaheo's prophecy, there was a tense silence while the assemblage looked expectantly to Queen Kalama's ranking orator—who took precedence over all other chanters there—for the customary pre-birth recitation of the mother chief's glorious past. The orator, in turn, waited for the Queen's signal, but she made no sign for him to begin. In the silence, a white-haired Hawaiian, ignoring the Queen's chanter, began the old chant of Aikanaka, great and powerful forebear of Ane Keohokalole:

"High is the land of Kau,
    Blessed by the wind . . .

It is a calabash,
    Misty with long waves . . .

O look! Observe thy lands,
    Retain them, Child of the highest rank!

Overthrown are the foundations of lands . . .
    Overthrown on the coral rocks of Kau . . ."

Queen Kalama angrily screamed for the old man who had dared to defy her. As he crawled to her she struck at his head with a whip until his white hair was bloodied; then she commanded: "Away with this descendant of *iole**! Fill this rat's polluted mouth with salt and whip him as he walks tomorrow naked in the sun, until his breath is no more."

Within the bedroom, Ane's labor pains had begun in earnest. Grandmother Tutu, supporting her, walked her to and fro while the sweat streamed down Ane's face and body; but the only sound was the whimpering of the boy husband.

* *iole* means rat.

Then Tutu helped Ane to a kneeling position, knees wide apart, while Haaheo helped to support her back. Within thirty seconds, delivery was completed and Ane sank into the strong arms of Haaheo, gasping, "Tell me, is it a man child?"

"Certainly," exclaimed the delighted Haaheo.

"And his *ma'i**, is it long?"

"Indeed, *halala!*"

"Good, we will name the penis, Halala," said Ane, and closed her tired eyes.

As Haaheo cut the umbilical cord with a sharp ceremonial bamboo sliver from a god-blessed grove, she warned Tutu not to announce the birth as yet. She tied the cord with an *olona* string, leaving but two inches. The placenta she put in a calabash and ordered the boy-husband: "After I am gone, bury it secretly under the tree nearest the palace. The tree will be the babe's and he will be King! I myself shall prepare him for that office; he will save us."

With a piece of soft *tapa*, made from the velvety bark of the *mamani*, wound about her finger, she cleaned the infant's eyes tenderly. Finally she reached below her dress, took off her chamois-soft tapa underskirt and wrapped the infant in it, the true signal that he was a member of her ruling family of Maui. She could easily slip out on foot, unseen, and within reach were the homes of a score of members of her family. They would receive her, without question; she was Haaheo, Governor of Maui.

As a blinding flash of lightning split the dark heavens, she slipped out of the house with her precious babe well wrapped and protected. The future King was hers.

---

* Among Polynesians, the penis was more freely discussed than, say, the nose or eyes. Sexual parts were always given names. Thus the babe's *Halala*, which meant 'generous,' was to become celebrated in songs and dances—more than a hundred songs and hulas were dedicated to it.

2 Kalakaua's Naming Banquet

Early the next morning the silver-haired Chieftess, Hoapili-wahine*, who had arrived before the sun's rays entered the Punchbowl, sat upon many layers of Niihau mats spread on a wide settee in the courtyard outside Ane's home. In her lap lay the infant, which Haaheo had brought back for its naming ceremonies. Hoapili-wahine sat with her legs crossed, her back as straight as a ramrod, her head erect, a difficult pose for a woman of sixty-eight, but she carried it with great dignity. She wore a loose-fitting Mother Hubbard and her sole ornament bespoke her nobility: a finely woven human-hair necklace from which hung a whale-tooth hook.

The day was still cool and the wind from the sea, which she faced, was gentle. The rain had washed the air clean and sweet and the sky was cloudless. Behind Hoapili-wahine and the babe rose the high-forested Koolau mountains hemming in the sunflooded, rich Manoa valley, while before them, white-capped breakers rolled in a turquoise ocean.

* Hoapili-wahine's name meant, Wife of My-Beloved-Companion, bestowed by Kamehameha the Great. When the King died, thirteen years before this biography opens, Chief Hoapili, her husband, was delegated to cook the King's remains in a temple and to hide the bones in a cave. So well did Beloved Companion perform his duty that to this day the bones, with the customary surrounding valuables, have not been found. She was also one of the favorite wives of King Kamehameha the Great.

14

Hoapili-wahine's seat outdoors was an invitation for even commoners to see the baby. Had she remained within, only high ranking chiefs could have entered to present their gifts. By mid-morning she and the babe were surrounded with Chinese umbrellas, stone pounders, spears, a feather helmet, rolls of tapa, calabashes, gourds full of cooked foods, wooden platters, sweet potatoes, banana stalks, coconuts, fish, taro roots, and barrels of salmon sides—all gifts for the unnamed chief.

Liliha came early with her large gift-bearing retinue—scores of naked children, and beautiful dancing girls. Liliha was even more startlingly beautiful than her girls. Her luminous black eyes sparkled, and when she smiled her teeth gleamed, their whiteness intensified by her smooth golden-brown skin. It was no wonder that a dozen years ago, in London, she had been the toast of salon and soirée. Her way of piling her hair high and ornamenting it with fresh flowers had created a fashion which spread to the continent; her low-cut revealing neckline set a new style. Liliha's curves had remained pleasing and her maturity added to her royal dignity.

As Liliha left her carriage, Haaheo appeared and joined her. At Haaheo's first words Liliha waved back her retainers, and the two women walked out of earshot. Contrite, because she had stolen the baby on the previous night, Haaheo wept. In the long talk that followed she explained that she had planned never to return him, but that although she still wanted him, her resolution had weakened.

Liliha listened without comment. The rude behavior of Queen Kalama the night before, the absence of the King, the acrid speech of Chieftess Premier Kinau had convinced her that the life of this child would be an acute and prolonged struggle. When Ane had promised her the child, Liliha had not foreseen all this. Haaheo's home on the island of Maui would give the boy his chance, away from the quarrels of Aikanakas and Kamehamehas and the growing animosity of the white settlers. Haaheo was rich; her lands were much greater than her own. Then there was the sign—the Southern Cross so clearly visible and alone in the sky; unmistakably this babe was destined for greatness. She would give him up.

When Haaheo heard the decision she stammered, "But, will your blessing go with him, Liliha? Will you be his god-mother?"

"Of course," Liliha assured her. "Come, we are neglecting him." Together they approached Hoapili-wahine, and those in the courtyard stood aside respectfully as they passed.

For the infant to be held by the old Chieftess Haopili-wahine was a great honor. In the entire Polynesian kingdom, only three others could sit on her lap: Lot Kamehameha, six; Alexander Liholiho Kamehameha, two; and Princess Ruth, aged ten, daughter of Kinau and Governor Matthew Kekuanaoa. A native holding a Chinese umbrella shielded the baby's brown eyes from the brilliant sunlight while another kept off mosquitoes, recently arrived with the white man.

Liliha's entourage approached the aged Chieftess on hands and knees, with Liliha and Haaheo alone remaining erect, although even they removed an article of clothing. As gifts were presented, the noble Chieftess said simply: "Thank you. The newborn chief also says *mahalo nui!*" Liliha placed her golden feather *lei* around the child's neck, a sign of royalty, and the wrinkled little fellow squawled and relieved himself. Unperturbed, Hoapili-wahine got up and removed the wetted top layer of her many tapa skirts. By wetting her, the baby had forever established his rank as equal to hers.

Liliha spoke impulsively: "Hoapili-wahine, I have selected a nurse for the child." Without turning, she called: "Kailua! Kailua Excursion!"*

A buxom girl with hard-swelled breasts came forward.

"Put aside your babe and nurse this chief," commanded Liliha. Turning to Haaheo, she added: "Take her to Maui with you." She demanded of a retainer: "Where is Bijou?" When the French poodle was handed to her she said to Kailua: "When the babe is weaned, give your breasts to Bijou until you are dry. He will be the boy's companion-of-the-breast and his close protector."

Haaheo took the girl to her and impulsively removed one of her soft skirts and wrapped it about her. "Ah, blessed are you my child. Your strength will flow into this chief. You are now *kapu*—your body is sacred. No man can touch you and you must eat only with women." In token of the great charge, the Maui chieftess rubbed noses with the commoner, thereby giving her rank far above all the other retainers.

Noon was approaching. Obviously King Kamehameha III and Queen Kalama were ignoring the christening feast. But with Liliha present, Hoapili-wahine gave orders for the christening to begin. A member of Ane's household took his position between Ane's two daylight burning torches and blew on a conch. Immediately, the assemblage of over three thousand became quiet. A chanter appeared. He recited Ane's illustrious ancestry. Then he gave the even greater geneology of the foster mother, the great governor Haaheo of Maui, after which he announced:

* Polynesians frequently named children for historical events such as Lord's Supper—the first celebrated by the missionaries in Hawaii in 1820—just exactly 200 years after the landing of the Pilgrims in America. Another was named First Reader when schools opened. Thus, historical events can be established. Kailua Excursion, however, was named for a pleasant outing at which, presumably, the girl had been conceived.

"*Aloha*. Know this: the man child sitting in the lap of our most venerated Hoapili-wahine, is a sacred *alii* of the heated *kapu*, the prostrating *kapu*, the *wohi* of the standing *kahili*, the torch that burns in broad daylight. He is a true Chief. Make your obeisance." After all the spectators were prostrate, except for Haaheo, Liliha and Hoapili-wahine, he added: "Forevermore, this glorious Chief will bear the name Laamea Kamanakaupuu Mahinulani Nalo'iaehuokalaii Lumialani Kalakaua!"*

Five dancing singers, naked to the waist, carrying large gourds, approached the infant.

Their first *hula* extolled Ane Keohokalole's many virtues, including her sexual proclivities. The pantomimic motion of the five dancers was perfectly coördinated, their hands in motion unbelievably liquid. There followed the orator's chant for the infant Kalakaua. It told of his conception, his life within Ane, the incidents of his birth, the help of Tutu and Haaheo, the prophecy of the Southern Cross, and of a glorious future. As the chanter ended, a singer began: "*Ko ma'i Hoeuneu, Moekepue, Ana oe*," the first hula to be dedicated to Kalakua's penis.

The hour was late and as the sun stood over the Waianae mountains, a long table was covered with fragrant *maile* leaves, hibiscus blossoms, and banana leaves for the chiefs, while mats were spread on the ground for the three thousand now assembled. To the accompaniment of ceremonial dances, chants, and feats of strength, sixty whole pigs were transferred from the steaming hot *imu* to large platters with baked bananas, sweet potatoes, fish wrapped in *ti* leaves, and salmon sides from New England.

Before the food was distributed, Tutu cut off the tip of one pig's snout; the tip of an ear from a second; and from

* Kalakaua means Victor, or day of battle.

the others a tip of tail, a piece from the feet, and bits of liver, spleen, and lungs. She put them in a wooden bowl and offered it to the three chief gods of the Polynesians—*Kane*, the god of light and life; *Lono*, the god of the harvest; *Ku*, the most potent of all, god of war and strength—and implored them to bless the infant Kalakaua and Ane Keohoka-lole and Haaheo. When her prayer was ended, she called for the mother. As Ane appeared and strode to the consecrated bowl, the gathering prostrated. She partook of the bits dedicated to the gods and then went to her child, lying in Haopili-wahine's lap, at the head of the chief's table. She nuzzled the baby's tiny nose with her own and after greeting those at the chief's table, sat down with Haaheo and Liliha and ate heartily.

By design, Queen Kalama came late. The King was not with her. No sooner did she sit down beside Liliha than she demanded loudly: "Was the King's loincloth* forthcoming?" At Ane's silence, she goaded: "How stupid of me, I should have brought one of black crow's feathers!"

Haaheo, defender of the tiny Kalakaua warned: "You Kamehamehas had better look to your future! A King was born last night and he sits at the head of this table!"

The Queen disdainfully dipped her finger into the commonly-shared poi calabash and sucked it clean noisily. "A king? Better to say, a Calabash king†!"

Attempting to restore peace, Governor Matthew Kekuanaoa picked up his ceremonial bowl of *awa*. "This is no talk for a christening, Kalama! Come, Haaheo, and you too, Ane, here's a friendship drink."

---

* An unfailing custom among Polynesians was for the true father to present his offspring with a loincloth. Paternities were thus established.

† Calabash King is a derisive term. It meant that among chiefs Kalakaua would be a commoner. It had the further implication that many men had dipped into his mother Ane's bowl.

The grateful women drank heartily.

Queen Kalama, as was her privilege, got up first from the table. Upon leaving, she fired a parting shot. "Take care of his *piko**, Haaheo, or the rats will eat up his paternity."

Haaheo, angry, had taken all the insults she could bear. On the instant she decided that she would take the infant away at once and gave orders for the leave-taking. During the ensuing commotion, the collection of gifts and retinue, and the confusion of weeping farewells, Ane's voice rose wailing in a paroxysm of grief. Unmoved, Haaheo carried the child to her carriage and, followed by her entourage of two hundred, began the journey to the wharf.

As they passed the missionaries' compound, a shoulder-high coral-stone enclosure, two children pressed against the bars of the gate. The five-year-old boy wore a short waistcoat and close-fitting velvet trousers. The girl, about seven, wore a belted frock and pantalettes that reached to her ankles. A pale-faced woman ran to the children, shook and scolded them. Haaheo looked straight ahead. Despite Liliha's protests these missionaries had taken some of her choicest land near the god Kane's spring, Ke-Puna-hou, to build a school for these fancily-dressed children who were too good to be caught watching her entourage go to the wharf. She thought: "Is it not enough that these 'long-necks' steal our land and thrust a new God upon us while denying us our own—but even in such things, they insult us?"

She looked down at the baby in her lap. Unconsciously, her hold on him tightened. The answer lay here, perhaps. Yes, it must be so. Through him their gods would again become strong, their lands restored, the white man driven out. Haaheo's entourage was now passing grass huts, about eight

* *Piko* is umbilicus. As a Caucasian says, "How are you?" a Polynesian asks, "How is your belly-button?"

feet high. Sitting in front were natives braiding human-hair necklaces, trimming feathers for kahilis, polishing tortoise shells, while from the background came the sound of tapa beaters making new cloth out of bark. The sharp-eyed Haaheo looked about with sorrow. The huts were miserably constructed, too close together; her people were disease ridden. Within twenty years, half of the population had died. Thousands of virgin girls, kept pure as in olden days for their day of sharing mats with their intended husbands, had come to Honolulu from the outside islands, solely for prostitution. Even fathers had put wives and daughters into whorehouses for profit. Disease had taken many to their graves. Others, sick, went back to their homes and spread infection.

The immediacy of Hawaii's dissolution was heavy upon her. Even now the weakling Kamehamehas, for all their arrogance, were negotiating with an English lord to cede the islands to England to forestall threatened seizure by the French.

As they neared the coral-filled wharf the troubled Haaheo saw that Fair Haven harbor, where once only native outriggers plied and the shore's sands were golden, was now dirty with garbage and a scum of stinking whale-oil. She resolved that she would keep Kalakaua away from Honolulu and the white man's demoralizing influence at least until he had passed puberty. Then, if she had done well, he could withstand the white man's civilization and reinstate her own.

Meanwhile, as Haaheo's heavily-laden entourage arrived, a great scurrying began. For the first time, the Maui governor entrusted Kalakaua to Nurse Kailua Excursion's arms and rushed here and there cuffing bare rumps, hustling her retinue of two hundred with the great store of cooked foods and gifts. Befitting her rank, she was last to get aboard. As she took hold of the taffrail, the impatient mate of the ship shouted "Anchor aweigh for Maui!" The capstan brought up the anchor chain, while laboring seamen chanted:

"Haul on the bow-line,
Our ship she's a ro-oh-lin';
Haul on the bow-line;
The bow-line, *H-a-u-l!*"

The sails bellied with the evening breeze. The ship glided past Diamond Point and within a half hour stood in the Maui channel. Once she was beyond the Koolau mountains, a full moon leaped clear of the saw-toothed peaks and sped through swiftly moving clouds. Haaheo, with the infant Kalakaua in her arms, came topside by the light of the whale-oil lamps swinging in their davits. As she looked down at the baby she thought, "It is for me: If I rear him right, and if there is yet time, this child will restore our people." She hugged the sleeping infant and hot tears stood in her eyes. The singing of the sailors and the plunking of a guitar diverted her. She crooned to the baby as the sailors sang:

"Oh welcome the seas and the fragrant breeze
Laden with odors rare;
And the pretty maids in the sunny glades
Who are gentle, kind and fair
And the pretty eyes even now look out
Hoping some day to see
Our snow-white sails before the gales
Rolling down to old Maui
Rolling down to old Maui."

A squall plunged the sloop's bow into the williwaw-roughened water and Haaheo went below, certain that Hawaii's future rested with the babe in her arms.

3 Liliha's Dramatic Prophecy

Day after day passed quickly for Haaheo and her adopted son. Kalakaua was well taken care of. There were three wet nurses and twelve *kahu* s*, grown men, servants who anticipated his moods and desires, and who contended for the honor of sleeping with him. Kailua Excursion and her assistant nurses were careful to support their heavy breasts so that the infant's tiny nose would not flatten; they saw that he slept first on one side, then on the other, so that his head would be well formed; the outer corners of his eyes were pressed inward to make his eyes large, and he was massaged every day. The sea was home to him. When he was a year old he could keep himself afloat.

When Kalakaua was two years old, Haaheo decided that he must be weaned and sent for his godmother, Liliha Boki, his mother, Ane Keohokalole, who was again with child, and Grandmother Tutu. They were delighted with the friendly boy, who put his arms about their necks, touching their noses with his cheeks. At the weaning ceremony Kalakaua was pronounced no longer in need of the milk of women, and the

* In Hawaiian *s* is not added to make the plural.

foods of the gods *Hina* and *Ku*—the poi of the land and the fish of the sea—were henceforth his.

Then Liliha declared, "Kalakaua is old enough now to have his Christian name."

Haaheo protested. She had kept the boy pure Polynesian; but even as she objected she knew that to rule and to impress the whites he would have to have a name as the other young chiefs had, Lot and Alexander, Princesses Ruth and Bernice.

Liliha suggested the name David as the name of a great Biblical leader, a name fit for any King, and she added shrewdly, "That name will please the missionaries."

After much parley it was agreed. Tutu, Ane Keohokalole, and Liliha returned to Hawaii, and Haaheo and David to their halcyon days on Maui.

When David was five an urgent message arrived from Liliha by special boat, asking Haaheo to hurry with David to Honolulu. Haaheo was both annoyed and anxious. Perhaps it was now time that David returned and grew up with the young chiefs; with reluctance she prepared to leave Maui.

Liliha had sent her carriage to meet them at Robinson's wharf. On the way to the Blonde Hotel, Haaheo regarded her little boy with pride. He sat erect. Around his neck was the yellow feather lei, Liliha's royal gift. As they rolled along, David's nose picked up new smells, spicy Guayaquil cocoa and fragrant Brazilian coffee. Bijou, at David's side, was also excited; his tail pounded vigorously against the dashboard.

As they drew up and halted, Haaheo caught her breath. Before the hotel stood scores of carriages and hundreds of retainers: Such attendance could only mean that Liliha was dying.

Entering the large, luxuriously furnished room with its French bed, Haaheo saw that the chiefs were all there; even the King was present. Hoapili-wahine came forward to greet them, embarrassing the boy by fondling him. As Haaheo approached the bedside, Liliha saw them and, with a glad cry, held out two wasted arms to her godson. He hurried into them, and she embraced him and wept.

The room became silent. David and Haaheo stood apart. With the exception of one small girl, Princess Victoria, who came to stand by David, everyone avoided them. The arrogant Princess Ruth, thirteen, hurried forward and snatched at Victoria. "You are a Kamehameha! Leave this cow-dripping of Aikanaka alone!" She spat upon David's feet.

Liliha was seized with a fit of coughing. As spittlebearers held up a small receptacle, blood came with her spittle. Again the room hushed. With David beside her, Liliha summoned strength.

"Hear me, O Chiefs! I go back to the sea, the mountains, the air which made me. Know this to be true. There is a man-child among us who will lead you back to our old ways. As the Heavens proclaimed his kinship with the gods at birth, this Kalakaua will restore these islands."

Drunk with whiskey and anger, the King stalked forward. He did what had never been done before. He slapped the dying Chieftess and said thickly: "Liliha, as you die, you make our gods lie!"

Princess Ruth, emboldened by the King's action, kicked viciously at David. "This bastard, a king! Would you have the gods give us a calabash bowl to eat out of in which every commoner has pissed?"

Haaheo was about to come to his defense when Kamanawa, David's grandfather, shouted: "Even if his father says nothing, I come to the rescue of my grandson! Kalakaua springs from the loins of Aikanaka, the man-eater. Even now, this boy's placenta is in the palace grounds. His name shall forever be fragrant!"

The bewildered David Kalakaua clung to Haaheo's hand tightly.

As though there had been no interruption, the dying Liliha went on:

"Listen, O Chiefs! Within this generation you Kamehamehas will die. Your wombs will be barren, your penises impotent. Your *mana** will die with you."

With that curse, an awful hush filled the room. Even the drunken King and brash Princess Ruth were silent.

"Now I go to my husband, to Boki . . ." She set her mouth upon David's and expelled her last breath into him. Her spirit now would live in her godson.

There arose from those in the room a dismal wail, the first low notes swelling as they were joined by those who waited outside. Liliha Boki had been loved, and as widow of a former Governor of Hawaii she was a person of consequence. Mourning was her due. As the cry was borne from one to another within the hotel and to the watchers along the street it grew in volume until passionate grief filled the air. Hearing that cry, the white residents throughout the city hustled their children and their belongings into their homes, closed and bolted doors and shutters. They knew that the night would be hideous bedlam, with an orgy of drinking, raping, burning; there would be ears mangled, teeth broken, eyes gouged out, and tongues tattooed.

Within Liliha's room, Hoapili-wahine, Ana Keohokalole, Haaheo, and Grandfather Kamanawa gathered around David to shield him. Some of the mourners tore off their clothing;

* *mana*: spirit.

others bashed their heads against the walls. Hair was torn
out by the handful. A spear flashed near David and a man's
ear dropped to the floor.

Drunken yells and screams of pain lasted throughout the
night. By sun-up the orgy was spent. A few wanderers on the
street, with teeth missing and bare spaces on their scalps
where tufts of hair had been pulled out by the roots, kept
repeating over and over, "How dark, oh how dark are our
hearts!"

Within the house of death the five-year-old David obe-
diently did what was required of him. Haaheo decided to
observe a month of mourning. In that time she would decide
upon the future. She saw that Honolulu had changed since
she had last visited it five years ago. Then the King was a
strong figure. His subjects "lay with their mouths in the
dust" when the King's drinking water was borne through the
street. Now even a bulbous-nosed white drunkard could
lurch into the King and, through his consul, demand an apology!

Haaheo reluctantly came to the conclusion that she must
remain in Honolulu. If David were to become a leader of
their people they could no longer stay away from the center
of the islands. She resented the whites, the missionaries and
the Kamehamehas. Yet she saw that the Kamehamehas were
weak and the whites and the missionaries strong. David Kalakaua would need support. To understand these people he
must learn something of their ways. But if she and Tutu
stayed in Honolulu and kept in close touch with the boy, the
teaching of the five years and the love of their own way of
life would surely prevail.

She had to make her decision at once, for a law had been
passed in Honolulu that all Hawaiian children must attend

school. The missionaries had recently built a schoolhouse for
the royal children near David Kalakaua's placenta tree in the
palace courtyard. As a child of royalty he must attend, meet
these arrogant Kamehamehas, know them and study with
them. If the years on Maui had counted, David would be
able to hold his own against them.

Despite her constant self-assurance, the Governor of Maui
started for her first visit to the squat, whitewashed adobe
boarding school with considerable trepidation. David was
with her, but was far more interested in the four-horsed
carriage which conveyed them than in the prospect of school.
When the couple who ran the school, Amos Star Cooke and
his wife, Juliette Montague, appeared to greet them, Haaheo
took one look and recovered her poise. Amos weighed only
about a hundred pounds, was short, and his skin was pallid.
Juliette was slightly larger than her husband but, squinting
in the morning sunlight, she looked cross. Haaheo decided
that there was little to fear from the Cookes and imperiously
ordered the twelve male kahus, David's servants, who had
walked behind the new carriage as a matter of course, to
cease their wailing.

Addressing the larger and more important looking
Juliette, she said, "I have brought my Chief Kalakaua to
attend your school."

Mrs. Cooke, with ready sympathy, asked, "What is his full
name?"

Ignoring the audible taunt "Nigger" from Prince Moses
Kekuanaoa peeping out of the near-by classroom, Haaheo
replied with composure, "David Kalakaua."

Amos Cooke said gravely, "I trust he will be as steadfast
in the Lord as was the Biblical David."

Trying to put the Chieftess at her ease Juliette asked,
"What does Kalakaua mean?"

"Day of Battle, or Victory," replied Haaheo. Won over to the friendly white woman, she raised her large tapa under-skirts and displayed the calabashes of Hawaiian food she had brought for David, who was unaccustomed to white man's fare. Mrs. Cooke raised the lid of a covered dish. Black claws gripped the rim, and she shrank back. Haaheo reached in, took out a live rock crab, bit into it and chewed it up, shell, pincers and all.

Amos Cooke reached up into the carriage for David, to give the little fellow a lift down. But David, who had never been held by a white man, kicked Amos on the shoulder and the teacher staggered back. Juliette's heart sank. They already had eight little chiefs to tame, and besides, there were two children of their own and a third on the way.

These chiefs had been accustomed to eat only when hungry and to dip their fingers in a common calabash. Their attendants had humored and amused them; they had no re-sources of their own. When, on the first day of school, Gov-ernor Matthew Kekuanaoa had brought his three princes—Moses, eleven; Alexander, six; and Lot, ten—he had to come back and sleep with them three nights before they learned to keep quiet. Juliette had to oversee their dressing, laundry, attend to their food, their amusement, and nurse them during illness. And here was another untamed chief!

Haaheo came to Amos Cooke's rescue. She scolded David fondly, took him in her powerful arms and handed him screaming to Mr. Cooke. Then she ordered the kahus to begin unloading. David's screams were the signal for a gen-eral fracas. Moses hurled his geography at his brother Lot; Jane pounded King-Designate Alexander's head with her Bible; Lot yelped, "You God damned bastard," and leaped to close with Moses. The royal children's kahus, always about the grounds but forbidden to enter the classroom, peered

through the windows and saw Amos Cooke pull Lot's ear.
"You can't do that," shouted Moses, who at eleven was
taller than Cooke. "Lot's ear is *kapu*, you Christer."

Jane shouted, "Kick him in the crotch, Moses!"

Abigail yelled, "Scratch his bloody eyes out."

Juliette, fearful for her husband's safety, asked Haaheo
to hurry and fetch the boys' father, Governor Matthew Kekuanaoa. David, the immediate cause of the outbreak,
stopped his cries to look on in bewilderment.

As Moses and Amos Cooke struggled, Alexander unbolted
the door and called in a dozen angry kahus. Cooke tried to
throw Moses, but one of the powerful Hawaiian attendants
jumped the slight man and bore him to the floor. Murder
was averted by the arrival of a neighbor of the Cookes who
ordered the kahus, "Begone, swine excrement; this classroom
is kapu." They obeyed, but the boys did not, and because of
their high rank the neighbor did not dare to touch them.
Fortunately Matthew Kekuanaoa arrived with a detachment
of six soldiers and ordered his sons to sit, as his presence
demanded.

Alexander and Lot obeyed, but Moses struck at his
teacher, shouting, "This pig touched me. I'll cut out his
heart and eat it."

The Governor ordered the soldiers to carry Moses out.
The first soldier who touched the boy yelped; Moses had
bitten the man's hand. Clinging desperately to a desk, the
boy fought on, but four soldiers overpowered him and
carried him away.

That broke the spirit of the rebellious children. Quietly
they settled into school routine, David with them as a matter
of course. Haaheo, with discretion, did not return that day.
David settled into his new and strange surroundings without

difficulty. His week ends were spent with Haaheo and Tutu.
After this unusual outbreak, Moses, chastened, became more
tractable for a time. The days flew by and the Cookes began
to think that their teaching really was reaching the children.
Then, one morning when Amos and Juliette returned from a
sunrise horseback trip, they caught Moses slinking out of
Jane's and Abigail's bedroom and found that the three, all
under thirteen, had been having sexual intercourse for two
months. Again Moses was punished but he continued to be
the bad boy of the school. He stole into the near-by Dowsett
home and put sand in the dough; he stole money from the
collection plate in the Congregational church, bought wine
and got his brothers Lot and Alexander drunk in the school-
room. He daubed little David's face with lampblack and
dubbed him "John Blossom" for his alleged Negro father. He
could no longer visit the girls in the school so he sneaked off
and sought sexual release in the white man's whorehouses.

The Cookes were sincere and conscientious. But they had
never dreamed of children like these. They struggled on,
and at times it seemed that they accomplished something.
Music was a bond of common interest. In the evenings the
girls played the seraphine and the boys accompanied with
flutes. All the Hawaiians sang and usually sang well. And
they learned, for their minds were quick and retentive. Unfortunately the Cookes had no understanding of Hawaiian
tradition or history or any respect for it. Their duty was to
their church. They were unable to understand that the children, naturally gracious to their instructors as they lived
with them and began to like them, deliberately adopted ex-
pedient attitudes of acceptance of beliefs in which they held
no credence. The Cookes taught white and Christian supremacy but the children knew that the white settlers—and

sons of the missionaries—really wanted power and money and had few scruples as to how they got them. If the Hawaiian gods were no gods, was the God the whites preached about any more real? What did this religion offer? In church, much; in practice, little. Perhaps there were no worthwhile gods at all.

4 The Missionaries Hang a Royal Chief

Months slipped into years. For young Chief David Kalakaua they were years of struggle between contesting interests. Pulled one way by Haaheo, whom he visited every week end at her Waikiki home, David became a true Polynesian. Haaheo insisted that he shed his detested *haole** clothes, wrap on his breechcloth and live as a native chief. During the week, at school, the Cookes pulled firmly in another way, pouring their teaching into lessons well seasoned with prayer and precept tending to the abandonment of heathen Polynesian ways and the acceptance of Christian doctrine.

Outwardly the children accepted David, but he knew that within their tight little circle the Kamehamehas regarded him as an interloper. One girl, Princess Victoria, seemed free from prejudice and became a friend. In this never ending tug-of-war only the growing boy was not fully aware of the great stakes. Haaheo was convinced that some day this royal chief would rule their kingdom. The Cookes, aware of the intense dynastic rivalry between the Kamehameha and Aikanaka clans, sensed that eventually David would play a dominant role in the kingdom's affairs, including those of the

* *haole* is a derogatory term applied to whites, foreigners, outcasts.

missionaries. The Kamehamehas, although discrediting the royal paternity, were fearful of the death-bed prophecy of Liliha Boki. In self-defense they constantly humiliated and provoked him, the more easily since he was the youngest child at the school. Unknowingly they were helping David, building within him strength which would stand him in good stead when the powerful Haaheo was gone.

As the boy grew the softness left his face and its structure showed the full features of a Polynesian. His brown eyes were large; his wavy hair black; his nose was straight, the nostrils slightly flared; the cheekbones rather prominent. Supple of body, he was erect, his bearing dignified, even for a boy. The *mana* of Prophetess Liliha was upon him like a mantle.

When Governor Haaheo called at the school for David every Saturday afternoon, to the dismay of the Cookes, she always brought the aging Grandmother Tutu. Usually they drove directly to Haaheo's seaside residence, which was filled with the prized symbols of nobility. There, to Haaheo's vast delight, her little boy kicked off his shoes, shed his haole clothes, wrapped his *malo* about his slender hips and called for a dish of poi. Although Chief David had twelve kahus to attend him, Haaheo and Tutu supervised his more intimate needs. When he was seven, these two women had taken him to the Big Island of Hawaii and cut bamboo from the god Kane's sacred grove. From it, Haaheo had made a sharp knife and gave it to Tutu to slit the boy's foreskin. Over the wound, to help it heal, Tutu had placed the blossom of the morning glory. After that time, David had worn the malo, signifying his circumcision.

Each week, Haaheo and Tutu planned carefully for the coming Saturday, so that they might impress upon Kalakaua something new and significant in their culture. One day, Haaheo drove up to the school in a new carriage, the most beautiful David had ever seen. The surrey had red plush cushions and as the matched white span trotted, the golden tassels quivered. Upon this special occasion, Haaheo ordered the coachman to drive beyond her home to Waikiki.

On the way, his foster mother pointed to the southeast and told Kalakaua how his Aikanaka ancestors had breasted the trackless oceans in frail canoes, setting their course by the stars and the flight of birds long before the Caucasian dared leave his shores. In discovering Hawaii seventy generations ago they had made a three-thousand mile voyage without sight of land from their South Sea islands, carrying poi, dogs, pigs, and breadfruit along with their families. But greater than their splendid navigation was his ancestors' mastery over the fear of the unknown.

"The blood of these courageous men who rode without fear through the gateway of dawn, Kalakaua, flows in your Aikanaka veins," she told him. As Haaheo intended, each story seemed to the young chief to be a part of him, even as the fiery volcano Mauna Loa in Hawaii, the swift flight of the *iiwi,* or the rapacity of the shark in the waters of Kaaina.

At the Waikiki palm groves, the Maui chieftess took him to Aikanaka's famous canoe.

"Hear me, Kalakaua," she said, lapsing into the chanter's poetic form of speech, "many years ago when I lacked pubic hair, Chief Aikanaka's skilled craftsmen built this canoe."

David ran his hand over the smooth polished surface, sat on its worn seat and picked up one of the light paddles. This famous canoe had made three trips to the South Sea islands. In graphic word pictures, the white-haired princess gave Kalakaua the chant of his ancestor Aikanaka's canoe:

"The venerable craftsmen took their stone adzes to the temple of Kane and first offered prayers to make the adzes light in the hands of the workers amid chips flying;

"The adzes hot and brittle through friction were driven sizzling deep into the core of juicy banana stalks to cool them;

"The builders lashed planks to the sides to make the canoe walk safely in the ocean, across short waves and long waves, to reach near and far horizons;

"The chief artisan invoked the aid of the gods of the forest, the sky, and the sea;

"The canoe, amid the glad shouts of the people, slid on round skids into the waves, gracefully poised;

"All the people of Kealakekua, wearing garlands of flowers of Kona and sweet-smelling herbs of Puna, shouted and marvelled at the fine craftsmanship of the canoe, and the feasting lasted for days."

David Kalakaua was deeply stirred by this tale of past glory, and Haaheo continued to tell him old stories of their ancestral greatness all the fragrant afternoon.

Heading into the sunset spreading like a flaming fan over the Waianae mountains, when she had finished, they drove slowly and silently back to Honolulu.

But when David returned to school on Monday, the Cookes opened with a Christian prayer and there were no gods but only one God, and the morning's first lesson in theology bewildered the boy: Who was right, and did it matter?

Haaheo had impressed and enchanted him with her marvelous legends, and although the Cookes' stories seemed less wonderful, some of them were appealing. He was thoroughly confused. Then suddenly a sharp test of faith came to him, which led to a decision.

Kamanawa, his grandfather, who had always been friendly and had come to his defense during Liliha's prophecy, was arrested and was to be tried for breaking the new missionary-inspired marriage laws. Kamanawa had left his fat wife Komo and was living with another woman. This was a custom followed by many Polynesian chiefs in times past. But the court directed that according to the new laws Kamanawa could not have intercourse with the second woman until his divorced wife found another legal husband or died. Six weeks later, Kamanawa was arrested for poisoning Komo. His trial was held in the coral-stone fort built by the Russians near the waterfront. Judge Matthew Kekuanaoa presided and there was a full jury.

In his defense, Kamanawa contended that Polynesian chiefs had the prerogative of changing mates as often as they wished. To make matters quite plain he accused the presiding judge of sleeping with the female Prime Minister, Auhea. This angered the King, who attended the trial, because he himself knew the woman well in bed. Kamanawa made no defense on the poison charge, frankly confessing that he had a sea captain concoct a violent poison and arranged a large Awa drinking party at which he had served Komo the poisoned drink. He considered this his inherent right. "Did not my grandfather, a chief as great as any of you Kamehamehas, rip his wife's belly open with a shark-toothed knife so that her guts burst forth?"

The Judge, consulting his pocket watch, a gift from George IV during his visit to London, called a recess and had coffee served to the King, court, jury, distinguished visitors, and the defendant. When court resumed he charged the jury: "Hear me. You listened to the talk of Kamanawa. Now decide the man's guilt and come and tell me."

That afternoon Kamanawa was handed a document which read: "In accordance with the sentence of death passed upon you, we hereby notify you that the day of your execution will be the twentieth day of October at 11 o'clock. Happy indeed will you be, Kamanawa, should you improve the present few days by repentance that your heinous sins may be forgiven through Jesus Christ." It was signed by King Kamehameha and his popular co-ruler, Prime Minister Auhea.

The gallows were built above the gate of the fort, within plain sight of the royal children's school. Returning from a pre-dawn horseback ride, the Cookes were horrified to find that the older boys had strung up David by the heels from a tree in the grounds. Amos anxiously lowered him, and felt the boy's heart beating wildly, but Kalakaua would not cry. He slipped out of Amos's grasp and ran to the school, where Juliette found him hidden behind his bed, sobbing bitterly.

A curious throng gathered to witness the first chief's hanging. When the hour approached, native soldiers could not be found to do the deed. One gave the answer for all: "This chief is a descendant of Aikanaka. How can my gods, which are few, contend against his, which are legion?" Governor Kekuanaoa bribed three dissolute whalers to do the ugly task, promising them two gold doubloons each. As the hangman's knot was placed about the chief's neck, the Hawaiians wailed: *"Au-we, kuu Alii*—Alas, our Chief!" To Hawaiians his death was the most ignominious in the islands: Even the Kamehamehas who had signed the death warrant were ashamed and soon realized that every Hawaiian had suffered in the eyes of the whites. And every Hawaiian knew that a chief had died without breathing his mana, his spirit, into the body of another. Now that spirit belonged to evil and roamed free to enter anyone.

When David Kalakaua stepped out of his classroom at noon, he saw his grandfather's dangling body turning slowly in the wind blowing from Pauoa valley. He fought back his tears, and when Cooke spoke that day on "the wages of sin is death," he sat there hard-eyed. He felt he must do something to avenge his grandfather. The missionaries had inspired the new laws. In the late afternoon David waylaid a missionary boy, almost a head taller and a year older, and whipped him soundly.

5 The British Navy Takes Hawaii

The hanging of David's grandfather, Chief Kamanawa, presaged events that threatened the existence of Hawaii. White men did not differentiate between the descendants of the two great dynasties, Kamehameha and Aikanaka; to them Kamanawa was Hawaiian royalty—and he had been hanged for transgressing what was, in reality, white men's law. The status of all Hawaiian chiefs was therefore dubious. Friction between them and the whites increased. The subject Polynesians, who had believed all chiefs sacred and above law, were bewildered and regarded their royal chiefs with lessened respect. In Haaheo's household the result of the hanging was a fiercer determination on her part that David Kalakaua must rule and restore the greatness of the Aikanakas. From the boy's changed behavior to all whites, since the beating David had given the missionary boy, she knew that he was now securely in her camp. He had enlisted to avenge the many indignities heaped upon their people.

But she could not know how soon additional insults were to be heaped upon Hawaii. Emboldened by the hanging, and by the fact that there was no outbreak among the Polynesians, white men began to make preposterous civil and land claims. To back up the British demands, a frigate rode into

Fair Haven with scarlet-coated marines drawn up on deck and guns manned. Her Captain, Lord George Paulet, refused to fire the customary twenty-one gun salute, and instead of making the usual diplomatic call on Governor Kekuanaoa, Paulet drove to the British consulate. The bewildered Governor could not know that the British Consul Charlton had met Paulet in Mexico, on his way to Europe, and had convinced the commander of the British squadron that a series of indignities had been imposed upon British residents. Charlton told him of the unrest in Hawaii due to the hanging of a prominent chief, and hinted that the islands were just as ripe for seizing as New Zealand, occupied recently by Great Britain. Eager to curry favor with his queen, the young lord resolved to seize the islands in the name of Queen Victoria.

At the sight of the armed ship, apprehension stirred in Honolulu. Now, when unity was most needed among the chiefs, dissension ruled—the hanging had blown the smoldering coals of the Kamehameha-Aikanaka feud into a hot flame. To spite the ruling house, some Aikanakas were even prepared to give the islands to England or France—even America, if it would destroy the rule of the hated Kamehamehas.

A boat was sent to bring the King from Maui to Honolulu. The British lord was demanding that the King give him a private interview; that an acting consul be recognized; that Britishers now in prison or arrested in the future be tried only by British law; and the immediate settlement of all land claims, including an outrageous one by British Consul Charlton to more than one-fourth of the city of Honolulu; and to submit to these demands by four o'clock the next afternoon or "I shall be obliged to take coercive steps."

Although it was late when King Kamehameha returned from Maui, he called his chiefs for a midnight meeting. The shame of the recent hanging seemed to pervade the group. In view of what they had done before, they seemed ready now to knuckle down to the degrading terms of the British.

But not Haaheo. If ever her David Kalakaua were to rule the islands, she knew that they must remain independent. "These whites, with their missionary-inspired laws, have brought shame enough upon us, already. As for me, no white man shall ever rule these islands." With that she turned to David. "Come, Kalakaua. At least now these fearful Kamehamehas know where we stand."

A respectful way was made for the two as they left. At that moment, Kalakaua took added courage from his foster mother.

Next morning the British and American consuls notified their nationals to evacuate the city. The word was that the King would not comply. For Britishers there was an English brig anchored in the roadstead, for Americans there was a Yankee sloop. Streets were soon crowded with carts loaded with pictures, cradles, books, lamps, featherbeds, and clothing.

On the British man-of-war, men cleared decks for action. Springs were put on the ship's lines to prevent them from snapping from the firing recoil. Guns were loaded and trained on the Punchbowl battery, the government buildings, and the fort.

Ignorant of the effects of disciplined gunnery, hotheaded Hawaiians gathered in the fort with clubs and an odd assortment of weapons. A leader urged Governor Kekuanaoa to board the British ship with a hundred men and destroy it by exploding her own powder magazines.

At the royal children's School, at three o'clock, an hour before the British ultimatum expired, Amos Cooke left and hurried to the wharf. At four the schoolhouse windows rattled as the first shot was fired. The children rushed out the door; only Bernice and Victoria remained inside. At the second explosion, Mrs. Cooke dropped to her knees with the two princesses and prayed: "Dear God, let no harm befall my children." She listened for the shots and noting they were regularly spaced, realized that it was not a bombardment—it was a salute from the fort to which the British man-of-war was replying. The King had complied! The islands were British.

Within an hour of the King's submission, Britain's Acting Consul pressed new and even more ridiculous demands: One hundred thousand dollars damages; a two hundred and ninety-nine-year lease for Consul Charlton's spurious land claims; and the instant reversal of law cases involving British nationals. Behind the Acting Consul were Lord Paulet's guns. The King wavered.

Haaheo said sharply: "If we yield to these terms, other nations will make like requests."

While the chiefs were debating, a second ultimatum demanded instant compliance or outright cession to Great Britain. Rather than comply, the King signed a document of provisional cession.

Then came a degrading act which even the Kamehamehas could scarcely stomach. Paulet ordered the old Governor, father of the King, himself to strike the Hawaiian flag despite his withered arm!

At this humiliating change-the-flag ceremony, Paulet demanded that Hawaii's royalty attend. On one side of the fort's enclosure were grouped the old Governor, his son, King Kamehameha III, Premier Auhea, Governor Haaheo, with David Kalakaua, the other chiefs and children, American residents, and native troops. Opposing them were the British marines, Lord Paulet, the acting consul and his wife, and

British townsfolk who took no pains to hide their elation. As the governor lowered the flag, King Kamehameha III wept. At a smart command the Union Jack was briskly hoisted. Paulet saluted and the ship's band broke into "God Save Our Gracious Queen . . ."

As the song ended, the King asked: "Lord Paulet, may I address my chiefs?"

Paulet consented grudgingly: "To your chiefs, but in my language."

King Kamehameha cried in Polynesian: "Where are you, Chiefs, and commoners from my ancestors?" It was an ancient chief's appeal.

"Hear me! I am in great perplexity by reason of my difficulties into which I have been brought without cause. Therefore I have given away the life of the land, hear me! But my rule over you, my people, and the privileges of you Chiefs will continue . . ."

Before he could finish, Paulet ordered the band to play.

That night windows of British and American homes were smashed by angry Hawaiians. Stones were hurled at the British men-of-war. To halt disturbances, armed British marines drove the natives off with bayonets. In the morning Paulet posted a proclamation announcing the cession of the Sandwich Islands to Queen Victoria and appointed a commission of four men, which he headed, to rule the islands. The King was represented by Dr. Gerrit P. Judd. To defray the commission's expenses, Paulet imposed a one per cent duty on imports. To prevent word of his occupation from going out to the world before his special messenger, the acting consul, could present the cession to his Queen, Paulet commandeered all foreign ships, seizing King Kamehameha's three vessels for himself.

The commission's first act, Judd dissenting, was to deny the *Gazette* the right to publish the King's interrupted speech. At the same meeting, auction laws were altered to give British residents preference; liquor licenses were revoked and new ones issued at one hundred and fifty dollars each; and foreign shipowners were ordered to secure British registries. The blustery Yankee skipper, Captain John R. Cummins, who refused to comply, was sentenced to three months in prison.

Two nights later David Kalakaua was awakened at the Cooke school by Governor Matthew Kekuanaoa and taken, with the other sleepy young chiefs, to meet the King in an American ship. Commander Long, of the American sloop-of-war *Boston,* had risked the meeting and had offered his own cabin. King Kamehameha III received the children. He was dejected but firm.

"I go to Maui tonight," he told them. "I will not return until I am the undisputed ruler of these islands." He put his arm about Alexander's shoulders. "You will be my successor, Alexander Liloliho Kamehameha." Reaching for David, the King pulled him under his other arm. "And you, Chief David Kalakaua, will be his strong right arm. From today, dissension between Kamehameha and Aikanaka must cease. Our danger is great; the life of our land is in the balance; we must stand together."

It was the first time a Kamehameha had shown such consideration for an Aikanaka.

Moses burst out: "Why do we meet secretly here by night on this American ship? Why do you not wear your royal uniform? We are dead." He ripped the insigne from his coat and threw it to the floor. "You are not King of the Islands and I am not Governor of Kauai!"

Tears filled the King's eyes. He said sadly: "Perhaps, Moses, you are right." He asked the others to remove their badges of royalty and they handed them to him in silence.

For the commission's third sitting, Lord Paulet and his guard of honor arrived late. He sat down, shot out his ruffled sleeve-ends, tapped his snuff box and took a pinch for his right nostril and one for his left. Judd studied the man critically. He had heard that the English lord was having sexual relations with a young native girl.

Paulet began: "Gentlemen I find nothing but stinking corruption in Honolulu despite the cloak of gentility thrown over it by some of the long-frocked residents." He ignored Judd's studied glare. "To clean up this mess, I propose we revise Hawaii's fornication laws." He read at length from a current statute a list of fines and prison terms for men and women. He called the law "absurd" and stated that he had visited men and women confined in one cell, that officers of the jail were extorting money from the female prisoners.

"Now that Her Majesty's flag flies over the fort," he summed up, "this commission cannot condone such practices."

Judd was on his feet objecting that the Hawaiian government had taken drastic steps to "stamp out vice, depravity and debauchery—"

Paulet cut him short. "Your laws cannot work with natives. Who knows but that the natives were vastly better off under their own moral codes, Judd, before you missionaries came and made prostitution necessary—"

Judd was furious. "Lord Paulet you dare not say prostitution came with the missionary. Harlotry came with the sailors, the whalers, and your own ships. The real trouble is that a few Britishers like Charlton want to increase their income from their Cape Horn property by removing all decent restrictions!"

He had spoken truth. But Paulet ignored the charge. "Judd, Honolulu's Cape Horn is known in London, Hamburg, Valparaiso, San Blas, everywhere, as the most immoral spot in the world. With these fornication laws you locked the front door and left the back door wide open. This stupid hanging of a Hawaiian chief . . ."

When he saw Judd's angry face, he eased up. He turned to his secretary: "Mr. Sea, summon our first witness."

The prisoner testified that he had been confined in the fort four months and two days. "Tell the commission about the women confined there," Paulet ordered. "Are they used by respected townspeople?"

The man replied: "Sir, I have seen females in the naked embrace of our leading townspeople under the trees on the rampart of the fort."

Judd, unconvinced, said peremptorily, "I do not believe it."

"Tell us what happened if a woman refused."

The prisoner said: "One woman was shackled with irons and made to lie naked in the open, exposed to the hot sun."

"Can you produce that woman?" demanded Judd.

"She got a blow on the head," replied the man, "for not being responsive and jumped into the water and was drowned."

Another member of the commission asked: "Did whaling captains arrange for female prisoners at the fort to go aboard their vessels?"

"Yes," replied the man, "I have heard police tell whaling captains: 'Go on in and test the *wahine* for yourself, first,' and then these captains would go into the cells with the women and remain a long time."

Paulet turned to Judd. "Do you still think your suppression of vice successful?"

"Certainly. This man's statements are hearsay."

Paulet asked his secretary to summon the next witness, a Hawaiian woman. At one time she had been Liliha Boki's favorite dancer.

Secretary Sea asked, "What is your name?"

"Leilani."

"Is that all?"

Without more ado she uncovered her chest and exposed her limp, drooping breasts. Around them were the healed white scars: C A P E H O R N. "That's my working name," she said.

"How did you come by your profession?" Paulet asked.

She shrugged. "Money!"

"How long have you been confined in the fort?"

"Two years."

"In irons?"

"Except nights when I was let out."

"Why do you go out?"

"To earn food."

"Aren't women prisoners given food?"

"Only those who take on the townspeople get food. I'm not much for looks since I had my teeth broken."

"How do you make your money?"

"At night I swim to the whaleships in the harbor. Last night I was on the *Stewart James*. For twenty-five cents, Officer Noa takes my irons off. For another quarter, he puts them on again in the morning."

"Do you wish to cross-examine the witness, Dr. Judd?" Paulet asked. As Judd shook his head, he continued: "There are six other witnesses."

It was over Judd's opposition, which culminated in his resignation from the commission, that an order was posted saying "No male or female is to be imprisoned for the crime of fornication unless committed in the open streets or thoroughfares." The new order was operative at once.

Whaling captains, who knew it would be much easier to recruit crews if the men could have unrestrained sexual freedom in Hawaii, rejoiced. As Judd predicted, Charlton's land values around Grog Street increased immediately.

One hundred and thirty days after the loathed British occupation began, the American frigate *Constellation* arrived, with Commodore Lawrence Kearney in command. He refused to salute the British flag, and after dropping anchor, hastened to pay his respects to Governor Kekuanaoa and received the princes aboard his flagship with a nine-gun salute, hoisting the Hawaiian flag from the frigate's fore. He sent a letter to the King inviting him to come aboard and receive due honors. The American Commodore further posted a protest declaring that he would not recognize Paulet or his illegal commission.

Kearney's action at once fomented disobedience to British officers. Hawaiian soldiers who had joined the British were stoned. Many residents, even in the British colony, were glad of the change: they had resented the arrogance of the British naval officers and men, and after the repeal of the fornication laws, sailors had raised a stench in the nostrils of all decent citizens. Disgusting scenes were enacted in the streets in daylight. Men now deserted from the British man-of-war to join the better-paying American whaling crews or the more democratic American *Constellation*. The Hawaiians wanted their royal line restored and the presence of the young chiefs without their royal insignia was a daily humiliating reminder that Hawaii must rid the country of the foreign oppressor.

On the one hundred and fiftieth day, a second British frigate appeared off Diamond Point. Aboard was the flag of Rear Admiral Richard Thomas. Ignoring Captain Paulet, the Admiral sent a note seeking "the honor of an interview with His Majesty, the King."

As the King had returned to Honolulu, the next morning was named for the interview. It was soon clear that the Admiral's purpose was to restore the independence of the islands. Provisional arrangements were agreed upon as to the rights of British subjects in Hawaii, subject to confirmation by London. When the King and Admiral Thomas had signed the agreement, complete restoration of the kingdom was ordered within five days.

It was a day the young chief David Kalakaua and many other Polynesians would never forget. After all the humiliation, Hawaii was once again to be free. The day was brilliant. Thousands gathered in holiday mood. American and English marines flanked by artillery corps, faced the sea. Promptly at nine forty-five in the morning, escorted by his troops, King Kamehameha III arrived astride his white stallion. Following him in a body rode sixteen young chiefs led by King-Designate Alexander and Chief David Kalakaua.

The order to strike the Union Jack was given upon the sharp command of Admiral Thomas to Lord George Paulet. As the Hawaiian colors were once again hoisted, the King said: "*Ua mau ke ea o ka aina i ka pono!*—The life of the land is preserved in righteousness."

Admiral Thomas had no intention of leaving his task unfinished. He remained in Hawaii for six months with his flagship, the frigate *Dublin,* until the arrival of the new

British consul, General William Miller, to succeed the detested Charlton. The Admiral was immensely popular with
the Hawaiians, who named the site of the restoration ceremony Thomas Square, as it is known to this day.

Before he left for his Pacific station in Mexico, Admiral
Thomas invited the royal children with their teachers for
dinner on his flagship. The Admiral sat at the head of the
table with Prince Alexander on his left, Princess Victoria on
his right, and next to her, Chief David Kalakaua. Admiral
Thomas lifted his glass to King-Designate Alexander. "To
the future ruler of these pleasant islands."

The prince, lifting his water glass—the Cookes would permit no wine—responded: "To Queen Victoria, the queen of
hearts."

"Bravo!" applauded General Miller, "And I give my toast
to Princess Victoria, a jewel worthy of a fine land."

Victoria bowed. Turning to her host, she said: "We are
indebted to you, Admiral Thomas, because you gave us back
our land, our King, and sent us General Miller."

The Admiral turned to Juliette Cooke. "Mrs. Cooke, I
have never met a better reared family. May I propose a toast
to you?"

Blushing furiously she bowed her consent. It was the first
time that she had ever been toasted.

Before the dinner was over, Admiral Thomas's aide
handed him a note. The Admiral excused himself.

"What brings you here?" he demanded gruffly of a native
girl waiting for him. "This is no time to come aboard ship."
Then, as he looked at her closely, he was sorry for his gruff-
ness. She was beautiful, with deep brown eyes and wavy
black hair and her skin in the lamplight was golden. And she
was pregnant. "Tell me, child, what is it?"

"What am I to do with Lord Paulet's child?" she burst out. "He told me that he would send for it and take it to London, but he has been gone now for a month. He sends me nothing to proclaim the child's blood. Where is he?"

Admiral Thomas put his hand on her shoulder. "I will do what I can." He looked at her intently. "How old are you, child?"

"Fifteen."

Thomas pulled a handkerchief from his sleeve and gave it to her. "Dry your tears, child."

His kindness was balm to her sorrow and with the child-like frankness of a Polynesian, she said: "You have made my name fragrant." Impulsively she reached for the old sea lord's hand, rubbed it against her cheek, and before he could learn her name or where she lived, fled hurriedly, taking with her his handkerchief. That would serve as her child's malo.

6 David Kalakaua's Initiation

With the departure of Admiral Thomas, Honolulu slipped into its workaday groove: Captain Cummins had been released from prison; King Kamehameha returned to his Honolulu palace; old Hawaiian women sold breadfruit and mangoes at the street corners, giving a fragrant *pikake* lei with each purchase; the fornication laws were restored; and the Cookes were having their usual difficulties—Prince Lot got one of the students in a family way and Prince Moses was caught in the act of having illicit relations with his aunt, Queen Kalama. Amos and Juliette hastily married the pregnant girl off to a commoner so that the child would have a father; Prince Moses was called to an extraordinary session of the King's Council and at the angry King's insistence the Privy Counsellors took away the seventeen-year-old prince's governorship and property while the Queen was quietly suspended from the Congregational church.

This problem of sex control was a baffling one to the missionaries: rules of conduct they established were broken by the actions of their own countrymen. They had persuaded the King to ban females from going aboard Yankee ships for the night—including the American man-of-war *Dolphin*. But Captain Jack Percival of the U. S. Navy demanded that the

53

missionary-inspired ban be dropped and when the King refused, he opened fire on the King's palace. A few salvos brought the King around in a hurry and the females were allowed aboard again.

Dismayed but undaunted, the missionaries attempted another solution for the student sex problem. On Governor Haaheo's island of Maui, they built two schools twenty-two miles apart, one for adolescent boys, the other for girls. Guiding Cupid's fickle darts, the teachers took daguerreotypes of the older girls, indexed them, and distributed them among those closely-confined boys whose voices were changing. By an intricate system of bookkeeping the favored girls were given portraits of the boys to study and formal letters were exchanged to fire the romance. Two months before graduation, senior boys were escorted to the female seminary, and quickly assisted through awkward proposals. Thus, within two working days, eighty girls were apparently assured of spouses upon graduation. But the deep-laid plan miscarried. Out of a possible one hundred and sixty, only fourteen joined in wedlock: girls with haole education preferred white husbands while educated Polynesian boys found untutored lasses vastly more compliant.

Haaheo and Tutu scoffed at the missionaries' fumbling efforts. "The white man's way is not good for Hawaiians," Haaheo told David, who was now eleven. "Mating is an art with the Polynesians and it must be learned carefully and correctly."

"Your famed ancestor Aikanaka had many hulas dedicated to the prowess of his penis," added Grandmother Tutu. "I myself experienced his skill."

David flushed and Haaheo saw that the time had come for the young chief to have his first sex lesson before the whites destroyed the age-old procedure. She nodded to Tutu. "It is time for the Aikanaka malo," and left the boy with his white-haired grandmother.

From a sea chest, Tutu took the most prized treasure in the household. She said: "When Aikanaka's hair was white as mine, he gave your womb-mother, Ane Keohokalole, this malo, saying: 'Give it to him of my descendants who is most deserving of its glory. But see that he is taught my secrets of pleasing women!' When I assisted at your birth, Kalakaua, in the thunder and lightning of the night, and Ane named your *ma'i* Halala, then I knew you would wear it."

To Kalakaua, who had been taught the names of one hundred and fifty stars, the genealogies of twenty generations, the royal kapus—why Ane alone was permitted to carry a lighted torch in the daytime; and the intimate distinctive names, such as his own Halala, given to the sexual parts of all the chiefs—this conversation was a very natural one.

"But you have yet to learn the greatest art of the Hawaiians, Kalakaua, the art of arousing never-failing pleasure with your ma'i and bringing forth new generations. But mind, what I teach you is secret, the secret of our ancestors and of Aikanaka. Of all people, we Polynesians alone do it thus."

As Tutu spoke, David's heart-beat quickened. There was a natural desire upon him.

Tutu placed her finest tapa on a pile of mats, slipped out of her clothes and told the boy to disrobe and join her. "This act," she said, "demands great skill, and it will make you beloved by women. You see, David, I am old. But yet, when it is properly done, I derive great pleasure from intercourse. Look, I have already plucked the blossom of the *hala*, pandanus." She guided his hand. "Here, you do it, David. When a woman does not respond to your touch and is cold, the pandanus juice will make her pleasurably excited."

Carefully, step by step, the old grandmother unhurriedly instructed the boy how to excite her sexual passions—the massage, the position, the ever-increasing rhythm—as well as the equally-important peaceful falling-off of the passions.

When they were resting quietly, David asked innocently if Tutu would now bear him a child. She put her nose to his affectionately. "Would that I could. No, Kalakaua, I am sixty-four. The time comes when women cannot bear children, but the pleasure of the connection, properly done, is never lost. We Hawaiians take it to our graves.

"These whites. I know, I've offered them hospitality. You saw what happened to Lot—who learned his sexual conversations the evil way of the white man's whorehouse? And then the Cookes married the pregnant girl off to a commoner trying to make everything pure by a curious ceremony in their church with a frocked man presiding.

"David, before the white man came, I never knew a woman to be discontented with her man. Married, the whites go to their bridal bed untutored; the women afraid. Then, do they stay home and please their women as you did me? Oh no, they go to the Blonde Hotel. They are cold, then hot, then cold: they know nothing of inciting or calming. David, men must be trained as you've been today—procreation is not an art of the gutters."

"But, Tutu, what of our girls? Who is to instruct Victoria so that she can do what you did, on our first night?"

Tutu laughed. "Never fear, your foster mother will instruct her massagers and she will remain a virgin, untouched by man, until the day of your union. But when you sleep with her the first night, there will be an intimate understanding and your embrace will be like a song at dawn."

Girding Aikanaka's famed loincloth about his slender hips, she repeated the chant of Aikanaka:

"High is the land of Kau,
Blessed by the wind,
A chest weathered . . ."

As the old *mele* ended she added: "You have more to learn, but now Haaheo must summon the chiefs and let them know you have been inducted into the secret lore of Aikanaka . . ."

"No, now that I wear Aikanaka's loincloth," said the eleven-year-old Kalakaua, "it is for me. I will summon them myself."

7 California Discovers Gold

That spring, while David Kalakaua was growing into manhood, an event in faraway California had a tremendous effect on his native islands. Gold nuggets were found in Captain John Sutter's mill-race. News of the discovery, which arrived in Honolulu in mid-June—several weeks before it reached New York—turned the city upside down: a native started across the two thousand miles in an outrigger; a bookkeeper absconded with eight thousand dollars to head for the goldfields on a fast whaler; the Blonde Hotel whoremaster hastened to the diggings with a bevy of Hawaiian females including Leilani, the branded "Cape Horn;" outgoing ships stripped even the outlying islands of vegetables and staples; prices doubled and then quadrupled.

With each ship's departure, thousands collected at the wharf and gave leis of flowers and fragrant *maile* to friends lucky enough to scrape together the necessary seventy-five dollars passage money. It was such a mob that witnessed the departure of Foreign Minister Judd and the Princes Lot and Alexander, who were bound for Paris on a diplomatic mission.

Almost forgotten in the excitement of finding "thirteen-pound pure-gold nuggets," as reported by the local paper, was the threatened seizure of the islands by a foreign power —this time France. Admiral de Tromelin, commander of the French Pacific fleet, who had seized Tahiti, now wanted Hawaii, seeing that the British had backed down. Like Lord Paulet, he made some ridiculous demands—French should be made the official court language; the tax of five dollars a gallon on French brandy must be removed; a French hotelkeeper must be reimbursed for damage done by British sailors—and when these demands were not granted, he stormed the Hawaiian fort, spiked guns and hacked trunnions off old brass pieces including the original Russian cannon, and set powder charges under walls and brought them down.

The King accepted the insults and, wisely, offered no resistance. Instead, he ordered Judd to Paris to mediate what differences might exist and, if possible, collect reparations. Taking the two princes along, however, was Judd's idea. He told the King that as future rulers of Hawaii, they needed the broadening influence of travel. Actually, however, he wanted to get Prince Lot Kamehameha out of the way and thereby help to bring about the marriage of his dollar-a-day customs clerk, Charles Reed Bishop, to the fabulously wealthy Princess Bernice* and thereby get the first solid hold upon Hawaii's royalty. So far, both the Kamehameha and Aikanaka dynasties had steadfastly resisted white intrusion. The princess, at birth, had been promised to Lot. With the prince in Europe and with the Cookes' support, Judd thought the marriage might be consummated. To promote Bishop's ardor, he promised the young man the lucrative position of Collector of Customs, should his suit be successful.

---

* Princess Bernice Pauahi Paki. Her lands, today, known as the Bishop Estate, constitute about one-sixth of the total of Hawaii's choicest lands and are worth millions.

The hubbub at the ship, with thousands milling about, was heightened by the loading of bellowing cattle, squealing pigs, and hissing *nene** to be killed for food on the way or sold in San Francisco at fabulous prices. On deck, "Cape Horn" led a boisterous group of singers. She sang: "Whiskey, is the life of man" to which the group responded: "Whiskey, Johnny, Oh!"

Cape Horn:	I'll drink whiskey when I can
Chorus:	Whiskey for my Johnny!
Cape Horn:	Whiskey killed my poor old dad,
Chorus:	Whiskey, Johnny, Oh!
Cape Horn:	Whiskey druv my mother mad,
Chorus:	Whiskey for my Johnny!

A Hawaiian missionary, embarking for the goldfields with thirty-four Bible-carrying native converts,† looked on in displeasure. Less than an hour ago they had taken the temperance oath in the Congregational church and had partaken of communion—because they were natives, however, Reverend Armstrong had substituted water colored with molasses for the wine.

The irate missionary shouted back to the tipsy singers:

"You old whiskey bottle, I'll love you no more,
    You've ruined me, body and soul.
I'll dash you to pieces, and swear from this hour,
    To give up you and the bowl.
And I'll now go and sing (I couldn't do worse)

---

* Perhaps a score of *nene,* the native Hawaiian goose, are still extant in Hawaii's National Park although at that time there were hundreds of thousands. Because of the Hawaiian Islands' remoteness—the most isolated islands in the world—they contain more distinct species of flora and fauna than any other comparable spot.

† These converts applied themselves industriously in the goldfields; saved money; many married Digger women; taught them to read the Hawaiian Bible, and how to pray in Hawaiian.

On that pledge all my hopes I repose,
And I'll get back my money in pocket and purse,
And I'll get back my beautiful nose!"

As the ship stood against the wind, sails billowed, the ir-
repressible "Cape Horn" started the song which was making
the rounds at the waterfront:

"Then blow ye winds, Hi-ho!
For Kaliponi-oh
There's plenty of gold
So I've been told
On the banks of the Sacramen-toh!"

With stiff breezes the ship passed the Farollones de los
Frailes within a fortnight and a swift incoming tide bore the
vessel rapidly through the rocky gates, past White Island,
and into the broad beautiful bay of San Francisco. The harbor was cluttered with two hundred and fifty ships whose
crews had abandoned them for the goldfields.

To the princes their first foreign port, San Francisco,
looked like a miserable dump. Of the population of about
one thousand, only fifty to sixty were in the city in the early
afternoon—the rest were in the goldfields. But when night
fell, the filthy streets came alive with lurching, bragging,
puking drunks. One pot-valiant rider spurred his mount up
the front piazza of the Brown Hotel where they were lodged.
At the fandangoes, flourishing everywhere, bearded men
and their women smoked cigars and spat on the floor. Men
danced in shirt sleeves and kept their hats on. In a side
room of one combination dancehall-saloon, a barker adver-
tised: "Human, live-flesh show demonstrating the intricate
art of intercourse in every conceivable position." This was
followed by a "Beauty and the Beast" performance in which
a boar served a sluttish female.

Judd got the princes out of the unsavory settlement on the first ship for Panama, where they crossed the Isthmus and sailed for Paris, arriving at the height of the social season. The foreign minister engaged a French tailor, a tutor, and a fencing master; and within a week the swarthy princes would not have been recognized. Paris lionized them at reception after reception topped by a soirée given by President Bonaparte, who was later to create the Second Empire, as Napoleon III. The contrast between Paris' perfumed powdered society at Versailles and San Francisco's fandangoes could not have been greater.

Nevertheless, Judd tried valiantly to emphasize the ways of democracy: the idea of free people seeking liberty, equality, fraternity—a concept, he said, which had begun to spread like a flame over Europe since 1848 and would someday reach Hawaii. Two years before, the people of France had overthrown the Bourbon monarchy of Louis Philippe and declared themselves again for individual freedom, he told them; from Paris a party of Polish emigrants had returned to their native land to advocate rebellion against monarchy; a revolution had broken out in Prussia and the dynamic Prince William of Prussia (later Emperor William I of Germany) had fled to England; Hungary had declared herself a republic; Ireland clamored to be free; Holland had just gotten a new constitution; in Rome, Garibaldi was hailed as the George Washington of Europe. But Paris entertainment had a much stronger appeal to the princes than any concept of government.

Despairing of his mission to Paris—to get the French government to punish the admiral who had sacked the Honolulu fort, and failing to educate the princes in the ways of democracy, Judd hastened to London and thence to Washington, en route to Honolulu.

Hardly had the party arrived in Washington when they received invitations from President Zachary Taylor to a levée at *The Mansion*.

The President, in citizen's clothes, greeted the visitors at the door. Judd was resplendent in diplomatic regalia and the princes were in full dress even to cocked hats.

Judd began: "Your Excellency . . ." but the President cut him short, saying: "I prefer 'General'," and scanned his visitors' attire with a certain amusement.

"What is your real purpose in this country?" Taylor asked bluntly.

"General Taylor, I come as King Kamehameha's emissary to obtain a treaty," Judd began.

Their host replied: "Step right in. Make yourselves at home and mix with the rest of the folks. We'll see later what can be done about a treaty."

Alexander scoffed: "Imagine a President receiving his guests at the door like a butler!"

Lot pointed to a man talking to the President. "Look at that fellow in a white overcoat and a dirty wrinkled shirt."

Later, reading newspaper accounts, Alexander quoted: " 'A brilliant reception at The Mansion' and 'A gay society'." He laughed contemptuously.

Seeing that his royal charges were far from being impressed with America's democracy, Judd decided to quit Washington—treaty or no treaty. While waiting for the luggage to be checked and placed on the train, he suggested that the princes go on ahead and hold a compartment.

As they attempted to enter the coach, the conductor ordered: "Go to the rear. This coach is for whites only!"

Alexander stormed: "We paid for first-class accommodations and, by God, we'll stay here."

The conductor grabbed the King-designate's sleeve and tore it, whereupon Prince Lot was upon him.

"What goes on?" called Judd, pushing through the crowd.

"This pair of niggers is trying to tell the conductor how to run his train."

"These men are Hawaiian princes," Judd cried. "I'm an Ambassador. Diplomatic immunity is involved."

Judd ordered the princes into the coach. As the train started, fifteen-year-old Alexander vowed that when he became King, he'd even the score with "these dirty, liberty-loving Americans."

While Judd mourned the futility of his trip, and Alexander and Lot raged against the ways of democracy, in Honolulu Charles Bishop had been ardently wooing Bernice Paki. He liked Bernice and he liked the idea of being married to a rich princess. At seventeen the girl was tall and stately with a slender figure, firm rounded breasts, full lips and the merriest of black eyes. Aided and abetted by Amos and Juliette Cooke, opportunities to be with Bernice were many. The girl herself was disturbed. She knew that she had been promised at birth to Lot Kamehameha and that Lot might be a King some day. On the other hand he was not nearly so attractive as Charles Bishop—who was white. And the Cookes pointed out that with the coming of Christianity such heathenish customs as betrothals at birth were outmoded.

Gossip carried news of the courtship to Bernice's father and mother, who called at the school at once and gave explicit directions that the wooing should cease and that Bernice was to marry no one but Lot Kamehameha. But Bishop was always about and Lot was in Europe or Washington. Bernice decided to marry Bishop.

The Cookes lost no time in sending out the marriage invitations. Bernice's mother, receiving hers, tore it up and shouted, "Tell Bernice she will not have enough of my land to cover her excrement." It was a very private wedding; the bride wore white muslin, and only the King's aide, young Chief David Kalakaua and Princess Victoria were guests. Charles Bishop seemed extremely happy.

David and Victoria were uneasy. That afternoon Haaheo had declared herself ill. There were so many new diseases about and Haaheo was feverish. As soon as they could, they left the wedding party and returned to Haaheo's home.

They found her no better. Since Honolulu had become the world's crossroads for California-bound ships from New York, the Aleutians, the Spice Islands, Australia, Cape of Good Hope, England, there had arrived at the islands the human scum of the earth, pimps, whores, convicts, murderers, thieves, embarked upon a desperate last voyage for gold. Many got no farther than Hawaii, their money gone or health broken; they somehow stayed on in that easy and beneficent climate. But they carried with them whooping cough, amoebic dysentery, and measles, which swept the land.

Thousands sickened. When fever ran high the natives did as their ancestors had done, plunged into the restorative cooling sea waters of Kane. The results were terrifying. In one month in Honolulu alone, eight hundred and twenty-six, including the unregenerate Prince Moses, died of the measles.

Haaheo had watched the plague with frightened eyes and kept David beside her whenever she could. As she saw hundreds of her Polynesian countrymen die she wailed, "David, it is we who die of these diseases, not the haole. This curse is destroying the bulwarks of our land; the old people who alone have clung to the true way of our ancestors and our gods."

When Haaheo herself succumbed to the disease her feverish mind tormented her. The terrible spectre of white supremacy hovered over her. "Kalakaua, you are growing into the ways of the white man."

When David attempted to deny it, she railed against his studying military tactics with the Prussian captain who was training the King's soldiers.

She worried about the Aikanaka loincloth. "You must treasure it always; it is your badge of honor."

She worried about her prized treasures of Niihau mats, calabashes, and feathered cloaks which, with her lands, she had willed to David. "What value have these if you live in a white man's house, use a white man's bed, his dishes, his clothes? Anyone can buy those things with this damned gold which has become the meaningless goal of every man's living.

"And don't trust the Kamehamehas. Forget Victoria; she will never do you any good. Look how Bernice betrayed Lot and took a white man for a husband."

Grandmother Tutu, embarrassed for Victoria, laid a finger on her lips and beckoned the girl to follow her out of the sickroom so that she could apologize.

Kalakaua summoned Tutu and whispered to her to call old Governor Kekuanaoa.

Haaheo was still talking. "Beware of the missionaries. Their children will have lands when ours go begging."

David put his hand on her forehead and she paused. He said softly: "I swear by Lono, and Kane and Ku, dear Haaheo, that what you have taught me I shall never forget. I will make your way our way of life in Hawaii."

A smile passed over her face and her eyes closed. He waited. Then his fingers slipped to her wrist. There was no pulse. He was aware of a great loneliness. Haaheo had given him love and in her zeal for the future of Hawaii had filled his days with meaning. He was empty of feeling; sorrow would come later; now there was just vacancy. He laid her hand gently by her side and went from the room to take the news of Haaheo's death to Victoria and Tutu.

8 America and England Fish in Troubled Waters

In his new role of lieutenant and aide to the failing King Kamehameha, the eighteen-year-old Kalakaua learned that Haaheo's terror of the whites was well founded. Conspiracies and counter-conspiracies were under way which he could not fathom, and rumors swept through the palace until the weary King could find release only in liquor. Ugliest of all to the proud Hawaiians was the overbearing, contemptuous attitude of the come-lately whites of California, tailings of the gold rush, many of them shanghaied for the whaling fleet.

One sailor, arrested for disorderliness in a saloon, threatened the turnkey, who promptly used his club, bashing in the sailor's skull. Next morning the sailor's shipmates headed a mob of four thousand who roared their demand for the turnkey. There was no violence until the return from the funeral. Eight thousand whalers roamed the streets and a native constable used a club in attempting to arrest one belligerent. His companions chased the constable to the police station, broke down the door, beat and kicked the man senseless and fired the building.

At the fort the Marshal of the Kingdom called for action. Knowing that a bloody race battle might result, Lieutenant Kalakaua wisely parried: "Marshal Parks, it is not for the

Hawaiian troops to disperse this mob. Let the white men do it. Their property is threatened. By turning Hawaiians against white men, we'll stir up greater trouble."

Parks railed: "Stir up trouble! My God, man, they're already beating up my police, and a fire is raging at the waterfront!"

Flames from the police station had spread to the harbormaster's building and a burning shingle started a fire on one of the oil-soaked whaling barques. Although shorthanded, sea captains frantically cast off lines, knowing that once the fire spread amid their fifteen-million-dollar fleet loaded with whale-oil, all would be lost.

White merchants, worrying lest the flaming oil should spread over the water and destroy the entire waterfront and the business district, organized a fire brigade under the leadership of Alexander Joy Cartwright* and hurried to the waterfront. While one band of more sensible sailors swarmed over the burning whaling ship to protect their own season's oil-take in the other vessels, a much larger group of several thousands, bent on plunder, stormed up Grog street and, while the city was fighting its fires, broke down the doors of whorehouses and saloons. The thousands caroused, drank and raped and by midnight were so demoralized that they offered little resistance to the businessmen's volunteer militia. The riot ended; but new fagots had been thrown on Hawaii's dangerous fire of racial hatreds. Although Kalakaua's shrewd appraisal of the situation—keeping armed Hawaiians from meeting rioting whites head-on—had averted what might have been wholesale murder, the day of decision was hastening on, with ever-increasing tempo.

---

* A member of the New York Knickerbocker Club, Alexander Joy Cartwright is frequently credited with having founded the game of American baseball.

Just how far this growing race hatred was being inspired by the Americans was difficult even for an onlooker to estimate. However, when the customary toast to the ruling King was proposed at the American Fourth of July banquet, George Lathrop, a doctor employed by the United States government, jumped to his feet and shouted: "I object to this damned nonsense. On our glorious Day of Independence it is neither becoming nor proper to drink to a God-damned nigger, even though he wears a crown."

A tight little band of come-latelies cheered the shocking insult but few knew that Lathrop was one of a group, called the Committee of 13, which was actively engaged in a plan to foment trouble between the whites and the Hawaiians. They planned to seize the palace, take the King prisoner, and set up a Republic of Hawaii. They would issue bonds; petition to be annexed to the United States, and have that country assume all financial obligations, including the outstanding bond issue. Enterprising Texans had made ten millions this way: the Committee might do equally well.

Meantime, this seditious group was not aware that the newly-arrived American Commissioner, David L. Gregg, had been sent to Hawaii by Franklin Pierce, newly-elected President of the United States, with the secret order: "The United States wants Hawaii—get it!" Before leaving San Francisco for his post, Gregg had sought out a filibuster leader who could round up a gang of cutthroats and bring them to Hawaii, if necessary, to exert a little extra persuasion should the King be reluctant to agree to a treaty of annexation. He found George Ryckman, owner of several old sailing ships, and made a secret agreement.

When Gregg arrived in Honolulu and presented his credentials, his job seemed even easier than he anticipated. The

King, who was drinking heavily, confided: "Gregg, my race is doomed. My people are dying. I myself am dying. My troubles are never-ending. My successor, Alexander, will inherit nothing but grief."

Having learned of Alexander's intense anti-American feeling, inflamed by his recent trip, Gregg proposed immediate annexation to the distraught King.

"Before we can do that," replied the King, "we must know exactly what terms your country offers."

Jubilant with that auspicious beginning, Gregg made the mistake of confiding his success to his fellow-American, Dr. Lathrop, not knowing, of course, about the Committee of 13 which was out to doublecross him. To forestall any positive word from the State Department, Lathrop immediately wrote a letter to the American Secretary of State denouncing Gregg. Then Lathrop and the Committee of 13 sent for their own professional organizer, George Wilkes, in San Francisco, who demanded a cut of a quarter million dollars.

Secret as both the Committee of 13 and the American commissioner had been in their plans to take the islands, their intentions were ferreted out by the suspicious British Consul, General Miller. Shrewdly, he decided to put the American commissioner against the Committee of 13; work on the anti-American prejudices of the chiefs—King-designate Alexander in particular; and, to forestall any filibuster action in Hawaii, to send for the British Pacific squadron based on Vancouver Island.

After sending a fast sailing ship to British Columbia to summon the men-of-war, he saw Prince Alexander and warned him of both Gregg's plans of annexation and the seditious plans of the Committee of 13 for establishing a Republic of Hawaii. That done, the Britisher went to Gregg, and in a seeming burst of confidence told him of the treasonable Committee of 13, naming the leaders, Cartwright, Monsarrat and Lathrop. Dumbfounded, Gregg hurried to the United States Marine Hospital to find Dr. Lathrop. Lathrop not only admitted the conspiracy and the fact that he had sent for Wilkes to organize a revolution, but attempted to bribe Gregg to join them, offering a handsome share of profits for the American Commissioner's help.

In desperation Gregg wrote to his own man Ryckman in San Francisco ordering Ryckman to come at once with his men, "to put pressure on the King," before Wilkes, Lathrop's man, could arrive. Then the triple-crossed Gregg saw the King and demanded a "yes or no" reply regarding annexation. When the King replied that the decision was Prince Alexander's, Gregg demanded a hearing before the Privy Council.

Nothing could have suited General Miller better. Through Prince Alexander the Britisher had received an invitation to attend the Privy Council meeting. Miller asked that it be an official diplomatic session.

The unsuspecting Gregg, innocent of diplomatic procedure, arrived in plain clothes and on foot. The fact that troops were drawn up to receive him meant nothing to him. But Miller arrived in a carriage three minutes later and, of course, was in full dress. In the council room the King, surrounded by the chiefs and chieftesses, was in full uniform. Princes Alexander and Lot stood on either side, before the throne, holding ancient spears. Aide David Kalakaua was at the King's right, Victoria at his left. Thrown over the back of the throne was the priceless Kamehameha feather cloak, worn only on state occasions. Gregg's dress was plainly an insult to the court.

King Kamehameha opened the conference: "My chiefs, we are convened to discuss annexation with the United States." He added that he was a sick man and that he wanted the problem of annexation settled before he died. Turning to Gregg, he said: "For my Privy Council to give this matter its unbiased consideration, we took the liberty to invite General Miller."

Gregg spoke first. After reviewing the hazards of Hawaii's independence—pointing out Lord Paulet's and Admiral de Tromelin's threat of seizure—he told them bluntly of the imminent danger from the Committee of 13. In a final burst of oratory he spoke of the great future of Hawaii as a sister state in the union—"A union of free people where every man has a chance to become president."

King-designate Alexander asked coldly: "If the United States is all this, why must you have slaves?"

Before Gregg could answer, Alexander's father, Governor Matthew Kekuanaoa, interfered: "All this matters nothing, Alexander. How much does the United States offer us in cash?"

"Two and a half million dollars outright or a settlement of three hundred thousand dollars a year for the King and chiefs with the amount diminishing as the nobility lessens in number."

Astonished at the liberal offer, the Governor advised his son: "Alexander, we are small fish in an ocean of big fish where the big eat the little. Let us take the money while we can."

Alexander asked that they hear General Miller, who began: "In years past even as your ancestors were following the Morning Star into uncharted seas, England had its inception from a small island, a kingdom not unlike yours, and today the sun never sets upon its empire. When that royal cloak of Kamehameha the Great was still being fashioned, we were great mariners, too. Sir Francis Drake sailed into the Pacific, the sea of your illustrious ancestors—the Kamehamehas and the Aikanakas. . . ."

After ten years in Hawaii, Miller knew the Hawaiians' predilection for historical narrative. Every eye was fixed upon him.

"Today, your nation which is still small, is faced with a crisis which affects the future of every true Polynesian and it calls for resolute action worthy of your forebears: shall you maintain your independent sovereignty or shall you become slaves . . ."

Governor Kekuanaoa interrupted: "You did not always speak thus, General Miller. Less than four years ago, this same Privy Council was forced to send a complaint to your government because you swore at me, ridiculed my officers, and called us barbarians. You said then that we were not fit for self-rule. Be practical, Miller. We desire a compact today so that we chiefs may die in peace and have no more of your Lord Paulets to harass us. If your country has an offer to make that is better than that of the United States, make it!"

Without instructions from his government, Miller could only appeal to prejudices: "Selling your self-respect for filthy gold will never bring you peace of mind or content-ment, Governor Kekuanaoa." Turning to the other chiefs, he said: "Remember you are bargaining with a country that is demoralized, corrupt, and on the verge of civil war over the question of slavery."

The implacable Governor raised his withered arm. "Lis-ten, General Miller, your own Lord Paulet forced me, an old man, the father of the king, to haul down my own flag with this crippled arm." He turned to his Chiefs: "Our best protection against filibusterers, or Frenchmen, or Britishers is to be under the protective custody of our great neighbor, the United States, and the money Commissioner Gregg offers will permit us to live decently."

"The money Gregg offers may come for four years, until there is a new administration," reiterated Miller. "If you wish to be protected by a strong nation, choose one at least that respects your color. Wasn't your Chieftess Liliha received like a Queen in England by the King himself? If you joined the United States, how would you be treated by your fellow-Americans? You remember the sailors' riot earlier this year? The insult your King received from this Doctor Lathrop at their Independence Day banquet? Should you become a state, how would your Polynesian representatives be treated? Would southerners detect the difference between Polynesians and Negroes? I know that at Charleston, South Carolina, our British subjects from the West Indies are thrown in jail overnight. How would you travel when you are barred from their first-class compartments?"

Commissioner Gregg broke in. "Miller, you speak of slavery. The United States abolished slave ships while yours still sail. You speak of intolerance. Your illustrious Queen Victoria decreed just this year that Catholics could not profess their religion publicly throughout England. You speak of the spoliation of natives. England shelled Canton, China, last year because that country dared interfere with your opium traffic."

The old general, outflanked, fired his last round. "Your Majesty, I do not advocate that Hawaii become a part of the British Empire. I advocate that you maintain your independence—get a guarantee from France, England, and the United

States for joint protection. If at the end of six months, you cannot get such joint protection, then by all means consider annexation."

King Kamehameha turned to Gregg. "Six months is not long. Certainly that must meet with your approval."

Even Miller could not have known how well his counter-proposal would work. Within a month his Pacific squadron arrived and Gregg's filibusters were forced to remain on an outer island. Before the six months were half up, the King died and, to prevent an uprising by the Committee of 13, armed marines landed from the British men-of-war while Chief David Kalakaua rode through the streets proclaiming Prince Alexander as Kamehameha IV.

9 A Glimpse of Past Glory

King Alexander Kamehameha appointed Chief David Kalakaua as aide-de-camp and, to prevent a coup by the Committee of 13, enlarged his Household Guard and placed David
in charge with the honorary title of Lieutenant General.
This position scarcely kept David busy and he spent much of
his time making a Polynesian shrine out of Haaheo's beautiful Waikiki estate—as she would have wanted it. The promise he made on her deathbed—"by our gods, I will make
your way of life, Haaheo, our way"—remained fresh in his
mind. Happily, Victoria joined him.

The spark touched off by their restoration of things Hawaiian kindled a fire which swept through the land: old
chanters and famed dancers and singers, long forgotten,
suddenly converged upon Haaheo's home, coming from the
remotest parts of Hawaii. Chanters told stories of Hawaii's
legendary past; the old dancers taught younger ones hulas
which had been banned; and sweet singers revived melodies
of old mating songs which had not been heard since their
childhood. But best, said Victoria, was the bright light that
shone in the eyes of these old artists. Humiliated and despised and shoved aside all these years, suddenly again they
had a part in Hawaii's life.

"David," said Victoria, "you are building a true monument to the memory of Haaheo. Everyone you contact, benefits. It isn't that Haaheo's lands have made you rich, but that you share those riches. What you are doing will live forever. No wonder I love you, David."

The tall, handsome young man looked down at her and smiled.

"For all my life, Victoria, Haaheo decided and I agreed. When she died I was lost. But now as I see our dancers in the hulas that have almost been forgotten, as I listen to the chants and songs of the years gone by, I feel the mana of Haaheo upon me and her assurance that our way of life will prevail. It is our way, Victoria, the Hawaiian way of life we both love."

These were halcyon days: In the mornings old crafts were revived, in the afternoons Hawaiian men tried out boxing, wrestling, surfboard riding and the catching of hurled spears. In the evening there was dancing, singing and chanting. David frequently chanted the old stories Haaheo had taught him, while Tutu, never far away, paced him by beating out a rhythm on a gourd.

Sometimes David's immediate family were with them. According to the white man's familial pattern, a curious relationship existed among them. David's womb-mother, Ane Keohokalole, had borne two girls, Liliuokalani and Likelike, and a son who had died young, but David felt no close kinship to them. This loose family pattern was a result, perhaps, of the Hawaiian custom of adoption at birth. Mothers were often very young, knew little of child rearing and so gave their children to older, more experienced women to rear. David Kalakaua had a greater regard for Ane as a high ranking chieftess than as a mother. For his father, the boy husband upon whom the pangs of his birth had been visited, he had no feeling at all.

Ane Keohokalole's interest in David was keen because he was the last male link in her chain of descent from Aikanaka; her lands were his, and she was extremely jealous of his hereditary rights and would fight for his ascendancy over the ruling Kamehamehas.

While Kalakaua and Victoria were happily restoring old Polynesian traditions, making friends among Hawaiians and enemies among missionaries "for reviving heathen customs," King Alexander Kamehameha was dissipating his energies and gathering about him a dissolute group of drunkards. The palace became headquarters for drinking, gambling and whoring. Two months after his accession, the King and his drunken companions broke into the Merchants' Exchange saloon at midnight, drank their fill of Schryder Champagne, smashed chairs and billiard tables, and left the place a shambles. A thousand-dollar settlement, paid by the King, did not hush up the affair. Another night's poker session broke up in a fist fight in which the King suffered a black eye. While fishing, the King split a native's skull for daring to disturb his royal fishing grounds. His instability and restlessness were perhaps aggravated by his continual moving from one of his island residences to another, accompanied, of course, by the same rowdies.

Doctor Thomas Rooke, his physician, could have given an explanation for the bachelor King's excessive indulgences: his breath-taking asthma, and piles, robbed him of sleep and so he played poker and billiards all night and drank himself to stupefaction.

Two years after he was proclaimed King, Alexander announced his engagement to Emma Rooke, his physician's adopted daughter, a girl partly Polynesian, partly white. The responsible element in the kingdom hailed the engagement with relief, hoping it would put a stop to the man's roistering. The Americans, however, were openly critical because Emma was half English. Already irritated by the King's pro-British tendencies, they said the alliance smacked of British domination. The Congregational missionaries, of course, objected to Emma's Episcopalianism—"British Popery." Nor did the Hawaiians approve. Among those who gathered in David Kalakaua's home, resentment was particularly bitter. Princess Ruth—who had spat on Kalakaua's feet at Liliha's deathbed—bellowed her prejudices about "half-breeds with foreign blood usurping high places." And Ane made no bones about the fact that the young King should have married David's sister, Liliuokalani.

"It angers me, David, to see these haole-loving Kamehamehas usurping our throne," she confided. "These Kamehamehas never have loved the Polynesians. You saw how Matthew Kekuanaoa would have sold us into slavery to this scoundrel Gregg."

David smiled. "Ane, it is not becoming of my womb-mother to speak this way of her future relatives."

She spat.

"The gods of Aikanaka forbid." She forgot that just a few moments before she had advocated the marriage of Alexander and her daughter Liliuokalani. "What do you mean, 'future relatives'?"

"I am marrying Victoria."

"Remember how Bernice forsook Lot to whom she was engaged to take up with that customs clerk, Bishop!" she warned. "These Kamehamehas are deceitful. They cannot be trusted even in their bedrooms. Beware that Victoria doesn't have a white man rob her of your wedding-night gift." Despite the warning, she accepted the news with evident pleasure. Victoria was the highest-born chieftess in the islands. "Ha, once you marry her, we will rule the islands. We Aikanakas are fertile: the Kamehamehas lack lead in their pencils. I will disown you as my womb-babe if you can't produce ten children for every one of these Kamehamehas!"

David cautioned: "Say nothing of our intended marriage, Ane, for the present."

Victoria was busy supervising the palace preparations for Alexander's wedding. But she was restless. She had promised her brother that she would not marry for two years, when she would be twenty. That seemed an eternity, the more so because she saw less of David, who was now reading law and giving much time to it.

When she could, Victoria lured David away from his lawbooks and then they talked as most intended mates do—of their love which was as no love that had ever happened to man and woman before; of their future home together; the children she would bear him; and then of the night when they would walk together to the mats in his bedroom and she would remove his loincloth of Aikanaka, and on the morning, refreshed, they would face the rising sun in their doorway, naked, man and wife.

On the evening before King Alexander's wedding, David turned over Haaheo's home by the sea to guests who came from the outside islands. There were singers and chanters of note. As the brilliant sunset hues faded from the clear skies, the guests assembled in front of the house, facing the sea. A gentle ocean breeze rustled the tousled palms. The old chanters took their places. Victoria sat on the mats next to David. There were several chants before Palea, a chanter of Kau, came toward the assembly and intoned:

"Hear the chant of Keoua, chief of the Rising Sun. An ancestor slain. Great were his bones and great were his deeds and great was his trust in men living."

The drums of the beaters rumbled with strength of waves striking a cliff, and of thunder, and of waterfalls. As the echoes subsided, Palea continued:

"Thrice Kamehameha went out to do battle with Keoua and thrice he was roundly defeated!"

The gourd pounders made their voices ring with the sound of battle, followed by the victorious shouts of Keoua's men. Intermingled was the undertone of the dying, vanquished men of Kamehameha.

Palea went on:

"Then the thrice defeated Kamehameha sought out his gods. His Gods said: 'Hast thou built us a temple, a great temple, greater than any?'

"And Kamehameha asked: 'Where shall I build such a one?'

"'There, where the sands of the sea sing with the water, at Kawaihae*, and make the temple large with great stones, for upon them you will sacrifice the bones of a high chief! Yes, even the greatest, your cousin, Keoua!'"

The great drums sprang to life and thundered and then slowly their tremendous roar died in the whisper of the palm fronds.

"'But this Keoua has defeated me three times in battle.'

"'True, but cunning failed thee.' The spokesman of the gods leaned forward and whispered: 'After you have built the temple at the singing waters of the sea, send Keawe to your enemy—him will Keoua believe.'

* Kawaihae means singing sea water. Remnants of the temple built by Kamehameha the Great are standing today, and Hawaiians hold the spot sacred.

"This messenger Keawe was your ancestor, Chief David Kalakaua, famed descendant of Aikanaka," said the chanter.

"Kamehameha sent the messenger Keawe to the thrice victorious Keoua and said: 'Kamehameha sends me to make peace that shall last as long as the pillars of the islands. Come, dedicate with me our new temple.'

"While the cunning messenger spoke, his many retainers spread forth rich and rare gifts.

"Thrice victorious Keoua asked: 'How can I believe this message of peace?'

" 'Am I not a cousin by your mother?' demanded the sharp one. 'Come I with warriors?'

" 'Truly great is thy bravery Keawe to come alone and without warriors,' said Keoua. 'I will go at once with a thousand warriors and we shall throw our spears away, and our war clubs shall be consigned to the fire!'

"There was one voice lifted, only one, that of the oldest *kahuna*. He warned: 'Trust not the wiles of this thrice defeated Kamehameha. Only a victor can offer peace.'

"Keoua thrust the suspicious one aside. 'No, old one. Bloodshed shall cease on this island; tranquillity prevail; fear banished; and we shall wake in the morning rejoicing.'

"Gift-laden with fine tapa and calabashes worn smooth, the victorious Keoua then took his warriors, and his canoes steered a straight course for Kawaihae, the home of the water which sings on the sand of the sea. And the passage was smooth as a liquid mirror with the peace of heaven reflected."

The melodic gourd accompaniment faded. Then, startlingly, it roared out like ominous thunder. In the audience, not a person stirred, Palea continued:

"Lo, as they rowed, Keoua and his thousand warriors saw massed thick in the distance a great fleet of canoes, double and single, a warlike array, and he knew there was no escaping. Reading his doom, he cried to his unarmed men: 'Behold the wind clouds are gathering in the heavens. But come forward, my comrades, steer the prows of our canoes to the beach where Kamehameha himself stands watching. In him we trust.'

"Taut muscles sprang into action, willing the paddles to obey the command of their glorious chief, well aware of the murderous betrayal under guise of friendship and peace. And when Keoua's canoe bounded up against the shore, Kamehameha hailed him: 'Rise, and come here, that we may know each other.' Keoua leaped out and chanted a praise to Kamehameha: 'Great is thy strength,' and as he cried, he was seized from behind, held, disemboweled, and his guts spilled to the ground at the feet of Kamehameha the traitor."

David's guests joined in the awful lament:

"*Alas, alas. Great was the deceit of Kamehameha.*"

When lamentations had ceased, Palea continued:

"The waters of Kawaihae were red with the blood of the thousand warriors of Kau. All, all were killed save one man who took the word back to the quick-sorrowing land of Kau. Thus ends my story." *

The gourd beats were swallowed up in the night and upon the people seated in front of Haaheo's home fell a great stillness broken only by the sobs of old folk from Kau who remembered. This was their past.

In the distance rose the sound of a violin from the Hawaiian Hotel and the singing of drunken white men:

---

* This chant, now recorded for the first time, was obtained by the author from Mary Kawena Pukui, a direct descendant of the famous chanter, Palea. She is an accomplished nose-flute player, and the Hawaiian translator at the Bishop Museum, Honolulu.

"My Mary's got the whooping cough
    Johnny's got the measles,
That's where all my money goes
    Pop goes the weasel!"

Victoria stirred in David's arms. "Love, I must go. Remember, tomorrow is Emma's wedding."

10 Romance and Disillusion

Before the shadows of night lifted from Oahu's valleys, natives were coming to the palace grounds burdened with the huge bundles of reeds to spread on the road. Flags of a dozen nations fluttered from ships and consulates while the King's standard floated above the great stone church. When the King's cavalry company arrived, more than three thousand had crowded into the church, which was festooned with orange blossoms, jessamine and ginger.

It was almost noon when the bride, accompanied by her foster-father, drove out of the Rooke grounds off Great Britain street. Emma, delicate and small, looked lovely in a lustrous white silk gown. Her Brussels point lace veil was caught in her black hair with a wreath of snow-white *pikake* and fragrant orange blossoms. Following came Princess Victoria and David's sister, Liliuokalani. As the bride's cortège passed the entrance of the palace, the King with his train gallantly dashed out and the two companies joined. In the bridegroom's carriage sat his father, Governor Matthew Kekuanaoa, and Prince Lot. Kahili-bearers ran alongside while the King's aides, David Kalakaua and Marcus Monsarrat rode horseback. David smiled at Victoria as he dropped back beside her carriage. "You'll make a prettier bride, Victoria, when the time comes."

As the royal procession approached the church, soldiers and natives suddenly prostrated, while friends ripped off their outer garments and threw them in the pathway. The three thousand within the church stood as the kneeling bride and groom exchanged vows, first in Hawaiian and then in English.

At the palace reception, hundreds wished the young couple health and happiness. For the evening ball, Queen Emma changed into an exquisite airy fabric of lace, embroidered in white and silver, adorned with marabou feathers.

Among the guests were missionaries, some of whom had been in Hawaii for more than thirty years. Watching the schottisches, minuets and quadrilles, the dainty frocks of the women, the lithe grace of the men, their memories went back to the first royal audience granted a missionary. The Queen of the Islands of that day had been clad in a single piece of tapa cloth. She received them sprawled out on a grass mat while receiving a massage. The King, in a loin cloth, squatted on the floor of his grass house tippling from a bottle of Holland gin. Civilization had substituted iced champagne for gin, minuets for hulas, flimsy dresses for tapas, and had replaced grass huts with substantial dwellings. The missionary guests were bewildered but not happy.

At midnight a supper of chicken, lobster salad, and boned turkey was served, after which dancing continued until three. Hundreds of transparencies were hanging from the trees in the large palace grounds as Kamehameha IV took his bride to her new home. Despite the hour, Palea, the chanting kahuna of Kau, was waiting. With a prayer to the gods to bless their royal home and a hula to Emma's *U-u*, to make it fertile, Palea dropped a thin tapa sheet over the shoulder of the royal pair, telling them that henceforth they would share the cares of state, the sorrows and joys of life. When dawn came two hours later, the King and Queen stepped out naked and faced the new day's rising sun, thus observing Hawaiian tradition.

Dances, musicales, box-auction suppers, horseback riding, and theatre parties to see Edwin Booth, the talented American actor, enlivened the honeymoon. Queen Emma persuaded Commissioner Gregg to learn the quadrille. In the evenings she gathered young people around the rosewood spinet; Victoria, Liliuokalani, David, Bernice Bishop and her husband Charles were good singers. Mornings she read *Vanity Fair* aloud to Alexander and together they discovered Wordsworth. Knowing Oliver Wendell Holmes's island relatives, they read with added relish his *Autocrat at the Breakfast Table*. In the sun-filled afternoons they rode to Nuuanu Pali. From that two-thousand-foot eminence they beheld one of the sublimest sights in the world—far below them was the turquoise sea, the subtropical foliage and this backed up with the huge green-clad monolithic cliffs.

Emma wanted to establish a well-behaved royal class. Missionaries blamed her for countenancing the devil's pastimes, dancing and champagne. Wagging tongues spread the tale that she was the illegitimate child of her foster-father, Dr. Thomas Rooke, and therefore a nobody. Palace entertainments aroused diplomatic irritations. General Miller demanded that his chair be six inches ahead of the French consul; the American Commissioner contended that his rank carried over to his assistant and both of them should stand ahead of the British Commissioner General in the receiving line.

Annoyed by all this pettiness, Ane Keohokalole, David's mother, who seldom interfered with his life, demanded,

"David when will you raise your hand against this damned haole living?"

Ane's high rank forced David to moderate his response. He told her that he and Victoria liked this haole-aping no better than she did, but that Emma was Queen. Then he rubbed her cheek affectionately with his own. "Try to be agreeable with my future wife, won't you, Ane?"

One morning, David Kalakaua sent Victoria a present of two poodle pups, and Victoria sent him a message that he must come that evening. As Kalakaua turned his perfectly matched greys out of the palace grounds at the beginning of their evening drive together, Victoria kept running her tapered fingers around the tight little curls on the snow-white puppy's forehead. She playfully lifted him to her face and imitated his rapid snuffing noises to amuse David. The poodle, in his excitement, began to drip. Victoria took David's handkerchief, spread it over her lap and said: "Now little Piko's rank is royal."

They saw Prince Lot walking down the street with Commissioner Gregg. David stopped the basket phaeton beside them and offered them a lift. As Lot got in, the carriage springs settled with his two hundred and sixty pounds.

"How did you like the new goods that arrived on the *Messenger Bird*?" Gregg asked Victoria.

Behind David's back she raised her finger to her lips, afraid that he might spill the news. She had kept the arrival of her wedding dress secret. It had come from Paris in a sealed tin box to protect it during the long sea voyage around the Horn.

"Very much! Isn't this lace nice?" Victoria asked, smoothing her frock. The white lace next to her olive skin was lovely and Gregg did not miss the beauty of the young chieftess—her shining black eyes, the erect bosom, the curve of her neck and shoulders. Turning to David, Gregg said: "I suppose you're planning a church wedding."

David retorted: "That's haole nonsense."

"But David," Victoria pouted, "you told me you wanted a big wedding."

"Don't forget, Kalakaua, weddings are by and for the women," Gregg hastened. He wondered if Victoria knew how appealing she was to white men.

By this time they were opposite the consulate. "This is where we get out." He turned to Victoria. "Allow me to wish the two of you much happiness."

As soon as Lot and Gregg had gone, Kalakaua asked: "What's all this wedding talk? He seems to know more about it than I do."

"David, we can marry April first, if you're still willing."

He promptly pulled her into a close embrace and kissed her.

"April first. This is January 6. Why can't we marry next month?"

"It's only three months and twenty-five days; I counted. And David, do you suppose I'll be frightened? My heart's pounding."

He put his hand over her heart and said: "I wish we were married already."

The following week, Monie Monsarrat was dipping flakes of Kona crab into lemon butter at the palace with Prince Lot. Aide to the prince, Monie had become an intimate of Lot and his sister Victoria. A good story-teller, his profession as auctioneer gave him endless anecdotes. As he raised a glass of Burgundy he saw his reflection in a large mirror. He studied it—gold braid and all—with no little pleasure.

He was tall, black-haired, and his worldly ease among women exerted an indefinable charm on the young Victoria. Her attraction to him was partly due to his race; for eight years at the Cookes' she had been taught the superiority of the white man.

Monie moved his chair the better to see her as she played a Scarlatti sonata on the spinet. As he listened, the young auctioneer looked about him. He had come a long way from his humble beginnings in England to marriage into one of the leading island families—the Dowsetts—having supper with the Crown Prince and wearing an aide's uniform. But Monsarrat forgot this as he looked again at Victoria. His heart pounded with the desire of possession. Forgotten were his duties as husband and father of three children, his position as aide to Prince Lot, Kalakaua's engagement to the young girl. He must have her.

The sonata finished, Victoria excused herself with some confusion in her manner. Monsarrat thanked his host for the enjoyable dinner and explained that he had to go to prepare an advertisement for the *Pacific Commercial Advertiser*. Once out of the palace, however, Monsarrat walked quickly into the heavy darkness. Looking back to see that he was not observed, he skirted the King's house and approached Victoria's apartment, where lights showed from her bedroom window. He whispered: "It's me. Monie. I've got something that I must show you."

He tried to keep his voice down although his heart beat furiously. Victoria, in a negligée, came to the window. She asked him to wait while she dressed and got Emma to join her.

Monsarrat removed his square-toed military shoes. He knew that he was a fool. If he were caught, Lot and Alexander would kill him. He stole toward her door, opened it slowly, and shut it behind him. He warned her not to make a noise. "I couldn't help coming to see you." He blew out the light.

"You must be out of your head, Monie," she whispered. "What makes you think I'd want you?"

He slipped his arm underneath her dressing gown and felt her body shake violently. "Victoria, I've loved you since I first saw you. I want you more than anything in the world. You belong to me."

Adroitly he led her to the bed, brushed the mosquito-bar netting out of the way and pulled her down beside him. She was breathing quickly and he would prevail if he did not rush his advances. Hawaiian women, he knew, were mad about white lovers.

"You don't think me a cheap strumpet, do you?" she asked.

For answer he slipped his arm about her tightly. Her half-open mouth fell against his. She drew close to him and shuddered, then relaxed in his embrace. Ecstasy, guilt and fear were mixed in her response. . . . Then, as they rested, she started violently and whispered: "Monie, someone's at the window." He raised his head, listened, then fell back. "It was your heart pounding, my love."

"No, listen," she warned. Voices approached, climaxed by her brother Lot's shout: "Monsarrat!"

Her heart jumped. "What'll we do? Oh Monie, where can I put you? Quick, put on your clothes."

"Open that door!" Lot's powerful voice boomed. "Open, or I'll break it down."

"Just a minute," she said. "I was sound asleep." She stood wringing her hands, naked, while Monsarrat straightened his clothes. When he reached for his shoes, he knew discovery was certain; he had left them outside the door. He went to the window and saw a group of servants before it, then rushed for the closet, knocking over a little Japanese sewing cabinet.

"God damn it!" he cursed.

Picking some clothes from her closet, he threw them at her. "Here, for Christ's sake, woman, cover your nakedness."

Under Lot's heavy impact, the door shattered and he loomed before the guilty pair. "You son-of-a-bitch! Come into my home as a friend and ravish my sister. Busy with advertisements, you filthy bastard!" As he talked he approached Monsarrat. "You knew she is about to be married to Kalakaua. Monsarrat, I am going to kill you."

Monsarrat backed to the wall and fell to his knees. Victoria saw her huge brother transformed into a killing brute. Kamehameha, their ancestor, had broken a man's back with his bare hands. Terrified, she threw herself between Monsarrat and her brother. "Lot," she cried, "I asked Monie to come to my bedroom."

He looked at her, doubting. Overcome with rage, he grabbed Monsarrat by the shoulder and lifted him to his feet with one hand as if he were a rag. He held him at arm's length.

Again Victoria interposed. "Lot, I tell you, it's my fault."

"So a white man nods and you fall into his hot embrace like a rutting bitch. What of David Kalakaua? Must you do to him what Bernice did to me?"

"I care more for this man."

Monsarrat found his voice. "If you'll let me out of here, I'll leave Honolulu. David Kalakaua will never know."

Lot stood undecided. With a tremendous effort at restraint, he said: "Under one condition can you go. Get out of our islands and stay out. If ever you even talk to my sister again, I'll kill you."

Monsarrat ran through the door, and received a kick from the giant prince which sent him sprawling. He picked himself up and shoeless sped into the night. He left the following day on a clipper ship for San Francisco.

Despite Monsarrat's departure, Lot felt duty-bound to call David and Alexander for a conference. David was certain that this meeting concerned Victoria, who had unaccountably refused to see him for five days. When Lot entered after the other two, he turned the key and told them that Monsarrat had come to his apartment, left after dark, and that Victoria's poodle had dragged one of Monsarrat's boots into the kitchen, whereupon servants had reported it to him. Lot added that the other boot was in front of Victoria's bedroom. At this Alexander jumped up. "Do you mean the son of a bitch was in . . ."

David cried: "You're crazy, Lot." Then he remembered that he had not seen Victoria for five days.

"I knocked down the door," Lot said, looking at his big hands. "Monsarrat pleaded for his life."

"Why didn't you kill the pig?" cried Alexander.

David had leaped to his feet. "By God, I'll finish off that dirty stinking white dog, myself."

"Where is he?" demanded the King.

Lot replied that Monsarrat was well on the way to San Francisco.

After a moment's silence David wiped his face. Then he said: "Victoria's too young to know what she was doing. It's these damned arrogant, superior whites, these whites. . . ." In helpless rage he balled his fists. Then he thought of the warning his mother Ane had given him: to beware that a white man should not rob him of his wedding-night's gift.

In the days that followed, his hatred for white men obsessed him. He saw Victoria and assured her that his af-

fection for her was unchanged but she was ill at ease, morti-
fied, cold, and did not reply to him. Hurt by her listlessness
he demanded, "Tell me, do you love me?"

The answer was a muffled "Yes," and a flood of tears as
the girl ran out of the room.

David's pride was hurt. Victoria was very young but he had
offered all he could and she ran away from him.

To make matters worse, raw stories of how Monsarrat had
been caught *in flagrante delicto* with Victoria spread through
the city. Even the Hawaiians incorporated the scandal into
an innocent sounding hula.

> "Where are you, Snow Blossom of Maleka?"
>   (White man of America)
> "I have no dread of the big size of Asia."
>   (Asia being Lot)
> "You have nothing to say, Snowland is mine."

David grew stern and morose under his constant humiliation; it was repeated day after day whenever he rode through
the streets. He avoided Victoria. One day he tethered his
horse and stood at the edge of Diamond Point. The harbor
was crowded as usual, and the *Yankee* was just rounding
the point. David mounted, rode back and reached the wharf
as the ship was moored. There was a man on deck who
looked like Monsarrat—it was he, beyond a doubt. David dismounted and was on the deck of the *Yankee* in a trice. It was
Monsarrat! But the man was already surrounded by friends,
to protect him if need be.

The following morning Monsarrat received a summons
from the King. He came accompanied by a friend and his
brother-in-law.

King Alexander Kamehameha asked "Am I to understand, Monsarrat, that you refuse to leave my kingdom?"

Monsarrat responded: "That's my intention."

Keeping his voice level the King read a statement which Gregg had helped him draft:

"Whereas you, Marcus Cummins Monsarrat, a naturalized subject of my Kingdom, are guilty of having perpetrated a grievous injury to Our Selves and to Our Royal Family . . . in due vindication and preservation of Our Dignity, you are hereby banished and strictly prohibited forever from returning to Our Dominions under penalty of death."

Monsarrat eyed the King. "I intend to remain, Alexander."

The King clapped his hands and eight soldiers appeared. Monsarrat was pinioned and carried off as a prisoner. News of the arrest and Marcus Monsarrat's banishment spread rapidly.

His brother-in-law and friends shouted protests to anyone who would listen, and Mrs. Monsarrat, heavily veiled, went to the palace to see her husband, who was held on an upper floor of the building. King Kamehameha offered to see her but she refused, and left the palace. Fifteen minutes later American Commissioner Gregg hurried to the palace. He said that because Mrs. Monsarrat had been refused an interview with her husband a large contingent of American seamen and townspeople were preparing to storm the palace and rescue the miscreant.

The King replied that he had asked General Miller for permission for Queen Emma to pass the night with Miller's niece and then turned to David. "General Kalakaua, tell what you have done to prepare for this threat."

Kalakaua replied: "I have five hundred armed men in the palace enclosure. The cannon are shotted and fixed to guard the avenue of approach. There are two hundred armed police guarding the streets."

Excitement ran high until 9 o'clock, the hour for all seamen to be on their ships, and the police combed the streets
and grog shops on the double. At 3:30 A.M. Honolulu slept.
Kalakaua went to the room where Monsarrat was waiting
his promised rescue.

"Marcus Monsarrat," said David Kalakaua, "by order of
my royal sovereign, King Kamehameha IV, I do hereby take
possession of your body and order you to follow me . . ."

Monsarrat looked at David's sword and at the armed guard
with him. He rose and followed to the waterfront. There he
spoke: "You can have Victoria with my compliments. You'll
find her well housebroken, for everything."

They had reached the wharf and were opposite the *Yankee*.
Suddenly Kalakaua grabbed the white man. With one hand
he caught his shoulder; with the other, the crotch, and heaved
him up aboard the deck, where Monsarrat fell sprawling.

"You God-damned haole! May God pity your soul if you
ever return to these islands."

Part **Two**

Upswells the Sea *(Nu'u Kai)* 1857–1881

11 President Lincoln's Roughhewn Ambassador

The early years of the reign of King Alexander and Queen Emma brought great rejoicing. Despite Liliha Boki's prophecy, the Queen became pregnant. Native Hawaiians doubted that the child would be safely delivered, but the boy arrived, a physically perfect baby, and the Kamehamehas now had a direct heir to the throne.

Queen Victoria consented to become the Prince's godmother and sent a huge baptismal font at which he was christened Albert Edward, for the Prince of Wales. Gifts of *kalua*'d pig, bananas, kona crab and other delicacies for the young Prince were heaped each night upon the palace steps. The land was happy.

The honor of rearing the Prince was given to Chieftess Kapiolani of Kauai, a tall, handsome, self-possessed young woman, who believed firmly in the Polynesian gods. Kapiolani, Hawaiian fashion, used but one name in defiance of the commonly accepted Christian style brought in by the missionaries. Her forebears were the powerful and arrogant Kauai Chieftesses whom Kamahameha the Great had been unable to subjugate. She was devoted to her charge and King Alexander and Queen Emma were well satisfied.

David Kalakaua watched the baby with mixed feelings.

Had Victoria consented, they would have been married ere this. But Victoria had not responded to any overtures from David. Made Premier by her brother Alexander, she joined the gay crowd about the palace and was usually with her cousin Prince William Lunalilo. Her pride, greater than her affection for David, ruled her, drove her to wild drinking parties which helped her forget her humiliation. In the eyes of the Hawaiians the brief romance between the two eighteen-year-olds was definitely over.

With the birth of the Prince, King Alexander's drinking and all night debauches were curtailed for a time. The King adored his heir and spent much time with him. Task after task was transferred to David. As the King's Aide, he learned to receive visiting foreign dignitaries, not only government representatives, but playwrights, authors, musicians, actors. Kalakaua was glad to be occupied and found himself struggling to keep pace with the growth of his country.

Navigation was drawing Hawaii deeper into the toils of the great nations. In ever-increasing numbers slow bottoms plying from Glasgow to Hong Kong; swift, beautiful Yankee clippers sailing from the Spice Islands to New York; heavily laden whalers returning from the Aleutians to New Bedford, put in at Honolulu. Because the United States was Hawaii's nearest neighbor, American currents flowed with the greatest intensity through the islands. The admittance of Oregon into the Union called for the draining of a half pipe of Martell's brandy—63 U. S. gallons—in Honolulu's National Dining Saloon. After Cyrus Field's success with the Atlantic submarine cable, negotiations were begun in the United States to link Honolulu with San Francisco and the Orient. When the clipper *Yankee* brought the news of Lincoln's election, the Stars and Stripes floated over Oahu's business houses. San

Francisco's first families sent their children to Hawaii's schools and their soiled linen to Honolulu laundries. But when firing began at Fort Sumter, American families in Hawaii were as widely split over the issues of slavery and states' rights as those in Kentucky. During the Civil War Hawaii prospered; sugar exports doubled and before the war ended the islands were supplying almost half the North's guncotton.

When Robert E. Lee surrendered, peace did not come to Hawaiian waters. The Confederate privateer *Shenandoah*, outfitted by Englishmen, kept on sinking vessels in the Pacific. More than thirty ships, including the *Hawaiian Harvest, Pfeil,* and *Victoria,* were destroyed in four months.

With Hawaii's growth, came aggressive foreigners seeking their fortunes. Cable negotiations brought an Italian promoter, Celso Caesar Moreno. The hope of controlling the islands through religious and political means brought an excommunicated Mormon, Walter Murray Gibson. On Lanai Island he established a Mormon settlement but his financial practices were questioned by Brigham Young, who promptly cut him off from the church. Undismayed, Gibson kept on working on Lanai and his colony was prospering. David Kalakaua liked him.

Little Prince Albert Edward was becoming a boy. Chaperoned by Kapiolani, he appeared on state occasions. At the annual diplomatic dinner at the palace, Abraham Lincoln's emissary, Colonel Thomas Dryer and his wife arrived late, well fortified with Monongahela whiskey. In contrast to the impeccably groomed diplomatic corps, the American representative wore soiled clothes, with pants-legs tucked into field boots.

Steering his unsteady course toward his royal host, Dryer put his heavy arm about the King's shoulder and whispered,

"I hear some of your *kanakas* are aboard the Confederate ships in these waters, Mr. Kamehameha. I'm reporting the facts to President Lincoln."

King Alexander replied, "I have issued a proclamation forbidding my subjects to engage in privateering. If there is any question about violation of neutrality, lodge your complaints with my foreign minister."

The awkward scene was relieved by the entrance of four-and-a-half-year-old Prince Albert Edward in a British naval officer's uniform complete to gold epaulettes. With him was tall, aristocratic Chieftess Kapiolani. They paused beside Mme. Varigny then went to Chieftess Ane Keohokalole and her three children, Liliuokalani, Miriam Likelike, and David.

As Kapiolani and Prince Albert Edward came to Ane, the boy shook hands with her, then with the two sisters and their husbands, and with David. Kapiolani led Albert to the Dryers. Dryer growled, "Why didn't you bring the brat to me first? Don't you realize we outrank the kanakas around here, including David Kalakaua?" Before Kapiolani could reply Dryer pointed an accusing finger at the Prince. "That uniform is a present from the British Commissioner, isn' it?" He dropped his hand roughly on the Prince's head. Had Dryer been a Polynesian commoner he would have been killed for placing his hand on a forbidden part of the boy's body. King Alexander approached with his fists doubled.

But the little Prince stepped aside and replied, "A British sea captain gave me this uniform, Colonel Dryer. I told him that I thought your American clipper ships better built than his slow British schooners."

The sigh that went around the room was audible. As Kapiolani and her charge were leaving, David complimented her.

"Prince Albert's behavior reflected good training on your part, Kapiolani."

She shrugged. "We Hawaiians must learn self-control early, David."

He looked at her sharply. With her following she was a strong political force in the islands.

At dinner everyone awaited the ranking consular representative's toast. Finally, Mme. de Varigny alerted her partner, Colonel Dryer, and suggested that a toast was in order. Dryer struggled upright, but instead of toasting the King, he tilted his half-emptied champagne glass toward Premier Victoria. In the four years since Monsarrat's departure, Victoria had cheapened and coarsened. Still, at twenty-two she was a handsome and voluptuous woman, arresting the attention of men while she seemed to scorn it. Looking at her through blood-shot eyes Dryer grinned, "I'm drinking to God's own bit of creation, there, that beauty!" He had forgotten her name.

Midway through dinner, Dryer slumped against his partner, Mme. de Varigny, and went to sleep. From across the table, Colonel David Kalakaua drove his military boot upon Dryer's foot. The man came to with a resounding oath, and Princess Ruth bellowed, "An oyster must have pinched our diplomatic friend," which produced the first effortless laugh.

Dryer was not through. When an iced dessert was served, he scorned it and searched his pockets for a plug of Luck's. He pushed back his chair and teetered with his knees against the table, emphasizing his general well-being by a discharge of tobacco juice on the rug. Silent and ashamed, everyone pretended not to have seen. The King rose, permitting the guests to proceed to the drawing room for music and a demitasse.

David started toward Dryer, but was restrained by Kapiolani. "Come along to the garden," she said, taking his arm. "It's time we did some talking."

"Their color can't give them immunity forever," Kalakaua stormed angrily.

Near the banyan grove, Kapiolani stopped and turned David about to face her. "David, the whites will insult us as they like until the day when respect toward the Polynesians is restored by the right leader among us. He must bear insults for the sake of his people. He must even have the self-control to overcome his fury at a white man's intrusion into his fiancée's bedroom . . ."

David took her arm and said rather roughly: "Come, let's walk."

As they approached the *mauka** gate, he stopped. "Kapiolani, if you'll stand by me against these whites and against the Kamehamehas—even Prince Albert, I will restore the respect of the white man toward the Polynesians. Join me and the throne is ours."

In that instant, David Kalakaua forgot the obstacles which stood between him and the throne: the King, Alexander Kamehameha; his son, Albert Edward; his brother, Prince Lot Kamehameha; the King's cousin, William Lunalilo. Not permitting Kapiolani to answer, he said: "Come, let's get back. The night air's chilly."

The Dryers had gone and the King had downed drink after drink to assuage the evening's insults. According to rank, the British first and the Chilean consul last, the con-

* In Hawaii, the directions "north," "south," "east" and "west" are unknown. Instead, it is seaward with a sweep of the arm. This is *makai*. Or mountainward, *mauka;* or toward the plains, *ewa;* or toward the beach of Waikiki, which is *waikiki*. Hence, *mauka* gate is the one facing toward the mountains; the *makai* entrance is the one facing the sea.

sular corps left. After they went, the King was seized with a fit of asthmatic coughing and collapsed. Queen Emma was beside him and attempted to assist him.

The King, fighting for breath, swore, "Damn it woman, let me alone."

Tears came to Emma's eyes.

The King shouted, "Your dirty mind is still on your lover Neilson."

A year before, King Kamehameha had accused his secretary of usurping his bed and had deliberately shot him through the lung. After a long illness Neilson died.

Emma dropped to her knees, "As I live I swear I have been true always." The King pushed her from him, left her sprawling, and staggered from the room. Emma met David and Kapiolani as they were coming from the garden, and sobbing, entreated, "David, help! The King—the King." Because she could not control her speech she ran up the stairs. David sought Alexander.

Between struggles for breath the King stormed, "How long will these stinking whites befoul our kingdom, Kalakaua? I shot one and I'll kill this son of a bitch Dryer, too."

David poured a large drink, waited, and then as the King became stupified, he put him to bed.

That evening started King Kamehameha IV on a drinking rampage. One night, a month later, he lurched into his son's bedroom to fondle the boy. Wakened out of a sound sleep, Albert cried out in alarm. To quiet him, the drunken father shook the boy angrily. The child, frantic, kicked at his father, broke from his grasp and fell to the floor, screaming. Enraged, Alexander dragged him to a basin and plunged the boy's head into cold water. The sudden chill was a shock and the lad went limp in his father's arms. Before Emma could reach him, Kapiolani had snatched the unconscious Prince from the King.

For two days and nights the King and Queen kept vigil at the boy's bedside but on the third morning, Albert Edward Kauikeaouli Leiopapa o Kamehameha Ka Haku o Hawaii, Prince of Hawaii, died.

As guns boomed and church bells tolled, distorted rumors of the death spread. "The child was illegitimate, the natural son of Henry Neilson, so the King did away with him." "Nonsense, the boy was an imbecile. He had an overgrown head and so the King killed him."

At the Merchants' Exchange the news of the death of the Prince stirred all the factions plotting to gain control of the government, but Dryer urged them to go slowly and his counsel prevailed.

In David Kalakaua's law office, Chieftess Ane urged immediate action. "Sooner or later it must be a Kamehameha or an Aikanaka. Strike now while the Hawaiians are divided and the whites are with you."

David shook his head. "If we stir up dissension among our own people now, we play into the hands of the whites. We must keep all Hawaiians together."

"This never-ending waiting does not become an Aikanaka," returned Ane. "If we do not act now we will have to wait until the Kamehamehas die out. Have you forgotten Liliha who said that the Kamehamehas would have no offspring on the throne? Her curse was working on the boy's own father when Alexander killed him."

Alexander's monstrous act reduced him to horrible self-judgment. His black-clouded mind gave him no peace and he began to drink to greater excess. Frequently, he would be found in a stupor at his son's grave. At the Queen's promptings a sea captain friend prevailed upon Alexander to take

dinner on board the *Hillman*. The King was so drunk he had
to be hoisted aboard the ship in a boat. During the evening,
the Captain warned him that foreigners were conniving to
displace him and his own people were beginning to talk of
putting David Kalakaua on the throne.

The next day a change came over the palace. For the
first time in months, the King was heard to laugh. He summoned the British commissioner: "Mr. Synge, my loss un-
hinged me. I have been selfish and unjust to my people
in spreading gloom over my land. Hereafter it will be different. This Saturday I am giving a ball at the palace. Will you
be so good as to lead the quadrille with the Queen? I propose to dance with Mrs. Synge if she will grant me the pleasure?"

The palace was decorated and the evening arrived, but
Alexander, too unwell to attend, sent a corsage containing a
diamond to Mrs. Synge and asked his chamberlain, David
Kalakaua, to escort her. He instructed the Queen to tell the
guests that he would soon regain his health and take an active part in court life. But on Monday morning, while his
Minister of Finance waited in the antechamber for an eight
o'clock appointment, Alexander, King Kamehameha IV, died.

12 David Kalakaua Marries

Chieftess Kapiolani was lonely without her small charge, and bitter against Alexander and the Kamehamehas. In her depression she saw David Kalakaua frequently. Two years his senior, Kapiolani was good for David. He needed the companionship of a superior woman who believed in his cause and in his ability to further it. Kapiolani's faith was justified at the first Privy Council meeting, a week after King Lot's accession. Outspoken King Lot, Kamehameha V, said: "We have heard loose talk about giving everyone the right to vote." He stared fixedly at David. "Frankly, we do not believe in wholesale suffrage. A child should not be given a knife and fork until he is able to handle a spoon."

As Kapiolani watched David she remembered that he had told her that to gain political power he would go to the common people whom the Kamehamehas spurned. This idea of universal suffrage was his. Her attention returned to the tense meeting. The old antagonisms of Aikanakas and Kamehamehas were stirring.

After his opening, King Lot became aware of the set stare of Ane Keohokalole. Behind her brilliant eyes lurked triumph. Lot's undiplomatic statement emphasized the growing insecurity of the Kamehameha dynasty, and it had been forced from him by her son's maneuvering. From Ane, King

Lot's eyes turned to Kapiolani, rested on her long enough to convey reproof and returned to Kalakaua.

"Some years ago, during British occupation, our predecessor, Kamehameha III, asked that Aikanakas and Kamehamehas work together to restore Hawaii's greatness. We seek that co-operation, too, but we want it understood that we Kamehamehas rule! In previous reigns there has been undue American influence. Hawaii's independence has been constantly jeopardized by the powerful missionary clique. This mistake shall not occur in Our reign. We repeat: We Kamehamehas rule."

David left the chamber first, with Ane. At the door, Kapiolani whispered, "David, the throne will soon be yours."

After Kalakaua drove his mother home he turned his span to Kapiolani's residence. She stood waiting on the *lanai* and David sensed anew her striking appearance. She was six feet tall and her full-bosomed figure was beautifully carried with the dignity typical of Hawaiian aristocracy. Her large eyes were deep set and her skin a smooth dark brown. There was no need for his invitation: she got into the carriage at once. They drove past Waikiki in silence. At Diamond Point Kapiolani said: "David, the white man's road is a dangerous one for the Polynesian. Those who take it first lose their fear of the gods, then respect for their forebears, and when it is too late, they cannot find the way back."

Kalakaua said nothing until they were stretched out on the mats of the beach near Black Point. He put his head into her lap. "Kapiolani, regardless of what Lot says, the white men have power, and to gain their confidence and support, I must join forces with them. A determined man can always find the road back."

She stroked his hair. "Perhaps I voiced the fear of a woman who loves you."

At this frank admission, he took her hand, but his next remark showed that his thoughts were still far from her. "Once
the throne is mine, I can effect my reforms."

Kapiolani waited for something which would include her
in his future but he said nothing. Angry with herself, she got
up. "Come, I want to go back."

Next day, when the morning dew was glistening on the
grass, David called for her with an extra saddled mount. By
age-old custom, most Polynesians arose before sunup to
plunge in the surf. "Come, let's go for a ride." As they rode
toward the mountains, up Nuuanu way, the bright rising
sun bathed the jagged mountain peaks in lustre. It was cool
and clear. On the last mile to the *pali,** they put spur to
horse, hurrying, keeping pace with their emotions. Once
again this view which greeted them seemed unbelievable.
Three thousand feet below the majestic, sheer cliff on which
they stood, stretched the vast, liquid green plain. Beyond, the
turquoise sea sparkled, tossing back the sun's beams in a
million silver flashes.

Kalakaua took her hand. "Kapiolani, join me in making
the rest of Hawaii like this: clean, undefiled by the white
man."

Her reply was forthright, Hawaiian. "I will bring my
Niihau mats to your house and we shall see what your Halala
knows."

They rode back quietly, possessed of the world's content-
ment.

A fortnight later, when the Chieftess Kapiolani of Kauai
came with her retinue of more than a hundred to Kalakaua's
seaside home, the cobalt blue heaven was brilliant with stars.

---

* *pali*: when used on the island of Oahu it means the great cliff or precipice
overlooking the plain below. (A truly great spectacle).

Kapiolani and Kalakaua sat in front of the house with their guests—many of the Kamehamehas ignored the celebration because the court was still in mourning for King Alexander. The famous chanters began softly, gradually lifting their voices as the dissonant noises of day gave way to the lengthened cadences of night. *Mele* singers sang of the coming bliss of the mating. "The woman's lying down on the mats," sang one group, "is like the murmur of an evening breeze," to which another group responded: "The man's entrance is like the fury of untamed winds."

During the chant, an old woman whispered to her neighbor: "Why did Kapiolani of Kauai, the widow of Namakeha, seek out this nigger-blooded Kalakaua? Does she not know that his mother, Ane Keohokalole, hawked his sister Liliuokalani from man to man until she had to take the white man John Dominis?"

The other cackled, "Kalakaua merely seeks rank to establish his right to the throne."

Kapiolani, for whose ears the remarks were intended, waited until the chant was finished and requested: "Let us have the chant of Aikanaka of Kau," and, seeking to rebuke the gossips, "The Kamehamehas and even my own ancestors feared Aikanaka, the man-eater."

Last there came a rarely done *ki'ik* hula, a marionette dance, which recited the history of the bridegroom's private parts with the aid of a puppet two-thirds life size. From the naming of the ma'i, Halala, through the ceremony of circumcision, the first intercourse with Tutu, the conquests and a final paean to the bliss of this, the wedding night.

The chanting ended, the guests departed. On the morrow at dawn, they would return and partake of prolonged feasting.

After a month of celebration the newlyweds, accompanied by twenty-five retainers, began a ceremonial tour of Oahu, returning the visits of their guests. In Hawaiian fashion, they remained at each house until food ran low, then hosts joined guests and the cavalcade rode on to the next house for more dancing, singing, sports, and feasting. But, as the entourage progressed around the island, an undertone of sorrow crept into their gaiety. With growing apprehension, Kalakaua and Kapiolani saw Oahu's ugly transformation. Sour smelling sugar plantations were crowding out taro fields. Valleys were denuded to provide cane-land. The songs of many Hawaiian birds were missing.

One morning Kapiolani asked: "David, what's become of our *mamo* birds? We haven't heard one."

The golden-tufted mamo limited his food to certain trees which grew in certain valleys, and once these were gone the mamo seemed to vanish overnight. The parallel was inescapable—David knew that unless drastic action were taken, his people faced similar extinction. The land all about them was filling with imported Oriental laborers who lived like animals and worked like slaves, shoving aside the Polynesians and increasing the white man's profit. Eight people— men, women, and children—were jammed into a single room, eating, living, sleeping, and breeding, in a space measuring no more than ten by twelve feet. One sugar plantation made provisions for married couples—three pairs were allowed one room, twelve feet by fifteen. Females over fourteen were paid fifteen cents; males, eighteen cents, for a twelve-hour day. Those younger depended upon the generosity of the planters. Under such conditions most newborn babes died and the mortality rate among workers was high. On one plantation, twenty of one hundred workers died within a year. Practically all of the imported laborers were

men who married Hawaiian women, which hastened the day
of the last Polynesian.

The white man's handling of this cheap contract labor
brought other evils. One morning David and Kapiolani's
wedding party of one hundred and twenty-five halted near
Waimanalo when they heard the ugly sounds of flogging.
They found an armed, mounted, white overseer raw-hiding a
Hawaiian who was crawling and twisting on the ground, trying to escape the cuts of a blacksnake whip eight feet long.
Stopping the lashing, Kalakaua learned that it was being in-
flicted because the Hawaiian had dared to remonstrate with
the white overseer when his sick wife was forced to go out
into the canefield, where she had collapsed and died. And as
Kalakaua and Kapiolani saw the fear-ridden Polynesians
grouped around their bleeding co-worker, with the Japanese
laborers near by working unconcernedly, they saw Hawaii's
future.

The thought of the beaten Hawaiian and the dejection
of his fellow-Hawaiians haunted Kalakaua. He turned the
wedding party back toward Honolulu, ending the tour. "The
time has come, Kapiolani. It's Hawaiian or white man." He
held up the ugly blood-blackened whip he had taken from
the white man, and said grimly: "Their necks are more fragile than ours."

"How, David? What are you going to do?"

"I'm going to organize a group of Hawaiians dedicated to
the rebirth of Hawaii; I'll drill them myself and when the
time comes drive out the white interlopers. I'll make our
home a rallying place."

At Honolulu, David went directly to King Lot to put a
halt to the importation of Orientals. Lot received him at
once and Kalakaua was shocked at the change in the King's
appearance. His hair was gray; the color of his skin had

grown lighter; his three-hundred-odd pounds had increased.
When, pressing his argument for stopping the influx of contract labor, David showed the blood-blackened blacksnake,
Lot replied: "The man and wife were hired laborers, weren't
they?"

As Kalakaua tried to explain that the pair were fellow-
Polynesians, the King seemed indifferent, yet, when David
ended, he said: "Kalakaua, I need a man with your convic-
tions. From today you are Chairman of the Board of Immigration. All plantation labor must be cleared through you.
If you like, go ahead and halt the importation of Oriental
labor." The sly monarch, who had worried over this problem, knew that the difficult post would ruin David. If he
dared halt or curtail contract labor, businessmen and planters would be against him; if he did nothing, Hawaiians com-
plaining about the Orientals would denounce him.

Deplorable as Kalakaua found the contract labor situation,
he discovered in it an even greater menace to Hawaii's security. The importation of Japanese was preparing Hawaii
for future invasion from the Orient! Men like Charles R.
Bishop seemed to be deliberately playing into the hands of
wily Emperor Mutsuhito. In the foreign office file, Kalakaua
found that Foreign Minister Bishop had written to Hawaii's
Consul General in Yokohama, Robert W. Irwin*, that plantation managers wanted field workers at twenty cents a day.

Imitating Germany, Emperor Mutsuhito, "Emperor of En-
lightenment," was scheming to make Japan the dominant
world power of the Pacific. To study Bismarck's method of
building an empire out of a group of disorganized central
European states, Mutsuhito had infiltrated the European

---

* Irwin was a descendant of Benjamin Franklin. He had married a Japanese
woman of high standing and had several children by her—hence some living
descendants of the signer of the Declaration of Independence are part-
Japanese.

continent with agents. As German troops stormed through the Vosges Mountains with new high-speed military equipment and routed French General MacMahon's forces at Sedan, Mutsuhito's observers were watching. When the German troops arrived in Paris, after the city had been looted by French Communists, Mutsuhito's spies were ahead of them. German occupation forces were still in the Verdun and Alsace-Lorraine sectors, bleeding the French of food and material, when Mutsuhito, without warning landed troops on Formosa. That operation went off like clockwork and, aping Germany, Japanese occupation troops looted the large island until Chinese officials came through with a thumping indemnity. Looking to future conquest, Mutsuhito infiltrated "laborers" into strategic islands throughout the Pacific, including Hawaii.

Quite alive to the Japanese emperor's ambitions, David Kalakaua had, in the course of a year, gathered about him more than five hundred fellow Hawaiians and trained them secretly in small groups. He had begun with a dozen trusted friends; and now he had an armed force ready for action. These followers were dependable and their loyalty gave David confidence. If he could not get King Lot to take action in stopping the entry of Japanese labor he might take a hand in the matter himself.

Kapiolani tried to dissuade him. Like most other Hawaiians she believed that Liliha Boki's curse was following the Kamehamehas and destroying them one by one.

"Victoria Kamamalu lies dead in the palace now, and within two years at most Lot will follow her to the grave."

David knew. Princess Victoria had died the week before and her emaciated body was lying in state. He had intended to go to pay her a last visit, but each night the fearful din that arose in the Palace grounds in honor of the dead Princess gave him pause. Half-naked Hawaiians of both sexes wailed and beat gourds, and hundreds seated on the grounds swayed and moaned to the rhythm of chanted dirges. Some of the wildest slashed their bodies; from the mouths of others ran fresh blood where they had knocked out teeth. Through this David must pass to arrive at the coffin with its six dignified kahili-bearing guards.

It had to be done. So David waited until Kapiolani had left the house and then started for the palace. As he passed among the howling mob, he was conscious of sudden silence. The inner circle took its cue from the outer; the mourners stood motionless as he entered the archway and stood by the coffin. The crowd in the grounds was still silent; only the chanted dirges went on.

David looked at the woman he had loved and there was no bitterness within him. His own pride had suffered throughout the last ten years. But her suffering must have been greater. She was still beautiful but thin and wan, worn out. She was twenty-eight, his own age. He remembered how she had come to be at his side when Liliha died, how she had stood by him in the Kamehameha-Aikanaka squabbles at the Cookes' school, how she had loved him and except for the greed of an unprincipled white man might still be loving him —he put his hands over his eyes, stood by the door a minute. Then Kalakaua raised his head and walked through the silence home.

Victoria would have worked with him if she had been there. She could not save herself but she would have wanted to save Hawaii from the Japanese. His decision was taken. He would go to the King. In addition to the problem of the Japanese, David had a personal grievance he wanted to take up with the King. Marcus Monsarrat, banished from the Islands more than ten years before, had returned to Honolulu.

Lot never seemed to agree with David, but he did give him a measure of respect. He was a Noble now, a member of the Hawaiian parliament. He had considerable electoral strength in the legislature. For a time he had been Hawaii's Postmaster General. Through diligent study he had advanced to the thirty-second degree of the Masonic order. Lot had admiration for his energy and achievement.

But Kalakaua found Lot in no mood to discuss either his personal feud or Japanese infiltration. Mutsuhito was three thousand miles away—what would he want of land in Hawaii? Kalakaua pointed out that Germany, a small power ten years ago, and still farther away, was gobbling up islands in the Pacific.

To this Lot replied: "The United States will not permit the Japanese to take Hawaii. Why don't you say what you want, Kalakaua? You want to frighten me off the throne?"

At Kalakaua's mystified look, Lot crooked his finger, beckoning David to come close to the great reclining sofa on which he was stretched, naked but for a loincloth, while a Hawaiian massaged his monstrous four-hundred-pound frame. The King asked: "Tell me, Kalakaua, who is your choice for my successor? Everyone wants the throne," he cackled, "Bernice, Ruth, Lunalilo, Emma. Now you."

Kalakaua turned the conversation. "What about the United States leasing Pearl River lagoon to develop it into a naval coaling station?"

Lot was not to be turned aside. "Yes, the United States wants my throne too. They've sent Colonel Alexander and General Schofield* to get the Islands."

Kalakaua went to Kapiolani and told her about the Ameri-

---

* Schofield Barracks, Oahu, one of the first targets during Japan's December 7, 1941 attack, was named for this General John Schofield, former Secretary of War.

can agents: "Lot will die soon; his mind is rattling. Kapiolani, our opportunity is here now that I have a powerful Hawaiian political organization. The first thing I'll do is to send Schofield and Alexander packing."

Events the following Monday outstripped Kalakaua's plans. King Kamehameha V was dying. The Attorney General joined those at Lot's bedside: "Sire, it is your duty to name a successor, now that no true-blooded Kamehameha remains."

The King replied: "Leave me alone." Then suddenly, Lot rallied. "You are all my *Alii,* my Chiefs. Give me light. . . . It is dark. . . ." And Lot was no more.

Without a successor to the King, the American Minister and the British Consul sent for warships to insure each other's neutrality while the Privy Council met in extraordinary session and convened the Hawaiian parliament for January 8, 1873.

Kapiolani, who sensed the feeling of the Hawaiians who had lost their last full-blooded descendent of Kamehameha the Great, advised David to abstain from electioneering. "We must show that our side reveres the dead King's memory."

Prince William Lunalilo, cousin of the late King, sought the advice of two white men: old Captain Cummins, owner of the Waimanalo plantation where David had interrupted the flogging, and Walter Murray Gibson, the planter from Lanai. Cummins summed up Lunalilo's prospects: "The missionaries hate you for your godlessness, your drinking and whoring around with your cousin; the legislators have no respect for you and the Americans fear you becaue they know you are pro-British."

The Prince laughed. "In short, Cummins, I'm not a likely candidate."

Gibson pointed out that Kalakaua was the most serious contender. The missionaries were behind him. His work as chairman of the Immigration Board had entrenched him with the common Hawaiians. "And I suppose it's no secret to you that Kalakaua has organized a strong group of natives with the slogan: 'Hawaii for the Hawaiians' and it has swept the island."

With that evaluation, they drew up plans to defeat Kalakaua.

Unaware of their scheming, Chief David Kalakaua went directly to the Hawaiian members of the legislature, who were in the majority, and told them that, as King, he would restore Hawaii to the Hawaiians. They in turn promised him their support. The throne seemed assured until, overnight, posters appeared throughout the Hawaiian islands calling for a special election by the populace to vote for Lot's successor. The posters had an electric effect.

"Prince Bill appeals to us directly," said Hawaiians on the street. "Lunalilo is democratic. That's the kind of King Hawaii needs."

Three days before the election, a vilification of Kalakaua appeared. It was a stuffed figure labelled "John Kalakaua Blossom," the face a jet black, its hair frizzed, its lips painted wide. It was borne through the streets in a hack driven by David Kalakaua's possible half-brother, John Blossom. Riding heralds proclaimed: "Vote for John Kalakaua Blossom, Calabash King of Hawaii!" Every time the half-naked puppet was raised to acknowledge the applause of the hilarious crowds, his loincloth stood straight out in front, pushed up by a broomstick. A hula troupe rendered several of the well-known hulas dedicated to Kalakaua's penis.

Anything but ridicule of birth Kalakaua might have overcome easily; this cut deep. Men in his own camp said: "Certainly we are for the restoration of old Hawaii, but why don't we follow a true-blooded Hawaiian? Lunalilo comes from pure Hawaiian stock."

With only two days remaining before the election, Kapiolani insisted that David abstain from cheap electioneering. Kalakaua railed: "The Hawaiians in the street must know that I, as their King, would have the courage to meet opposition." She tried to soften the inevitable blow. "If you don't succeed this time, the next election will be ours."

"The next!" stormed Kalakaua, "By God, I'm going to win this election. I'm calling a campaign meeting tomorrow."

The crowd next day at Thomas Square, where Kalakaua had called his meeting, clamored for more hulas. David finally stood up and waited for the noise to subside. "O, my people," he began in the traditional manner, but a man heckled: "Shut up, Blossom, we came for the hulas."

Kalakaua started again. "My people, I called you together at this spot, where, thirty years ago, Admiral Thomas restored our country to King Kamehameha III . . ." The reference to Hawaii's past quieted the crowd. Kalakaua went on. "Today Hawaii needs another restoration. The giant trees from which our ancestors hollowed their outriggers have been felled and the land planted to sugarcane to fatten the bellies of foreigners. Where we once worked them, now degrading slave labor forces us aside . . ."

"As chairman of the board of immigration," shouted a rude native, "why didn't you correct those abuses?"

Kalakaua saw that Gibson and Cummins had prompted the interruptions. "When the white man first came to Hawaii," Kalakaua resumed, "we numbered a half million Polynesians. Today we are less than sixty thousand, thanks to the white man's civilization, his sexual diseases, measles, and smallpox."

His audience listened intently.

"But the white man is not done with this. He must take the very land from us who remain. A strange man, General John Schofield of the United States, is plumbing the depths of our Pearl River lagoon and proposes to make a naval base there for the United States in exchange for the free entry of sugar so that the greedy whites among us can become even richer. Depend upon it, those of us who are true Hawaiians will not benefit . . ."

Another heckler interrupted. "Prove that you are Hawaiian."

Kalakaua flushed. "To you, I reply that I inherited the Aikanaka loincloth. Was there any Hawaiian greater?"

His rebuttal was interrupted by loud guffaws. Looking behind him Kalakaua saw the nigger manikin on the platform. Hot with embarrassment he concluded: "If you are for the restoration of our gods, our way of life, our land, then you are for me." He bethought himself of Kapiolani's warning: "I would say more but the remains of our beloved King Lot are still resting in the palace and we are in mourning."

From the light applause Kalakaua read his doom at the polls. The black manikin had defeated him. Sick at heart, he went home.

13 The U. S. Wants Pearl Harbor

Lunalilo was elected by a great majority and the legislature confirmed the public's choice.

With a new King on the throne, the American agents, Schofield and Alexander, were eager to push plans for acquiring the Pearl River lagoon as a naval base. The United States needed a coaling station where ships could refuel. Pearl River lagoon, safe, secluded, was an ideal spot. It was difficult to get King Lunalilo down to business as he had embarked upon a hundred-day drinking bout to celebrate his accession. One cabinet meeting was called during a temporary lull in the prolonged spree, and the Foreign Minister pushed a document across the heavy *koa* table.

King Lunalilo picked it up and read: *"I, Lunalilo . . . being desirous of the good of my Kingdom . . . do hereby authorize and empower Charles R. Bishop to conclude a treaty of reciprocity . . . and to include a cession of Pearl River on Oahu Island for a naval station . . ."* He turned on his cabinet members. "Why, you scoundrels!"

Foreign Minister Bishop explained: "Your Majesty, for this slight concession, President Grant offers us the free entry of sugar, and this naval base will yield millions of revenue . . ."

124

Judd counseled: "Your Majesty, once the United States establishes a naval base in Hawaii, she will have a very real reason for supporting our independence against future encroachment by France, Germany, Japan, or Russia."

"What do I care for these?" demanded the King. "Once these grasping Americans have two square miles, they will snatch ten, and finally my kingdom."

Bishop countered: "General Schofield is prepared to pay cash for any land outside the lagoon."

The King roared with anger: "So, your treasonable dealings have gone that far! You ministers of the crown are a disgrace!"

When the meeting was over, Bishop, who had campaigned for Lunalilo, said to Judd, "Anyone can make a mistake. We need a new King. I'm calling on Kalakaua this morning. Judd, you go this afternoon."

David Kalakaua was surprised at Bishop's call. As they talked he gathered its import. Bishop wanted to be assured that David would support friendly action towards the United States, even to the leasing of Pearl River lagoon, if the terms were fair. David was reticent about the matter. When Judd came that afternoon and asked if Kalakaua still advocated limiting all government posts to Hawaiians, David parried, "In the heat of an election talk one makes rash statements."

William R. Castle, David's third caller, asked Kalakaua bluntly whether he would be willing to write a letter expressing his views to be published in the *Advertiser*. "Some of us are casting about for an alii to take the throne," he said. "Bishop and Judd told me of their conversations with you. Are you prepared to publicize them in Whitney's *Advertiser?*"

Kalakaua agreed and when his letter appeared, Walter Murray Gibson sought him at Oehlhoffen's Delicatessen. "Kalakaua, I made a great mistake in supporting this drunken Lunalilo."

Kalakaua knew that the missionary group did not like Gibson. Yet he needed the man's powerful support because the *Advertiser* letter had angered many Hawaiians. If Gibson were to throw his support to Queen Emma, it might well tilt the scale in her favor.

Gibson moved his head nearer Kalakaua's. "Your buttering up of Bishop, Judd and the other Americans in the *Advertiser* was a smart move, David. To get the throne we must first have the support of the haoles. I speak as a native because I have the welfare of the Polynesians at heart. I'm not asking you to make any commitments to jeopardize your support from the Bishop-Castle contingent. But to prove my sincerity, I will destroy Lunalilo for you."

Kalakaua saw he was forcing Gibson's hand. "Why do you wish to destroy him?"

"Because I gave him the throne and he has ignored me. Frankly, to me the Polynesian is God's most perfect creature. His ways are reduced to the simplest elements of life. Away from the white man's domination, he is the happiest man in creation. You should see what I've done on Lanai island." He stood up to go. "If within a fortnight there is a mutiny among the King's troops and the citizenry clamor for Lunalilo's abdication, will you trust me?"

"We'll see," said Kalakaua.

Gibson left; he had gained nothing and had committed himself to action.

The following Saturday night, as officers of the King's Household Troops were carousing at a Gibson-endowed party at the Hawaiian Hotel, the wily schemer had accomplices smuggle five cases of square-bottled Palm Tree gin into Iolani Barracks. Sunday morning, a group of Gibson's hirelings among the King's troops were in possession of the barracks. The Hawaiian officer in command had been dumped into the barrack's fifteen-foot dungeon and the mutineers had barricaded the building. A bugler appeared at the windows and blasted naughty tunes at the horrified churchgoers. Gibson, standing in the background, sent a messenger to summon Governor Dominis, Commander in Chief of the Household Troops. By the time Dominis arrived, the rascals were hurling improvised coconut bombs—hulls filled with fused gunpowder—into the street. The noise was terrific. Seeing a soldier ready with a fused bomb, the Governor shouted: "I command you all to return to your posts or you'll be thrown into prison for the rest of your lives."

"What about more pay?" the man parried.

The crowd hooted with delight at the public haggling.

Governor Dominis, with great restraint, promised: "Those loyal to Our King Lunalilo will be properly rewarded."

Catching sight of the bandmaster at a barrack window Dominis shouted, "Captain, I command you to play the National Anthem." The bandsmen hastily assembled and began to play "Hawaii Ponoi." As the strains reached the crowd, the noise subsided, and the men within the barracks were silent. Then the Governor ordered the gates opened; he was obeyed. The mutiny was over.

Within a week Bishop was appointed Secretary of War. He dismissed the Household Troops, sent the ringleaders of the mutiny to prison, placed the band under Governor Dominis, increased the police force, and put the powder magazine in charge of a responsible white police squad. And growing out of this liquor-inspired rebellion came a cry from foreigners and Hawaiians: "We want a King—not this drunk who has no control over his troops." Kamehameha followers demanded that Lunalilo abdicate and give the throne to Alexander's widow, Queen Emma. The whites were for Kalakaua.

In the thirteen months Lunalilo had been King he had not solved one major problem; labor was sorely needed, the independence of the islands was threatened, and the white residents looked down upon the King and his fellow Hawaiians. Action was delayed because Lunalilo was obviously very ill. Dissipation and drink had taken their toll and consumption accompanied by hemorrhages weakened him. Then, one afternoon at dusk, before the thirteenth month of his reign had passed, King Lunalilo whispered, *"E maka ana wau"*—I am about to die—and within a few hours had gone.

The King's funeral with its ceremonies filled David's days, but his thoughts wandered. He could see Gibson's fine hand in the mutiny, but Lunalilo's death had settled the matter of abdication. As there was no heir to the throne there would be an election. David Kalakaua wanted that throne as he had never wanted anything before, and he intended to get it. He no longer confided in Kapiolani, who, sensing the change in him, was unhappy. She attempted to remonstrate with David about his new associates, but he flew into a fine temper. One night he arrived home at four to find her sobbing. Irritated that when he was working so hard he had to come home to a crying, unsympathetic wife, he said nothing.

"David," she called softly.

"What is it?"

"Of what good is the throne if you sell yourself body and soul to the whites?"

"Kapiolani, a year ago I sought the throne through the love of our people. At the Thomas Square meeting did one Hawaiian stand up for me? Drive past Queen Emma's tomorrow and you'll find where they stand today. This time I intend to get the throne by fair means or foul and your loyal Hawaiians be damned."

"David, do I mean nothing to you any more?"

"Even you cannot stand in my way, Kapiolani."

"David, we cannot go on like this."

But he was not listening. Queen Emma's growing power was disquieting. As sleep would not come Kalakaua mentally ran down the list of legislators and stopped at the name of John Cummins.

Cummins, son of old Captain Cummins, was a representative with an important following. Owners of the rich lands called Waimanalo, father and son were powerful potential adherents. Eight years ago John Cummins and David had quarreled over a woman, at a palace dance. It was a silly quarrel and David resolved to patch the matter up with Cummins.

In the morning he rode up Nuuanu Street, past Queen Emma's home, richly covered with masses of climbing roses. As he approached he saw a crowd gathered before the gift-laden verandah where stood the widow of King Alexander Kamehameha IV. A kneeling native was making a presentation. "Supreme One, Whose Flight to Heaven is Momentarily Arrested"—this was Emma's name bestowed upon her after marriage—"aloha. Grant me the pleasure of accepting this little gift." Emma took the calabash of pink poi from his uplifted hands. He kissed the hem of her skirt, "I give you my thought that you will become our Queen enshrined on the throne as thou art in our hearts."

Kalakaua had dismounted and stood behind some shrubbery where the voices were clearly audible. Emma spoke, "In the name of the King we all loved, I thank you for these gifts. So that others may know, this is my plan for the kingdom."

Emma then spoke of carrying out the policies of her late husband, King Alexander, of restoring some unspecified portions of the constitution of Kamehameha III, of reducing salaries of government officers including her own, and of labor for the well-being of the nation, promising that her religious opinions would not influence her governmental policy.

David mounted and rode off as one of Emma's most rabid followers was urging that, if Emma were not elected, they should use force to seat her on the throne. He found Captain Cummins at home and sat with him on the verandah. While they were talking, John Cummins entered the gate.

As he reached the verandah his father said, "John, David Kalakaua is waiting for you."

Kalakaua spoke first. "I was wrong, John. Forgive me."

Old Cummins laughed. "That is as it should be in Hawaii. It's a small land and you are men now, not boys. John, Kalakaua wants your support."

"I must think it over."

Fear of failure spurred Kalakaua. "John, in this election it is Queen Emma or I. She stands for the old Kamehameha tradition with no place for the white man. I stand for a reciprocal treaty with the United States and for the white man's rights in Hawaii."

"Suppose I give you my answer tomorrow?"

After Kalakaua left, Captain Cummins said: "That's the first time, John, I've ever heard a Hawaiian Chief apologize to a white man. Why didn't you agree to help?"

"Tomorrow he'll make me a better offer. How much are you willing to contribute?"

His father shrugged. "Make others put up the money, Kalakaua's white brothers-in-law, Dominis and Cleghorn, will help. So will the sugar interests. So will Bishop. You might invest four hundred, but no more. Get the old Shillaber place and provide free meals and women for the outside islands' representatives. The country boys look for a little relaxation."

Next day Kalakaua promised John Cummins crown lands adjoining his Waimanalo estate and Cummins agreed to give his support, but he warned: "Stay away from the old Shillaber place. Some of your missionary friends wouldn't understand."

A government vessel, well-laden with *okolehao** had already been dispatched by Kalakaua backers to the outside islands to pick up the legislators. Upon its return, the evening before the election, the assemblymen were put up at the Shillaber residence where they continued to drink, while pretty hula girls lulled away their cares of state.

---

* *Okolehao* is a powerful Polynesian drink made of the *ti* plant. Good "oke" tastes like a sherry-flavored Scotch.

14 David Is Elected King

Election day, February 12, broke clear. American flags flew as well as Hawaiian and the two American warships in the harbor—the *Tuscarora* and the *Portsmouth*—were festooned with special decorations.

With his future at stake, fear gnawed Kalakaua's vitals. He had everything to lose—the throne, his reputation among the Hawaiians, money, Kapiolani's love. She had left their home; he didn't blame her, but the election was more important. At the newsboys' raucous "Extra, extra!" he ran to the window and saw natives battling for the papers and starting bonfires with them. Kalakaua unlocked his desk and lifted out a brace of pistols given him twenty years before by the visiting Duke of Edinburgh. At a step behind him he whirled, pistols cocked. It was Bishop. Angry, Kalakaua shouted at his Minister of War, "Why haven't you provided me with adequate police protection?"

Bishop assured him that special police were on duty and that a hundred Hawaiians had been hired to guard the legislature. At any show of force aid would come from the American warships. "President Pierce wants to see you elected," said Bishop. "The United States wants Pearl River."

At the Beef Street drygoods store of David Kalakaua's

brother-in-law, Archibald S. Cleghorn, assemblymen were eagerly selecting free Prince Albert frock coats and silk hats!

The barkentine *Murray* had furled her sails and dropped anchor in Fair Haven. The bos'n from the U.S.S. *Portsmouth* reported to the barkentine's skipper and ran up the ladder to her crow's nest, the highest in the harbor. He was the lookout for the American minister's distress signal and would relay a message to the U. S. marines on the two warships.

At the legislative assembly hall, spectators overflowed into the hallways, the stairs, and the streets. Judging from the small red roses in their buttonholes, the majority had been at Queen Emma's residence. Now that noon approached, a group numbering almost a thousand marched to the accompaniment of fife and drum down King Street up to the courthouse. Cheers resounded for Queen Emma.

Upon the arrival of Bishop, Judd, and Hall the crowd became quiet. The silence was broken by a native who shouted: "Who votes for Kalakaua is a traitor to Hawaii!" The applause bespoke the temper of the gathering. A group of carriages, from the Cummins' livery stable, came from the direction of the Shillaber place, carrying most of the outside island's legislators. For two days there had been free food, free okolehao, and free women at the Shillabers'.

At noon, the Reverend William Kanui, who had led the group of Hawaiian gold diggers to California, twenty-four years before, opened the legislative session with prayer. Gibson had instructed him to make it long to calm the restless crowd. Following the invocation, the president and vice-president *pro-tem* were elected. The crowd hushed as the ministers of the crown rose together.

Bishop, their spokesman, stated: "Gentlemen of the Assembly, you have been convened by order of the cabinet to

elect by ballot an alii as successor to the late King Lunalilo.
May the God of All-Wisdom guide your deliberations."

On the platform, the vice-president sought permission to
speak. Pulling a handful of printed manifestos from his
pocket he said: "I have evidence here, sworn to by our revered Queen Emma, that King Lunalilo's will* still exists . . ."

There was an uproar. Assemblymen fought to get the floor.
The President recognized Gibson. "This is cheap political
chicanery! If such a will exists, why was it not presented before! I move that the vice-president be barred from using
his office for electioneering and that what he has said be
stricken from the record . . ."

A chorus seconded the motion. The president managed
to restore order. During the comparative quiet, the vice-
president ran to the window and tossed the papers to the
crowd below.

To hasten the balloting, Assemblyman Cummins moved
that each member deposit his ballot when his name was
called.

The chair appointed two tellers. As they took their posts
beside the ballot box, someone yelled: "Both are Kalakaua
men. Our Queen will be robbed."

Some of the legislators looked uneasy.

John Cummins spoke to them: "Fellow members, it is our
duty to vote as free men today. For my part, the ruling of
Hawaii is not the business of a female. I am voting for
Kalakaua."

The ranking member of the legislature, Charles Kanaina,
father of the late King Lunalilo, was called to deposit his
ballot. The revered Chief walked slowly through the assemblage. As he dropped his vote, he said: "I know my son

* King Lunalilo's will has never been found.

Lunalilo wanted Queen Emma to succeed him. I saw his will . . ."

Gibson was on his feet. "That is a Kamehameha lie."

The president rapped for order as, one by one, the votes were deposited. The last was a representative who was too drunk to find the slot and needed a steadying hand to cast his ballot.

When the ballot box was opened and the names were called off, there were two ballots for Emma. The next three were for Kalakaua, and the sixth for Queen Emma. Then, as votes for Kalakaua mounted, the crowd, in disbelief, remained silent. The president spoke: "My tally reads: Queen Emma, six votes; Chief Kalakaua, thirty-nine votes. Long live King Kalakaua! I hereby appoint—" The rest of his speech was drowned out by the roar of the angry crowd.

Within that roar were the accented high-pitched notes of women's screams, the sound of crashing wood as a fence broke under the impact of the seething mass. And then the crash of splintering glass!

A group of legislators rushed to the rear of the hall for their carriages. Behind them streamed the mob. One of the delegates appointed to notify Chief David Kalakaua of his election was dragged out of his carriage. The old man attempted to get up. Blood stained his white hair and streaked down his face. Hawaiians bore down again with clubs, and he lay motionless. An Englishman, John Foley, went to his assistance. Struck by someone in the crowd, he hit back, right and left. A moment later a picket stave crashed on Foley's head and dropped him. Hawaiian or white, there was no color line now.

All this was a matter of seconds, and then the crowd assaulted the barred rear door, from which a few of the representatives, including Bishop, had effected their escape. Using a section of the broken fence as a battering ram, the mob smashed doors and poured into the building. A dozen police looked on apathetically.

Outside rose the mob's yell "Kill them!" Men were climbing a leafy *kamani* tree in pursuit of their quarry. With a splintering crash, a branch broke and men fell out of the foliage into upraised hands. A dozen clubs, table legs, chair legs, and a shovel were aimed at defenseless heads which disappeared beneath the mob.

Men poured into the building and hunted down their victims. One representative was found crouching in the attic. He was pitched down to the crowd which beat him unmercifully. Another Kalakaua supporter hung by his hands from a second-story window. One of his hands was smashed with a club and he fell, his shoulder and hand broken. A fourth member of the five-man committee appointed to notify Kalakaua of his election—special victims of the crowd's insane fury—was found hiding in the map box in the Recorder's office and beaten.

Bishop, unscathed, hastened to the residence next to the palace where David Kalakaua awaited word of the election. Breathlessly, Bishop told him that he had been elected King of Hawaii and a mob was killing the representatives.

"And you came here to betray my presence!" shouted Kalakaua. At the King's distress, Bishop calmed. "If we act quickly, Sire, we can get the American marines!"

Wild with fright, Kalakaua cried: "You have not yet asked the Americans? Get out before I kill you with my bare hands."

Bishop backed away. "Sire, a note must be written."

Kalakaua ordered: "Hurry. Write the commanding officer to land forces at once."

Bishop parried: "The order must go through American Minister Resident Henry Pierce." While Kalakaua paced the room, he wrote:

"A riotous mob, having unexpectedly made a violent attack upon the courthouse and the members of the legislature, which we have not a force at hand to resist, I have to request that you will cause to be furnished at the earliest possible time aid from the United States men-of-war *Portsmouth* and *Tuscarora* to the Police in quelling the riot and temporarily protecting life and property."

Without waiting for the ink to dry, Kalakaua grabbed the letter and rushed a servant off with it to Pierce.

Bishop hurried to Queen Emma. She was at the Episcopalian Church, within five blocks of the riot. "Your people are rioting and seeking to kill our representatives and our new King," he said. Queen Emma looked at him steadily and responded: "If the people cannot express their sovereign rights through the ballot, what other recourse do they have?"

Within ten minutes of the receipt of Bishop's note, a hundred and fifty bluejackets and marines were marching on the double up Fort Street to the courthouse. According to plan, the *Portsmouth's* gatling crew took its position in front of the courthouse, while another force formed in line behind them with drawn guns. Then marines entered the building. A few violent Hawaiians attempted resistance, but when the marines started for them with fixed bayonets, they made for the windows, leaping out like so many frogs.

Night came. Kalakaua's fears were magnified by the darkness, the forebodings of the morrow, and by the sharp crack of an occasional rifle shot. He wondered if Kapiolani were safe. Then his heart caught up sharp, as he heard an American marine sentry give a challenge. After a few seconds, the front door slammed open.

Three men entered, announcing themselves as members of the committee to inform Kalakaua of his election. A bullet zinged through the glass door and the four, the King and committee members, dropped prone. At that instant the Marshal of the Kingdom ran into the hallway. He reported five men killed and seventy-six taken prisoners.

"Only seventy-six! Good God, go out and get the others," ordered Kalakaua.

One of the committee men held a bandbox. He set it upon the marble topped table, opened it and lifted out a crown* made of the paper ballots taken that afternoon.

"Moehonua sent it. He was hurt. We thought you'd like it as a memento of your election to the throne."

* This pasteboard crown made of the ballots and presented to King Kalakaua is now in the Bishop Museum, Honolulu.

15 A Royal Tour of the Islands

Under the protection of American bayonets, a sorry-looking band of representatives, nobles, and diplomats gathered for the secret swearing-in of the son of Ane Keohokalole. With blackened eyes, broken arms, and bruised faces, many of the guests looked like patients from an accident ward. The ceremony in the palace—former Hawaiian kings had been invested with pomp and circumstance at the Great Stone Church—was short and to the point.

Scarcely had the new King received his guests' felicitations than he ordered Bishop, his Minister of War, to get him a royal guard of two hundred, "all men over six feet tall."

"Sire, such action has always required the cabinet's approval," Bishop remonstrated.

King Kalakaua retorted: "I am my cabinet! I will inspect them at five-thirty this afternoon."

Next morning's news created a sensation. It announced the appointment of a new Cabinet—a Hawaiian, President Nahaolelua of the legislature, as the new Minister of Finance; a British shipper, William Lothian Green, as Foreign Minister; a German, Herman Widemann, as Minister of the Interior; and the American, Judge Hartwell, as Attorney-General.

Kalakaua's action was decisive. Within a week the ringleaders of the election riot were tried. Sixty-eight were convicted, one was hanged, fourteen sentenced to prison at hard
labor, and the remainder fined. Within a month, political
hatreds gradually eased.

David's personal affairs eased at the same time. He knew
that the election and his methods of securing votes had
irked Kapiolani, but he believed that now that he had the
throne, she would be willing to help. He sought his wife and
they discussed the election frankly. Bribery troubled her;
she thought Queen Emma had not been fairly treated. David
smiled, went to his desk and picked up a legal looking
document.

Over his shoulder Kapiolani read:

"We, Kalakaua, King of Hawaii, hereby direct you, William Lothian Green, Minister of Foreign Affairs, to termi-
nate instantly all negotiations with the United States for the
cession of Pearl River lagoon."

She sank to a settee and stared at him. "Why, why that
will alienate every white!"

"Do you want me to tear it up?"

"No, no. It's just that I've been so worried. David, I want
to go to my own people on Kauai with you. Can we?"

"There is a week before I have to convene the legislature,"
he said thoughtfully. "Time for a quick tour of Oahu. Later
we can go to Kauai and all the islands."

Kapiolani welcomed the suggestion. Everybody seemed to
approve of the newly elected King and his Queen visiting the
land. As there was but a week they started out the following
morning. It was clear, cool, and pleasant. After an early
breakfast for a company of almost two hundred, a gay cavalcade, led by the King on a snow-white stallion, and the Queen

astride a black mare, left the palace for Mauna Rose, the country estate of John Cummins.

It was a merry entourage, each rider bedecked with ginger blossoms, the Queen's favorite flower. The royal standard was carried in advance by cavalry, in white hats with havelocks, red shirts, and black trousers. The ladies of the court wore long green, red, yellow, and blue *pa'u* s—divided skirts —reaching within a foot of the ground.

Above them was the sharp whirl of heavy golden plovers, in the islands just long enough to fatten up for the next hop of their overwater migratory flight of seven thousand miles from the South Seas to Alaska. Over the white-capped channel water could be seen the faint outlines of Molokai, Lanai, and the Crater of the Sun on Maui.

As the royal cavalcade approached Makapuu Point, the company stopped to make proper obeisance to the fish goddess *Malei*. Pretty girls danced and each rider dropped a flower lei before the rock image. Suddenly they heard the tootling of a mail-man's horn. As Postmaster General, Kalakaua had known the old postman of the Koolaus and when he came alongside, the King reined up his mount and beckoned to him. "Here's a lei for you, John, with the wish that you will continue to blow your horn in the Koolaus throughout my reign. And here," reaching into his pocket for gold coins, "is a little remembrance for your four children."

Midway down the thousand-foot descent, the party was halted by six mounted knights, vizored in the traditional Hawaiian mask, which permitted only the eyes to show. Below the brilliant feather headgear flowed flaming scarlet-colored feathered cloaks, and they carried day-burning torches in deference to the royal son of Ane Keohokalole.

After the King and Queen were presented with flowered kahilis, to be borne by their escorts, the party continued on its way to the rich valley, while along the route the King's humble country folk lay prone on the ground.

Since dawn men, women, and children had brought baskets of Hawaiian flowers to Cummins' home; the yellow *ilima* for royalty, and red *lehua* interwoven with fragrant maile leaves for others. Fifteen cottages and the mansion had been festooned with flowers, ferns, and ti leaves. A twenty-one-gun salute heralded the royal party and from an unseen chorus came that best of all Hawaiian songs, "Sweet Lei-lehua," the King's favorite. Both he and Kapiolani added their rich voices, and soon the entire cavalcade was singing. Kapiolani was happy. Her heart beat again for her lord.

As they rode through a flower-covered gate, a corps of men blew on horns woven of *hala* leaves. As his Majesty and the Queen halted before the house, two natives locked fingers and made stirrups for them to dismount. John Cummins greeted them. In his late thirties, Cummins combined the easy grace of his English father, and the charming hospitality of his royal Hawaiian mother. Life at Mauna Rose was always gay and unconventional. For the men there was an abundance of beautiful women—gossips had it that the *Konohiki* (the Great One) of Waimanalo had eleven wives yet jealousy did not exist.

With pleasant words for everyone, King David Kalakaua went from group to group and then retired to the cottage prepared for him, to the seventeen-foot-long bed and a fifteen-year-old virgin who had been annointed with the King's favorite oils. Since puberty the virgin had been massaged to soften her muscles and to give her the proper control over her vagina for the ceremonial intercourse with Hawaiian nobility, an inherited privilege. With deftness, she helped her royal charge undress and then danced a graceful hula dedicated to their anticipated lying together. After intercourse, the royal monarch stretched out while she sponged him and covered him with satin-fine tapa for a nap before the afternoon's sports. When he awoke, she helped him into freshly-pressed white flannels.

While sports were in progress, the King sat on the shaded *lanai,* or porch, with the ladies, who had changed into colorful *holoku* s*, and sipped gin and bitters while eating sweetmeats with his host. On the sea, Hawaiian men rode their boards on the twenty-foot high surf, while along the sandy beach riders galloped by, pell-mell, picking up handkerchiefs from the ground. But the King's applause was for the Hawaiians who boxed and wrestled in old Hawaiian fashion.

Two hours before dinner, King and guests again retired for a nap, and when the women reappeared in the latest New York and Paris creations and the men in dinner jackets, they found flower-covered tables—eighteen inches high—laden with imported wines, vintage champagnes, and food which rivaled anything obtainable in Boston or Paris.

After the royal pair had taken their places at table, the guests sat on their mats, leaning on pillows. During the meal, which lasted three hours, a chanter recalled the prophecy of Liliha Boki and the King's partner of the afternoon obligingly repeated her hula, finishing it with a new verse telling of the afternoon's intercourse. Even Queen Kapiolani laughed heartily at the portrayal of Halala's greedy appetite. A group of little girls dedicated a hula to Kapiolani, ending with an entreaty to the gods to make her stomach bear fruit for the land. When the banquet was ended, there was ballroom dancing on the lanai lit by Chinese lanterns,

* As devised by the missionaries, the *holoku* was a loose-fitting garment, better known as the Mother Hubbard.

naked surfriding in the moonlight, and outrigger riding. Queen Kapiolani, in good taste, retired early, leaving her royal mate free for the pretty Hawaiian girl he obviously desired.

Shortly after midnight a second supper was announced and the young girl went out to fetch the King's food. Couples who stole off to the cottages were pursued and serenaded with appropriate music, while on the mountainside bright bonfires burned, signaling the presence of royalty. Few slept before five but, after a nine o'clock breakfast, Their Majesties, attended by singers, musicians, dancers, standard bearers, court attendants, friends, and the train of baggage wagons, continued their round.

At the end of the week they were back in Honolulu, so that Kalakaua could appear to convene the legislature. It was not necessary for him to remain, however, so he decided to defer the visit to Kapiolani's home no longer. With a large retinue they sailed for the outside islands.

Landing at Koloa, on the Queen's home island of Kauai, they were received by pretty girls dressed in flower costumes matching the bouquets they presented to the King's Royal Guards, members of the government band, singers, dancers, chanters, the Queen's specially appointed ladies-in-waiting, and the King's gentlemen. Gifts of the soil rose in piles at the rulers' feet.

Touched by this welcome, the King said: "My children, with the help of God I intend to do my duty wisely so that the nation may increase. The number of small ones gathered here gives promise of a greater population. Truly that father who provides for a large family and that mother who gives birth to them and nurses them should be rewarded."

An old man spoke up. "I've cast twelve, Sire. What's my

reward?" The crowd laughed. Entering into the spirit, Kalakaua replied: "Part of your reward was in the pleasure you
obviously derived." When the laughter subsided, the King
added seriously: "Your King intends to have a law passed,
exempting you from all taxes."

At Lanai, pursuing the subject of the birth rate, the King
summoned the young matrons for a special meeting. "There
are too many of you who want the pleasure of intercourse
but are too lazy to have children. It is this accursed abortion
plant. Would to God it had never been created. For as surely
as our women die without issue, just so surely will our land
pass out of our hands."

As Kalakaua spoke, he felt that at last he was to realize
his destiny. The prophecy of Liliha had been fulfilled; he
had the throne and now he must act to save his people and to
fulfill his birthright.

Despite their hearty welcome and the never ending beauty
of the islands, Kalakaua was longing for Honolulu and work.
By the time he reached Byron's Bay he was restless and felt
the need of diversion. He summoned one of the gay Hilo
blades, Curtis Piehu Iaukea.

"Get me a night's partner and if she suits me, I will give
you a permanent place on my staff."

When they left the next morning, a girl named Brown*
accompanied the party around the island. The news of the
legislative action coming through annoyed Kalakaua. It had
been a lively and expensive session. The assemblymen voted
themselves five thousand dollars to defray expenses at the
Shillaber home and another thousand for free refreshments
at the Hawaiian Hotel. The King's supporters demanded a
hundred thousand dollars for a steamer to take the legisla-

---

* A descendant of this girl named Brown, living today, boasts that she is
the only living descendant of King Kalakaua.

tors to and from Honolulu; a new half-million-dollar palace, a quarter-million for a standing army, including a royal guard of honor, and cavalry, and a million dollars for a submarine cable to San Francisco. Despite these appropriations, the legislators decreased revenue by abolishing the poll tax, and began debating the issue of tax-exemptions for all natives with more than three children. This was a direct result of Kalakaua's speeches at Koloa and elsewhere, on his island tour.

But there was other news, far more significant and exciting. President Ulysses S. Grant had sent a special invitation asking the King of Hawaii, David Kalakaua, to come to see him at Washington. Kalakaua lost no time in returning to Honolulu.

16 President Grant and the King of Hawaii

On his return to Honolulu, King Kalakaua found that President Grant had sent the frigate *Benicia* for his trip to San Francisco and it awaited his convenience. Kalakaua knew that this visit to Washington was of vital importance: Hawaii's trade was in the doldrums.

Within five years the whaling industry had slumped from five hundred ships to sixty. Hawaii's planters, hampered by the import tax, found increasing difficulty in competing with California's beet sugar growers. As the sugar trade lessened, imports dwindled. And the government budget had doubled. Disgruntled business men were arguing that had the King not refused cession of Pearl River lagoon Hawaii might have had free entry for its sugar. Kalakaua knew all of these things but he had in mind a larger possibility. He wanted to get free entry into the United States for all Hawaiian products! And the United States wanted Pearl River lagoon, had wanted it for several years and the need grew more acute.

If he, the King, could manage to wangle free entry for all products for the lease of the lagoon, prosperity would come to Hawaii and the King could have almost anything he asked for. Then there was the racial issue. If the King, a Polynesian, made a triumphal visit to America, was received as a social equal, it would increase the stature of his race in their own eyes as well as in those of the whites.

It behooved Kalakaua to prepare for the Washington trip in as short a time as possible. In a few days he was boarding the *Benicia,* without furore but with the good wishes of all his subjects. A smooth voyage made speed possible and they covered the distance in record time. As they entered San Francisco Bay, the army guns at Fort Alcatraz thundered. The ships along the wharves were festooned with bunting. General Schofield, with Mayor Otis of San Francisco in top hat, striped trousers and spatter-dashes, were the first to come on board. Both welcomed the royal guest heartily and the Mayor assured Kalakaua that his stay was on the house.

They had landed on Sunday and thousands of carriages thronged the city thoroughfares, while city blades on spirited mounts cavorted alongside. Along the route to the Grand Hotel, marines with muskets stood at attention.

Because of the King's large frame and regal bearing, the populace identified him at once and hearty applause rose from the sidewalks. The King looked distinguished. He had handsome black burnsides. He wore a steelpen coat, a low cut vest, a studless white shirt front with a turned-down collar and a black tie. In his lapel was a strip of parti-colored ribbon of the Grand Cross of the Order of Francis Joseph.

To avoid the crowd at the hotel, the King was hurried through the women's entrance to his suite, which was decorated with the Hawaiian coat of arms. No sooner was his standard hoisted than the mob shouted for him. Obligingly, he stepped to the open window to receive an ovation. Much as he enjoyed it, he soon rejoined his hosts to accept toast after toast drunk in champagne.

At noon the next morning he was asked to visit the Western Union office which had put a line through to President Grant. The visiting monarch wired:

KALAKAUA, KING OF THE HAWAIIAN ISLANDS, SENDS GREETINGS TO HIS GREAT AND GOOD FRIEND, THE PRESIDENT OF THE UNITED STATES.

Within fifteen minutes, came the reply:

THE PRESIDENT OF THE UNITED STATES EXTENDS THE CORDIAL WELCOME OF THE NATION TO HIS GREAT AND GOOD FRIEND, HIS ROYAL HIGHNESS KING KALAKAUA, AND HOPES THAT HIS JOURNEY ACROSS THE CONTINENT MAY BE GUIDED BY KIND PROVIDENCE.

For four days San Francisco outdid herself. Kalakaua received delegation after delegation with ready humor. When the Temperance Alliance of San Francisco called, he said: "Your society has done much good in my land, Gentlemen. I myself once led a cold-water parade in Honolulu, but I must confess it rained cats and pitchforks."

When the Temperance Alliance left, someone sent for brandy, and toasts were merrily offered to the Alliance, the cold-water parade, and to all who abstained from the demon rum. Between levées at which crowds of elegantly dressed ladies surrounded the King, Kalakaua managed to attend the theatre and to pay a visit to the Federal Mint, where a souvenir was struck off in his honor. One afternoon the King visited the California Club rooms and played billiards with Holmes, one of the city's crack shots—and Kalakaua defeated Holmes, to the great astonishment of the onlookers. On the last night, Kalakaua visited the Bohemian Club in the upper rooms of the Old California Market and enjoyed an oyster supper. A group invited the King to a poker session and Kalakaua accepted with pleasure. When they broke up in the morning Kalakaua had dropped ten thousand dollars, the exact amount, in fact, that the Hawaiian legislature had appropriated for the trip.

For the Washington journey, the Union Pacific attached two elegantly appointed coaches and a drawing room, with an additional car for the newsmen. It was Kalakaua's first train ride and the journalists made the most of it. Snow and ice coated the windows. Accustomed to Hawaii's subtropical temperature—it never dropped below fifty-five in Honolulu—the King shivered and dreaded to go out to meet the whistlestop crowds. His Aide, Governor Dominis, arrayed himself in Kalakaua's greatcoat and cap to satisfy the King-hungry populace.

At Omaha, despite a bitter snowstorm, Mayor Chase insisted upon taking the King for his first sleigh ride. When the King returned he was chilled to the marrow and went to bed. He stayed there until within ten miles of Washington, D.C., when he was greeted aboard the train by the Secretaries of State, War, and Navy. Huge crowds were massed at the capital's flag-draped depot. Still suffering from exposure, the King again went to bed. The President's personal physician came to attend him and issued hourly bulletins to the press. The fourth day, he was able to pay his official call at the White House. As his carriage appeared, the President advanced from the Executive Mansion to greet him. The return call—made by President Grant, accompanied by General William Tecumseh Sherman and the cabinet—followed. On the next day an immense concourse awaited the royal visitor at the Capitol where Congress assembled in joint session. Breaking precedent, women received permission to occupy places on the floor.

King Kalakaua was escorted to the Speaker's desk.

"I welcome you to this hall, King Kalakaua of Hawaii,"

said Senator James G. Blaine of Maine. "It is the first instance in which a reigning sovereign has set foot upon the soil of the United States. It is significant that your visit comes to us from the West. No single event could more strikingly testify the century's progress in your Majesty's country and ours. The rapid growth of the republic on its western coast has greatly enlarged our intercourse with your insular kingdom, and has led to a knowledge of your wisdom as a ruler and your exalted virtues as a man . . ."

King Kalakaua was too hoarse to respond. Chancellor Elisha P. Allen, Hawaii's representative at Washington, returned the King's thanks.

The American Government's entertainment was climaxed by a White House reception. The military was in full dress —the diplomatic corps in court dress while King Kalakaua and President Grant were in evening clothes. "It was the most brilliant gathering in Washington's history," reported the *Washington Star*. "His Majesty is tall, finely formed, and looked exceedingly well in his simple evening dress."

Grant, meanwhile, had instructed his Secretary of State, Hamilton Fish, to approach Kalakaua about Pearl River lagoon. Because Kalakaua had already turned down the cession of the lagoon, Grant wanted to secure a most-favored nation option in exchange for the free entry of Hawaiian products.

Kalakaua bargained shrewdly: "I would entertain such a proposal gladly, providing my country receives sufficient compensatory benefits." Drawing a long bow, he added: "Sir Edward Thornton, the British ambassador, stands ready to give me some fine concessions."

That spurred Fish. "Sire, would you be satisfied with the free entry of sugar for the assurance that no other nation can have the lagoon?"

Kalakaua was reluctant. "Your proposal would benefit only the sugar planters, mostly Americans. May I suggest the free entry of all Hawaiian products?" To Fish's assent, Kalakaua suggested the Secretary send a copy of such a treaty to his foreign minister in Honolulu for study.

Elated with the success of his mission, Kalakaua left for New York. When he arrived at the station, women broke through police cordons to kiss him. The second day of his visit was Christmas. The King attended service at St. Thomas's and in the afternoon went to Gurney's Gallery for photographs. He was still in his resplendent dress-white uniform when P. T. Barnum arrived at the Windsor House to take him to the Hippodrome. Barnum had brought a gold chariot, drawn by six milk-white horses. As Barnum and the King turned the second corner, they were joined by ten other chariots, on the sides of which were huge posters proclaiming the personal appearance of King Kalakaua at the Hippodrome with no advance in prices. Instead of taking his guest directly to the show, Barnum drove through New York's down town streets. Kalakaua heard a great deal of singing in the carriage following. When they arrived at the circus gates he heard the words of one of the verses:

> "Hoky, poky, winky wum;
> How do you like your muffins done?"
> "Soaked in beer and steeped in rum,"
> Said the King of the Sandwich Islands.

The King affably joined in singing New York's latest, and the incident, recorded in the nation's press, added to his popularity.

After the Hippodrome performance Kalakaua was resting at the Hotel Windsor when he was told that Celso Caesar Moreno craved an audience. Good natured as always, he admitted him.

"Your Majesty," began Moreno.

The King interrupted. "I have it. You are the man who proposed a cable from San Francisco to Honolulu. I recall seeing you in Hawaii."

Moreno drew himself up and squared his broad shoulders. He was a tall man, distinguished in bearing although he carried his large head to the right side, a result, he claimed, of a neck wound.

"In the next legislature," the King went on, "I intend to introduce a ten-million-dollar appropriation for such a project."

Moreno began to talk. He was suave, flattering, and acutely sensitive to any change in Kalakaua's attitude. He painted a future in which the proposed cable made Hawaii the most important nation in the Pacific, the key to trade between the East and West. It was music to Kalakaua and as the wily schemer went on to praise the Polynesians, Kalakaua beamed upon him.

"You seem conversant with the Orient," said the King.

Moreno began on his adventures. He had left the Italian navy to manage his own merchantmen and ran between Genoa and Singapore. He had married a Sultan's daughter and because of intrigue had to leave the Spice Islands. The French government had sent him to Indo-China and from there he had gone to China.

Gibson had something of a similar history, the King thought as Moreno went on and on. . . . Gibson had left home as a boy of thirteen. He had worked with a revolutionary general in Mexico and was sent back to New York to buy a ship. Somehow the ship never got back to Mexico: Gibson had persuaded the crew to go around the Horn and landed at the Spice Islands. He fomented a rebellion against the Dutch and was sentenced to be hanged, but the sentence was commuted to ten years in prison. He never served them. A native princess helped him to escape from prison and he was secreted on a ship sailing for Glasgow. From there he managed to get to Washington, went out to Utah and joined the Mormon church.

"Do you know Walter Murray Gibson?" the King interrupted abruptly. Moreno smilingly denied all knowledge of Gibson.

"The future history of the world, Sire," Moreno went on, "will be written in the Pacific. Hawaii, Your Majesty, can well be the hub from which greatness will radiate—"

The thought inflamed the King. He ordered more cognac and over it told Moreno of Liliha's prophecy that he would one day lead the Hawaiians back to their old ways; he spoke of Haaheo's teaching and the lore of the Polynesians.

"The white men upset our simple economy of growing taro, catching fish, making tapa clothes, building grass huts, braiding necklaces, trimming feathers for kahilis, and hollowing outriggers. After their coming my people wanted foreign clothes, bread, silver, and salmon sides. To pay for these luxuries, we cut down our sandalwood. And when the sandalwood was gone, we all became immeasurably poorer."

During the Hawaiian monarch's recital, Celso Caesar Moreno conceived a new idea, an idea greater than the promoting of submarine cables. He would go to Hawaii and be a Bismarck and a Garibaldi at once: form an Empire of Polynesia and free an oppressed people. He stood and lifted his glass. "Master, greatness lies before you and your people. May I be the first to propose the toast: "King Kalakaua the First, Emperor of the Pacific!"

The King bowed.

Aide Dominis, who had come in twice before, now said firmly, "Your Majesty, the Masonic reception held in your honor is already under way." He bowed to Moreno. "His Majesty is a thirty-third degree Mason. You'll understand, I'm sure."

Kalakaua turned to Moreno. "We will meet again."

As the King returned to San Francisco, the thought "Emperor of the Pacific!" haunted him. And the closer he came to home via U.S.S. *Pensacola*, the sweeter it grew, "Kalakaua the First, Emperor of the Pacific."

Thousands were awaiting the King at Honolulu. Kalakaua's Hawaiian subjects had read newspaper accounts of their King's triumphal tour and they greeted him with new respect. As the ship drew near the wharf, the King bowed to the tumultuous applause, but for him the thunderous ovation came not only from the people he saw, and the fine speeches given at the palace by white men—but from the illimitable regions of the Pacific and from the uncounted millions of Polynesians soon to be united under one King.

17 Enter Mr. Claus Spreckels—Sugar King

While Kalakaua and all Hawaii waited, one man blocked action on President Grant's proposed reciprocity treaty with the islands: Claus Spreckels, a California sugar-beet grower. Single-handed, he organized Western opposition and enlisted the support of Southern sugarcane planters and Eastern refiners in tabling the treaty. Hawaii's trade slowed to a standstill. Planters, still hoping to put their sugar down in the United States without a tax, withheld their shipments. Ships idled in the harbor. With depression upon the land, white businessmen, irked by the legislature's expenditures, formed a coalition with Queen Emma's forces so that the whites controlled the purse-strings of government.

After a year, upon President Grant's insistence, the treaty got to the Senate floor, and the roly-poly Spreckels himself appeared to lobby against it. Despite Spreckles' opposition, the Senate went into executive session. At the secret meeting, Secretary of State Hamilton Fish's special clause was read, which he was inserting in the treaty—and which would eventually tie Hawaii to the United States:

> *"It is agreed on the part of His Hawaiian Majesty that he will not lease or otherwise dispose of, or create any lien upon any port, harbor or territory in his dominion, or grant any special privileges or rights to any other power . . . !"*

156

That succeeded.

The Diamond Point ship's watcher was the first to see the be-ribboned *City of San Francisco* with rainbow bunting from bowsprit to stern. Like wildfire, his telephone information spread through Honolulu: "The treaty passed!" By the time the clipper stood off the roadstead two bands were contending with "Columbia, the Gem of the Ocean!" and "Shoo, Fly, Don't Bother Me," while youngsters set off fusillades of "astonishing" crackers, afterwards called firecrackers.

Foreign Minister Green had barely time to unseal his diplomatic tin from Washington and read the treaty, before Major James H. Wodehouse, the British Commissioner, arrived and demanded an audience with the King.

He warned Kalakaua: "This treaty, granting the United States exclusive rights to every harbor, port, and territory in Hawaii, has the appearance of unfriendliness and disregard of the imperial rights of Great Britain."

King Kalakaua replied, "Tell me, Wodehouse, how can I answer you about something which I have neither read nor approved?"

The British Commissioner again warned, "This act may sever diplomatic relations and provoke a state of war," and added that he was going to London to present the matter to the foreign office.

At the waterfront, it was a race between the *Murray* and the *Mary Belle Roberts* to see which would make San Francisco first with duty-free sugar, rice, tobacco, bananas, Chinese nuts, goat hides, *pulu**, and peanut oil. Other

---

* *pulu*: is the soft golden fuzz which covers and protects the uncurling tender fronds of Hawaii's twenty-foot-high tree ferns. It was used for pillow stuffing. After many years it was found to be extremely dangerous to sleepers. After use the pulu fuzz broke into minute particles and when inhaled induced lung inflammation.

ships were being loaded pell-mell; men were swearing in good humor, and heavy freight-laden wagons rumbled over the cobblestones of Sea Street.

The cost of living increased. Within a year, exports rose from $500,000 to $6,000,000! Real estate prices doubled. Heaviest land buyer was the Californian, Claus Spreckels. With sudden prosperity King Kalakaua's thoughts again turned toward empire. But he knew that he must first break the Queen Emma—white coalition in the legislature. He summoned Gibson, who had vision plus a strong following. From the moment Gibson sat down in King Kalakaua's study and looked at the luxurious surroundings, illuminated by a huge, icicle-bright chandelier, the King saw that the man was impressed. Ordering brandy, the King led a discussion of the problems of the Pacific, saying that it was most unfortunate that the Polynesians should be gobbled up by England in the Fijis, by France in Tahiti, by Germany in the Carolines and Marshalls.

The opportunist Gibson smiled: "Rex, Hawaii should be the hub of the Polynesian kingdom. Sire, you are standing today on the very threshold of the door marked 'Emperor of Oceania'!"

King Kalakaua pointed out that this would take an army, navy, jeweled orders, ambassadors, gifts. "And all this," he added, "takes money."

Gibson snapped his fingers. "Isn't the kingdom yours? In the olden days of Hawaii, the fruit of the land was the King's."

"My cabinet would never approve of such expenditures . . ."

"Sire, if your crown ministers disagree, sack them. Surround yourself with men of vision."

This led King Kalakaua up to the real problem. "The legislature convenes next week. So far, you have been aligned against me."

Gibson started bargaining: "I control a sizable following. If we join forces the assembly is ours."

The King asked: "What are your terms?"

"No terms, Sire. Let me serve you and Hawaii. Make me your Prime Minister and I will make you Emperor of Oceania."

Kalakaua was prepared to take Gibson into his cabinet, but this new post, Prime Minister, was another matter. "Every planter would cry to high heaven if I were to make such an appointment now."

"Let them. Threaten to throw in with Claus Spreckels," said Gibson, "that will bring them around."

Spreckels was a real threat to Hawaii's businessmen. After passage of the treaty, he had come to Hawaii with his son, John D., to go into the planting of cane for his California refinery rather than to compete with Hawaii's tax-free coolie-grown sugar.

Gibson went on: "Your subjects, Sire, will number millions. As Prime Minister, I will buy a man-of-war and man it with gold-skinned Polynesians. From its truck will fly an ensign of your own design. I'll augment your paltry army with a formidable striking force. I will make your court the meeting place of intellectuals and beautiful women. I will stock your cellar with the wines of Burgundy, the Rhine, Champagne. I will make this library the repository of the accumulated knowledge of the ages. . . . And, as you become great, Sire, your people will rise to greatness with you . . ."

"But all this takes money, Gibson."

"Money, Sire! I will multiply your income ten times ten.

Your Empire of Oceania will be one of the world's richest. I know the South Sea Islands, Malaya, the Indies. They float in wealth."

King Kalakaua recalled how Celso Caesar Moreno had told him that the King of Siam ate off plates of pure gold. The King called to his butler, von Oehlhoffen. "Here, Robert, another bottle. . . . Gibson, give me your support in the coming legislature and within a year I will make you my Prime Minister!"

In the Assembly of 1878, Gibson effected the coalition of Kamehameha-ites and the King's forces chiefly through raising the racial issue. To insure a majority, he had nobles appointed who were friendly to the King. Step by step, he gained power. He got a yearly subsidy of thirty-six thousand dollars for Claus Spreckels to have his vessels call at Honolulu on their Australia-San Francisco run. King Kalakaua's brother-in-law, Archibald S. Cleghorn, got a ten-thousand-dollar stipend for his new daughter, Princess Kaiulani. A proposition to cover the twenty-thousand-dollar deficit incurred by the King on his mainland trip to Washington passed with additional riders to defray the King's Household expenses of fifteen thousand dollars.

Such appropriations offended the white legislature. "Dollar after dollar is being squandered, while those who contribute the cash have no control," shouted one representative. Lorrin Thurston added: "Our population is overburdened with the expenses of royalty."

Gibson was on him like a hawk: "You missionaries think that Hawaii exists for the exploitation of you landgrabbers, Thurston! You and your kind have erected a colossal monument to selfishness! The native scarcely gets enough to eat while you money-changers gorge yourselves!"

Hawaiian representatives applauded with prolonged cheers.

The argument prefaced a proposed inheritance tax on property exceeding two thousand dollars, which affected most of the twelve hundred whites and only a few of the sixty thousand Hawaiians. Gibson had saved his big jolt for afternoon, the last of the session. At noontime most of the members went to the Hawaiian Hotel for their free lunch of deviled crab, apple pie, and wine. With a quorum present, Gibson called the members to order and proposed a ten-thousand-dollar statue to Hawaii's first King, and by acclaim was appointed to go to Boston to supervise its design.

Spreckels had bided his time until the legislature had adjourned and Gibson was on his way to Boston. He had eased himself into the King's favor until he was a steady poker companion during the night sessions at the royal boathouse. Actually, there was little profit in taking the King's I.O.U.'S and then lending him the money to cover them! When the King was in debt to him to the extent of fifty-six thousand, Spreckels opened the subject of the surplus water rights on northeast Maui island. That, the King informed him, would require the sanction of the cabinet, and he arranged a meeting for the following afternoon. At a stormy session, the cabinet refused, despite threats, to accede to Spreckels' demands.

Two nights later, at two in the morning, after the King and Spreckels had conferred at George Macfarlane's saloon, a royal messenger handed Foreign Minister Green and the other cabinet members identical letters of dismissal. Within forty-eight hours Spreckels had the desired water rights for five hundred dollars a year. The same day he announced the establishment of the Hawaiian Commercial Company, with a capital stock of ten million dollars, to build the greatest sugar plantation in the world. Work on the Maui irrigation flume began within a week. Five of Spreckels' vessels discharged cargo at Kahului, Maui. Locomotives arrived. Seven hundred tons of boiler tin came from Philadelphia. Three thousand skilled laborers were brought in from California. The skilled labor wage jumped from a dollar a day to two, and angry rival planters accused Spreckels of hiring away men by paying two dollars and fifty cents for a short nine-hour day! Planters who feared Spreckels sold their plantations, only to find that prices doubled within six months.

Never had such prosperity hit Hawaii, but over every businessman's head hung the sword of Spreckels' power. He built his own stores, his own bank, bought acreages on the other islands and the mainland, and began the erection of one of the biggest homes in Honolulu.

18 Mr. Gibson, Mr. Moreno, and the Empire of Oceania

A month after Walter Murray Gibson had left for Boston, King Kalakaua received the announcement that Celso Caesar Moreno was asking for audience. Kalakaua had often thought of the man who had fired his imagination and set him firmly in his vision of the future, the possibility of uniting all Polynesians in one great Empire. That vision was still with him. He received Moreno at once and the visitor sank to his knees and kissed the King's hand.

"Get up, get up, Moreno. Welcome to Our Kingdom. I have thought with pleasure of our talk in New York City."

Moreno bowed.

"With your permission, Sire, may I present my credentials?" He clapped his hands. Two pig-tailed Celestials appeared with scrolls—one in Chinese, the other in English. While the King inspected the parchment, Moreno explained: "I am here for two reasons: first, the Congress of the United States has delegated me to form a corporation for the laying of a submarine cable from the United States to Hawaii and on to the Bonin Islands, Japan and China. Second, President Tong King Sing of the China Merchants' Steam Navigation Company has empowered me to open commercial relations with your Kingdom. His company is ready to provide a luxury steamship line to operate between Canton and Honolulu for mail, cargo, and passengers. But what gives me the greatest pleasure is that I have the honor to be the bearer of some trifles from China, if Your Gracious Majesty will deign to accept them."

"Gifts from China!" said Kalakaua, "have they heard of my kingdom there?"

"Your brilliant trade agreement with the United States has proclaimed you in the world's capitals as an enlightened monarch. Should you visit China, the Emperor is prepared to bestow great honors."

"The treaty," Kalakaua said smiling, "does seem to fill our coffers almost faster than we can drain them. But what of these Chinese gifts?"

Moreno clapped and three Chinese ran up bearing gifts across outstretched arms. They prostrated before the King. Moreno took the first—a sword in a jewel-encrusted scabbard. "A gift from the Dowager Empress of China." The second was a heavily brocaded coat. "A trifle from President Tong." The third, a carved jade jewel-box was "an insignificant nothing from your humble servant."

The King thanked him profusely. Moreno summoned a pair of Chinese and they carried in a dozen bottles of iced wine. Kalakaua picked up a bottle of the *Chateau d' Yquem* and read the date, 1871. "How could you know it's my favorite vintage?"

Moreno had shrewdly noted an item in a New York paper during the King's visit. Pleased beyond measure at the man's thoughtfulness, King Kalakaua invited: "We'll have it for lunch," and the pair retired to the card room. As they drank with their cold fowl, confidence called unto confidence, and as the afternoon advanced Moreno pictured Polynesian navies and forts. "You have but to command me, Sire, and I will negotiate a ten-million-dollar-loan with China to build you a bastion rivalling Gibraltar. It is yours, Sire, to write a glorious record of achievement on the pages of history—a record of the welding of all Polynesians under one powerful hand, and their liberation from the white man's oppressive yoke."

"But I am hemmed in by a parcel of old women who know nothing of Empire!" complained the King. "To them, the future of my people means nothing—absolutely nothing. See that blacksnake?" He pointed to the wall. "I took it from a white man who was whipping a Hawaiian. I keep it as a perpetual reminder that all these greedy money-changers want of me and of my people is to make their filthy money multiply."

"Ambition, Sire, is God's great gift to few. Garibaldi had it; Bolívar had it; you have it! You, like them, must overthrow the complacent tyrants who worship the *status quo*."

"There is a place in history for my people, I know," the King mused. "You and I, Moreno, can carve that niche. Resign your commission with this Hing Sing and become my foreign minister."

Moreno knelt. "Sire, first I must discharge my obligation to the China Merchants' Steam Navigation Company. If they could have a trifling subsidy to defray the expense of having their luxurious liners stop over in your Kingdom, one like that granted to Spreckles, then I would feel free . . ."

Kalakaua waved his hand. "The subsidy is as good as yours."

Moreno again kissed the King's hand. "Master, command me, I am your servant." But the reality of the present still hedged the King. "For the present, Moreno, keep your cabinet position secret. There is an election coming in two months. When the time arrives I will make the appointment public."

A fortnight before the election, Gibson returned from Boston and hurried to the palace. He hastened to show the King a photograph of the statue's model, but he got scant response. He talked of Pacific conquest, heretofore a subject of never-failing interest, and the King smiled indulgently. As Gibson turned the conversation to the subject of organizing the government employees for the coming election, a man entered the room unannounced and Gibson knew the source of the King's indifference. Moreno and Gibson had been working in the United States files at the same time—Gibson trying to substantiate a $50,000 claim against the Dutch government, and Moreno searching for records to incriminate his cable rival, Cyrus West Field. As though they had never met, they bowed formally upon being introduced.

"Don Moreno," said Kalakaua, "is a graduate of the naval academy at Naples and he has helped me drill my troops in Italian evolutions that are vastly superior to the German. He has supervised the transfer of most of my military and ammunition to the palace grounds where it can actually guard my person. Today, thanks to Moreno, I can really feel safe."

Moreno's smirk enraged Gibson. The two men left together; the King was delighted that they had hit it off so well.

As they passed through the palace gate Gibson said, "Moreno, I did not expect to find you in Hawaii."

"Nor I you, Gentillissimo Gibson; well, shall we join forces for the common weal?"

They stopped and shook hands.

"Come home with me," invited Gibson. Moreno assented and as the evening progressed Gibson said, "If all the expenditures Kalakaua contemplates for his Empire of Oceania are introduced into this legislature, the whites will tear him apart. He would be dethroned and the people would select Emma as their Queen. She has a strong following. I have been offered a place in her cabinet."

Moreno raised his eyebrows. "But to gain this goal you would lose much. She is thrifty; he, generous to a fault."

Gibson smiled. "You have almost persuaded me."

Moreno lifted his glass. "To our future Minister of Finance."

As Gibson listened to young Robert W. Wilcox's campaign speech on the eve of the election, he knew that the *hapahaole** schoolteacher had become the mouthpiece of Moreno. Wilcox spoke of the need for making Hawaii a formidable fortress: "The guns of Russia and Japan are today trained at our very hearts and their soldiers are poised for invasion."

Volunteer and Household Troops huzza'd.

"Elect me, and I will turn all my efforts toward creating a navy and a standing army second to none in the Pacific. Hawaiians have too long tolerated the crushing boot of the Jesus Shouters who pray in their temples on Sunday and slip their hands into our pockets Monday through Saturday . . . Awake, men of Hawaii! Elect me, and we'll drive them out . . . !"

With the help of Royalist party contributions, illegal tax rebates, and free liquor, Wilcox and the other loyal followers of the King were swept into office. At Lahaina, Maui, it took forty cases of whisky. At Kauai, one thousand two hundred and fifty-six ballots were counted—double the number of voters!

When the Assembly opened shortly thereafter, Walter

* part-white, part-Hawaiian.

Murray Gibson outdid himself to regain his former place in
the King's favor. He championed an appropriation to record
the genealogy of Polynesian chiefs, all-important to natives of
the South Seas who loved to recite genealogy. The King's
sister, Princess Liliuokalani, was made chairman at five thousand dollars a year. A ten-thousand-dollar coronation bill
was introduced. Gibson had convinced the King that the
princes of the earth would foregather at a formal coronation
held in conjunction with the opening of his new palace, and
the dedication of the statue. Moreno added: "It will launch
Your Majesty's Empire of Oceania with the proper éclat.
Polynesian princes will love and revere you the more for it."

The bill was read and aroused heated opposition. Nevertheless the coronation appropriation passed. A bill providing
for the education of Hawaiian youths abroad in foreign military academies to prepare them for future military leadership was introduced. Approved, there followed a subsidy of
forty-eight thousand dollars for Moreno's Chinese Steam Navigation line. During the noon recess, Moreno's agents drifted
among representatives with bundles of bribe money. When it
passed Moreno felt secure and asked the King when his cabinet post would be announced. The King put him off. "As
soon as the legislature is prorogued, then I may proclaim you
publicly."

In the afternoon session Kalakaua's supporters delivered
the real blow—a ten-million-dollar loan to finance the King's
army and navy. Castle shouted: "As surely as you vote for this
measure, you hasten the end of the King's rule. We taxpayers
will express our resentment in a concrete manner!"

In the resultant uproar, part-Hawaiian Robert W. Wilcox
was the first on the floor. "Castle speaks from a heart of pure
gold! It shines every time he opens his mouth." As the laughter subsided, Wilcox cried, "Gentlemen of the Assembly!

The missionary has made our choice easy; the vested interests or the people?"

Furious, Castle retorted: "By your biased actions you Hawaiians make our King a hated man. A push will tumble him from the throne."

"Treason!" shouted Gibson.

The legislative hall was in instant turmoil. When the President secured quiet, he recognized Castle. Looking at Gibson, Castle said coldly: "That man speaks and acts treasonably who stirs up racial strife and corrupts the legislature. You are a political Ishmael, an outcast of your own kind. Since you have joined forces with the King's side, there has not been an election in which government authority has not interposed. Your despicable tactics of setting Hawaiian against white have forced me to hire guards for my home. Absolutism, Gibson, is a monster which devours its own kind!"

The silence which fell was broken by the applause of Claus Spreckels. Hearing of Moreno's growing power in the legislature, the sugar refiner had taken his swiftest vessel to hurry back to Honolulu. Upon his arrival, he had gone to his son, and learned that he was too late to stop the steamship subsidy to Moreno's rival Chinese line, but that a ten-million-dollar loan was up for second reading. He flew into a rage, "*Gott im Himmel*, this crook Moreno with my own hand, I will kill."

Spreckels and his son had found Moreno at Sing Chong & Company's offices. Claus lit into the Italian adventurer hammer and tongs. "Moreno, I of you knowing in San Francisco. *Du ein* cheading, lying schemer *bist*. Lower parasides der are none who licks Arsh und to thousands harm does. I in dis land twenty million haf und I the land to blooming make. *Und du?*"

"I am unlocking the treasure houses of China, promoting trade between the Orient and Hawaii!" Moreno retorted.

That recalled to Spreckles the proposed ten-million-dollar loan. "John, telling me you und dat good-for-nudding cabbagehead Gibson, the King's head mitt navies, armies filling. Ja? Und supmarine caples?"

Moreno smiled. "Claus, there are those who have Hawaii's true interest at heart. What has the King to lose? He is up to his ears in debt to you. That debt brought you here to protect your own filthy money."

"Fildy monies! My monies into productif channels going. A Navy! Army! *Ach du lieber Herr Gott im Himmel.* Day gif you apsolutely nuddings, but why am I mitt you yet talking, why? I go mitt de lechustlators talking."

Spreckels had worked fast and now as he applauded Castle's attack on Gibson it was clear that his timely appearance headed off the very likely passage of the $10,000,000 loan; among the King's loyal Hawaiians, there were too many in Spreckels' employ.

19 Mr. Moreno's Riot

Spreckels remained in Honolulu until the legislature adjourned after giving the cabinet a thirty-two to ten vote of confidence. No sooner was he on his way to San Francisco than King Kalakaua summoned Gibson to the boathouse, his favorite informal meeting place. When Gibson arrived he found Moreno and the King in close conversation.

King Kalakaua began, "Gibson, I have decided to form a new cabinet. Mr. Moreno is a world traveler and a diplomat. I am offering him the portfolio of minister of foreign affairs." As he spoke Moreno knelt and kissed the King's hand.

Gibson knew that it was cut and dried. Although Kalakaua had promised him the Prime Ministership, the smooth-tongued interloper would get top-billing. To forestall such humiliation Gibson hastened, "By your leave, Rex, my business duties are too pressing to permit me at this time to accept the Prime Ministership." He saw the smile evaporate from Moreno's face. "But Sire, if you should require my assistance at any time, you will always find me quick to serve you." He felt sure that with a little effort on his part, Moreno could be driven out of the country within a fortnight. He congratulated Moreno and after toasting the new foreign minister, left.

From his office Gibson telephoned Editor Henry Whitney of the *Commercial Advertiser*, and having reported the news added: "Better put a two-inch mourning border around page one. It's Hawaii's funeral."

When Whitney's black-bordered sheet hit the streets men gathered in small groups, discussing Moreno's appointment. "How does the King dare do this?" cried Castle. Banker Bishop put in: "Everyone in San Francisco knows Moreno's reputation. During the last legislature, Hawaii's plantation stock dropped from $1,500 to $800 without any buyers. Moreno's appointment will finish us."

"I tell you, it's not Moreno. It's not Gibson. It's the King we must dislodge," said Castle. "Men, this is our chance to run the black bastard off the throne."

Dole pleaded caution. "Moreno and the King have stored arms and ammunition behind the palace wall. If we are going to capture them, we must take the palace by surprise."

"If we don't take action now, a white man will never be safe again in Hawaii," insisted Henry Waterhouse. "I'm going to call a public meeting. We'll get together what arms and ammunition we can and issue them to everyone who will help."

Tight-lipped men walked into Hall's hardware store and walked out with rifles. Ships at the docks quickly filled with white women and children and turned about for San Francisco. Windows were shuttered and there wasn't a child on the streets.

The diplomatic corps met with the ranking new American Minister Resident, General James Comly. Ratard, the French Consul said: "I have seen riots in Paris. Murder is in men's hearts. I propose that we make our consulates 'havens of refuge' at once."

Wodehouse, who had lived in Hawaii longest, counselled:

"If we refuse to recognize Moreno as foreign minister, we may avert bloodshed." General Comly agreed.

Events outstripped the conservative diplomatic corps. As they conferred, Moreno called a meeting of all public-spirited Hawaiians at the Kaumakapili church, which filled quickly with excited men.

Moreno was in fine fettle. At last he was proving himself Hawaii's Garibaldi. Using the traditional Hawaiian greeting, he began:

"O, My People! Your ancestors came to Hawaii to be free. Their blood was spilled on this soil, defending it against foreign invaders!" Although contrary to history it sounded well. "But today our land is in the toils of shameless rascals. As we are meeting here in orderly manner, they are gathering guns and weapons.

"Hawaiians, awake! To you belongs Hawaii. With your help, the King's loyal soldiers are ready to fight to the death for this soil on which your ancestors' blood was spilled. I, your foreign minister, am ready to lead you. Are you ready?"

There was a thundering response.

"Go home then, get guns and shoot the white men . . . Get kerosene and burn them out. Get clubs and beat out their brains."

The frenzied hearers rushed out, voicing their deep-rooted hatred. Moreno hurried to report to the King the success of the meeting and the temper of the angry crowd. "Sire, the moment is here to strike the blow which will free your Polynesians and go ringing down through the ages."

"You are sure the Hawaiians are with you?"

Moreno looked for confirmation to the new Minister of Interior, John E. Bush, who had been at the meeting. When he corroborated Moreno, the King said: "Moreno, the portfolio of Minister of War is yours. Make what disposition of troops and equipment you deem necessary."

Moreno went into action. He declared a state of emergency; called up the Volunteer corps; commanded the Household Troops to place the field pieces so as to guard the avenues leading to the palace; ordered the artillery loaded with canister, arms stacked at strategic points; and, to stouten the hearts of his warriors, asked Kalakaua to inspect his forces. The King changed into the uniform of his Royal Guards and with Moreno beside him, inspected each field piece. The sight of the loaded artillery, the determination of his troops, roused Kalakaua. It was his hour. At last the white man's yoke would be thrown off. And once they, his people, were free, he would liberate all his fellow Polynesians in the Pacific. Wishing to convey something of this large feeling to his men, King Kalakaua ordered the troops to form for review.

Standing before them he said: "Soldiers of Hawaii, we are reluctantly called to resort to arms for the protection of Our Sovereign rights and those of Our people. We expect a mob and a rabble. Stand ready. Do not flinch. Maintain discipline. Prove your heritage as Hawaiians!

"Our cause is just. In that justness, let us charge into the battle always looking forward. 'Forever live Hawaii!' "

At the fierce shout of his troops, the King rejoiced.

Night came. The danger of the situation became more apparent and as during the election riot, Kalakaua felt his blood run cold. Unaccountably, he remembered old Haaheo's injunction: "If you want power, set haole against haole, foreigner against foreigner"—but by following the advice of Moreno and Gibson, he had pitted Hawaiian against white. He wondered why Gibson had not taken the cabinet post and suddenly thought: "He must be behind this trouble, somewhere." He hurried up the stairs to Kapiolani's sewing-room. "Come, Kapiolani, you must get out of here. The whites are rebelling. You will be killed."

Kapiolani went on sewing. "David, I knew this time would come. The white men would never let us be free without a fight. Now that it has come, my place is with you."

At his wife's composure, Kalakaua steadied. But as he sat alone in his card room, he heard a brisk exchange of rifle fire. He summoned the palace guard captain and learned that a group of whites was approaching. In his frenzy, he summoned a heavy guard and with the pretense of removing his headquarters from the palace to a place of safety, he fled across the street to Iolani Barracks.

Again a flurry of shots shattered the silence driving the King to a new resolve. His troops were not strong enough yet. He must compromise with the whites. He summoned his troops' physician, Doctor John Strayer McGrew, and after a hurried consultation, sent him to the American Minister, General James Comly.

"The King is hiding in the barracks under a heavy guard," Dr. McGrew told the sleepy-eyed, night-shirted American. "He wants to settle without bloodshed. He trusts your judgment and says he will do anything you advise."

"Tell him the diplomatic corps has agreed to take concerted action in all things. Therefore I am not a free agent. Anyway, it is after midnight and nothing will happen tonight. Tell him to wait until morning."

The doctor argued, "General Comly, the fear of night is upon Kalakaua. With daylight, he'll be of another mind. It is in your hands to prevent mass murder and to rid the country of Moreno without bloodshed."

Upon Comly's arrival at the barracks next morning, the King greeted him with embarrassed cordiality. "General Comly, I can't understand why the white community doesn't like Moreno. He's a true patriot."

"Your Majesty, the diplomatic corps considered it an offense to deal with the rascal. He has lied to Ratard, insulted Wodehouse; he's been driven out of the United States. Wherever he's been, there are writs against him—San Francisco, New York, Washington!"

The King interposed: "Moreno is a man of large views in economic, political, and state affairs which frequently coincide with my own. Of all white people in Hawaii, Moreno understands Hawaii's future better than any . . ."

Comly interrupted abruptly: "I came here for one purpose, Your Majesty. Unless Moreno is discharged, the diplomatic corps has agreed to ask their governments to send warships and intercede to protect the lives and properties of their nationals."

"You threaten war!" Kalakaua blanched. "What of my sovereign rights?"

Comly stated flatly: "Once there is a foreign intervention, you will never be a free man again."

"You give me no choice."

"Banish Moreno."

"Give me time."

"It is now nine. The whites are meeting in one hour for the distribution of arms."

Kalakaua demanded: "Where will you be at ten?"

"The Consular Corps is meeting at Doctor McGrew's."

Honolulu's business had stopped. Stores and auction rooms were bolted. Whites were hurrying to the Kaumakapili meeting hall. The packed house was called to order, after which

Castle told them that arms were available. "Each man will line up and get a rifle and ten rounds of ammunition." The audience cheered.

Meanwhile the Consular Corps met.

At ten there was a knock on Doctor McGrew's door. The doctor excused himself and returned promptly, saying: "Moreno demands to see you, General Comly." He added, "I think he is armed." Comly went to the door.

Moreno didn't wait for any greeting. "I ask one thing, Comly. Withhold your demands to the King a month, to give me time to procure documents from China, Italy, and the United States to prove my integrity."

Comly shook his head. Thereupon the Italian appealed to Comly's justice. That failing, he got on his knees and pleaded: "Comly, I swear by God in Heaven, it is my life to serve the Polynesian people. I love them. I may have made mistakes in the past, but if I lose this trust, my life will not be worth living . . ."

"Why come to me?" Comly asked. "Every responsible person in Honolulu is against you. You have fostered murder, set Hawaiian against white. There is a big public meeting now in session. They may even cause you bodily harm; do you realize that?"

In a flash Moreno's servility changed. Jumping upright, he swore: "God damn you, Comly. I'll quit the job, but I'll denounce you to your government, to every newspaper. You'll know what it is to have your reputation ruined, you sneaking, heartless coward."

Comly smiled. "This completes my picture of you, Celso Caesar Moreno. Good day."

Within a few minutes of Moreno's departure, an autographed letter arrived from the King.

*General James M. Comly, American Minister Resident
to the Hawaiian Islands, etc. etc. etc.
Sir,
Moreno has resigned his portfolio and I have accepted
his resignation.*

Kalakaua, Rex.

Alexander Joy Cartwright, who had been delegated by
the whites to attend the diplomats' conference, asked if he
could announce the news to the mass meeting. "No," replied
Comly, "it must not be disclosed that King Kalakaua acted
under duress, but the men at the meeting must know before
they take action. Tell them that the King has dismissed
Moreno of his own free will."

When Cartwright arrived at the church the men were getting their issues of guns and ammunition. The six-foot-three
messenger strode up the aisle. Every eye was upon his commanding figure. He turned to the audience. "His Majesty
has dismissed Moreno!"

That was not enough for Hall, who had supplied most of
the arms. "To hell with dismissing Moreno," he shouted, "I
move that we banish the rascal."

Cartwright held up his hand. "Moreno is out of office and
is a free citizen—entitled to the same treatment as any in-
habitant of Hawaii. I, for one, am ready to see that no harm
befalls him."

Coming from one of their own leaders, that halted the
crowd. Arms were turned in and the men dispersed slowly.

Moreno, however, was full of vengeance. He was resolved
to purge every consular member who had opposed him and
to go to each foreign capital to do so. To defray his traveling
expenses, he took along three Hawaiian government students, including Robert W. Wilcox, with their combined

nine-thousand-dollar foreign study scholarships. Supplied with letters he had forged on the King's stationery, he left for America.

A new cabinet of substantial businessmen was appointed. At the Queen's suggestion, the King held an official New Year's harmony dinner the following week. The clergy, the diplomatic corps, the judiciary, nobles, representatives, privy counselors, the bar, the medical profession, press, and principal merchants were invited. Kalakaua waited until the New Year, 1881, was striking. Then His Majesty slowly rose and raised his glass.

"My friends, the New Year is upon us. If there have been mistakes in the past, let us profit by the lessons of experience and with honesty of purpose press on to a future which I trust may be bright with prosperity and hope for one and all."

As one, the assembled guests cheered the speech to the rafters. Minister Green had to wait several minutes before he could respond: "I drink to His Majesty, Our King, the most popular sovereign in the world."

The King bowed as the men drank—many in water—and smashed their glasses against the fireplace. As the air resounded with breaking glass, King Kalakaua studied the sober-sided businessmen, the pinched lawyers, the complacent members of the cabinet, and he missed Moreno. He recalled that Moreno had said the Chinese ruler would treat him as an equal; the Duke of Edinburgh had once invited him to visit England; he thought of the King of Siam who ate off solid gold plates. The pyramids of Egypt, too, had always had a strong fascination. And then there was that unexpended ten-thousand-dollar coronation appropriation.

Part Three

Resplendent in Plumage of Mamo *(Ua Wahi' ika Hulu o ka Mamo)* 1881–1887

20 Kalakaua Visits the EMPEROR OF Japan

Kalakaua's resolve to see the world and investigate for himself the barriers that might exist between him and his dream of empire culminated in action during the week after the "harmony" banquet. The time was propitious; there was some money, and a definite feeling of good will towards him among Hawaiians. The Privy Council agreed that David's sister Liliuokalani should act as Princess Regent during his absence, and that he could make a round-the-world cruise, provided that he pledge his own income to defray expenses, and that he take along "advisors" Judd and Armstrong. The King's reaction to this chaperonage was one of disgust but he knew that some of the missionaries would insist upon accompanying him, and these two were as harmless as any. When their ship left Honolulu amid the shouts of the Hawaiians, neither Judd nor Armstrong had any idea that Kalakaua had quietly engaged his bibulous butler, Baron von Oehlhoffen, as a member of the party, on government salary as poet laureate and keeper of the royal archives during the tour. An hour out at sea, von Oehlhoffen appeared; the King grinned amiably, and Judd and Armstrong were furious but helpless.

First, the group went to San Francisco, where they took ship for the Orient, with the first port of call to be in Japan

As the S.S. *Oceanic* steamed slowly into Yokohama Harbor, Grand Chamberlain Charles Hastings Judd and Minister of State William Nevins Armstrong stood on deck open-mouthed. The party was traveling incognito, but evidently they were expected! The harbor was full of shipping and they moved in between an imposing array of forty-two Russian, British, and Japanese men-of-war. Rainbows of pennants descended from masts; sailors manned yards smartly; the Japanese flagship's band played "Hawaii Ponoi," and thirteen saluting batteries boomed two hundred and seventy-three times. Bewildered, Judd and Armstrong looked at Kalakaua reproachfully. But Kalakaua, personally innocent of violating the incognito, drew himself up proudly and conferred a patronizing smile upon his traveling companions.

"Do my Crown Ministers approve?"

Armstrong frowned. "Our purse cannot meet the strain of such entertainment as this promises."

Attempting to rebuke his penny-pinching aides, Kalakaua retorted, "Isn't it time you two were putting on your seven-hundred-and-fifty-dollar uniforms, which my government paid for? The Emperor's launch must be here before long."

When the uniformed aides appeared on deck beside their royal master, a trim military launch flying Emperor Mutsu-hito's crown ensign was just pulling alongside. Aboard were Foreign Minister Count Kaoru Inouye, a feudal baron; Ma-chinori S. Nagasaki, the Emperor's Minister of Ceremonies; and Hawaiian Consul General Robert W. Irwin. They welcomed the royal party with many bows and the master of ceremonies informed Judd that a special express train waited to convey the royal guest to Tokyo where a palace had been readied for his reception.

As the Hawaiians were driven to the station in the Emperor's gold and ebony carriage, armed troops guarded every step of the way. Behind them, hundreds of thousands of spectators prostrated. Judd, who was attracting great attention because of his fine gold-bedecked lieutenant general's uniform, complete to cocked hat, observed: "Such child-like devotion, Armstrong, gives one a new perspective of royalty."

At the railroad station four Imperial Princes of the Blood and ten high officials including the Ministers of War and Navy, greeted the Hawaiian monarch. At all times these dignitaries insisted that their royal guest walk ahead, alone. Once on the train, Kalakaua summoned the four princes to his compartment and paid special attention to young Hatsu, who understood some English. As the King talked with the eager adolescent, a warm memory of his niece Kaiulani came to mind. He reached into his pocket, pulled out a gold-plated compass and gave it to the prince, "When we return to Hawaii we will ship you one of our coal-black stallions."

As they left the train, again troops lined the route to the magnificent palace grounds where officers of the Imperial Household Troops presented arms. Mindful of protocol, shortly after they were guided to their rooms, King Kalakaua, flanked by his two crown ministers, went to pay his respects to the Emperor. As Kalakaua's carriage swept over the moat and into the Imperial Residence grounds the thirty-eight-year-old Emperor Mutsuhito descended the steps to greet his royal guest at the carriage doors. For the first time in Japan's entire history the Japanese Emperor, Son of Heaven, was descending to receive a mortal. President Grant, who had visited Japan two years before, was not so honored, nor did he walk side by side with the Emperor. Mutsuhito was small in stature and fragile, but his dignity of carriage impressed King Kalakaua, who towered above him. While Judd and Armstrong stood at a respectful distance, the royal guest was ushered into a private chamber where sat Her Gracious Majesty, the Empress. Kalakaua noticed her doll-like appearance. Her white shaven face was enameled; cosmetics accentuated her lips and eyebrows and her black hair rose in a high pompadour. Over richly colored silk robes she wore an ornate sash which caught the light in its intricate brocade.

As they sat on chairs, European fashion, a lady-in-waiting translated. The Empress complimented Kalakaua upon his courage in attempting a global trip. "I shudder," she said, "when I am forced to travel ten miles to our summer residence."

Within twenty minutes, King Kalakaua rose and took his departure. Again the Emperor accompanied him, walking beside him, to the carriage.

Returning to the guest palace, King Kalakaua found Baron von Oehlhoffen in a deplorable condition and to make matters worse, the Japanese dignitaries accompanying him witnessed the spectacle. In Yokohama the poet laureate had been ordered by Judd and Armstrong to remain with the luggage. All the way in the baggage car, Baron Robert had brooded over his humiliation. When they arrived at the station, von Oehlhoffen's plan of revenge was ready. No sooner had King Kalakaua, Judd, and Armstrong left than he took out the royal standard and bowed before it three times. To the further bewilderment of the spectators he repeated the same abracadabra before a shimmering golden coat— King Kalakaua's prized feather cloak. Tossing it over his shoulders, Robert clapped on one of the King's silk top hats and motioned to a Japanese lackey to follow him with the royal standard.

Completely baffled by this unscheduled appearance, Japanese prostrated right and left. King Kalakaua's cavalcade had been slightly delayed in forming the ceremonial procession and it was just moving again when some of the lesser dignitaries, including the Minister of Education, looked back and saw the butler, resplendent in the royal *mamo* cloak, with prone Japanese all about him. Believing they had made some horrible mistake, the rear of the procession broke off and returned to do homage to this fine-feathered personage. Then, as Baron Robert attempted to overtake the forward part of the entourage, the mystified public thought that it was really beholding the true sovereign and fell upon its knees all over again.

Once in the guest palace, Robert ordered liquor and geisha girls whom he commanded to dance. It was in this setting that Kalakaua, escorted by the princes, found Robert sprawled upon a large bed with the King's top hat drawn far down over his head and the sacred feather robe over the bedpost. The princes politely ignored Robert, but noting the brilliant feather cloak they respectfully asked its significance.

The King, in Hawaiian, spoke to Judd, "Explain that my official court taster felt it incumbent to sample all the wines. And tell them the robe is a symbol of royalty which the Hawaiian monarch may order an attendant to wear for convenience's sake." Then, when the princely escort had departed, the King ordered: "Armstrong, get that drunken son of a bitch out of my sight."

In the morning, before going to review the troops with the Emperor, King Kalakaua summoned his butler. Balancing the crushed top hat before von Oehlhoffen's stricken eyes, he said: "Robert, I have been like a lenient father, yet you persist in heaping disgrace upon me. This is the third top hat you've ruined. Henceforth, I command you to confine yourself to the servant's quarters."

Escorted by mounted lancers, Mutsuhito arrived at exactly ten. At the parade grounds two milk-white stallions with trappings of gold were brought forward. The rulers mounted simultaneously, while attendants kept the two stallions exactly abreast. Kalakaua sat his horse well. His imposing height of six feet one and his well proportioned two-hundred-pound frame dwarfed the fragile Mutsuhito. Even the Emperor's lancers, the tallest in the land, seemed puny.

They had scarcely mounted when they saw dust in the distance and eight batteries of six field guns, pulled by horses at top speed, dashed across the field. Halted instantly, horses were detached in a trice, guns unlimbered; and within five minutes the field artillery reduced a dummy fortress, three thousand yards distant, to shambles.

Kalakaua was impressed. "Such speed and concentration of fire-power could only be approached, perhaps, by Germany."

The compliment delighted Mutsuhito: "My observers studied the Prussian methods carefully."

Turning to his Grand Chamberlain, Kalakaua said: "Judd, order four hundred German-style field uniforms for my dragoons, footguards, fusileers, and musketeers! And one hundred and fifty dress-white uniforms. When we get to Berlin, inquire about these Krupp guns."

After an inspection of ten thousand goose-stepping Japanese, the Emperor, on behalf of his royal guest, declared a nation-wide amnesty to prisoners charged with minor offenses. Back in the royal palace, Mutsuhito finally got around to his question: "Pardon, worthy brother, but we in Japan are all of one basic hue. Your Majesty is dark brown; your Grand Chamberlain is swarthy, and the Minister of State is as white as a blood-less Caucasian."

Kalakaua laughed. "When the gods experimented with mortals they left the first in the oven too long and he came

out burned coal black—from him descended the Negroes. In
their anxiety to make the next one right, the gods took him
out half done, a chalky white—from him descended the Cau-
casians. The third was done to a turn, and he came out a nut
brown with overtones of golden yellow, like your own people.
My Minister of State, unfortunately, is only half-baked!"

At the fanciful reply the Emperor roared.

The entertainment which followed was climaxed by a state
dinner at Akasaka Palace, dampened not one whit by torren-
tial downpours. By comparison, President Grant's fifty-
thousand-dollar reception for King Kalakaua had been taw-
dry. Here, the menu, in both Hawaiian and Japanese, was
wrought in white satin with threads of gold. Even democratic
Armstrong was impressed when told that the gold service was
valued at two hundred thousand dollars. Emperor Mutsuhito
expressed profound regret that the gold fountain in the center of the banquet table had that day met with an accident
and refused to spout its diversified jets.

King Kalakaua responded: "But, Sire, the High Powers
of Heaven have been pouring out such a superabundance of
water to fructify your Imperial domains, that the little gods
and goddesses no doubt felt that it would be impious to add
their insignificant spouts at this time."

The Emperor laughed heartily and the remark ran around
the assembled two hundred and thirty-eight princes and princesses of the realm who had never seen their imperial ruler
in a more jovial mood. There followed a signal honor to
Kalakaua. His Imperial Majesty rose and proposed the
health of his fellow sovereign. The toast was drunk in *Veuve
Clicquot,* a gift from the Czar of Russia. With nicety King
Kalakaua withheld his response for the following day when
the Emperor would be his dinner guest.

As the minutes sped by the conversation became more informal. Kalakaua, who had drunk toast after toast, was getting sleepy. In a half wakeful moment he caught a question young Prince Hatsu asked him about man's noblest aspiration. He replied: "My son, man's noblest aspiration is to hear the birds sing."

The young prince pondered the cryptic response, and finally bowed. "Your Majesty, I shall always treasure that deep thought."

At the other end of the great banquet table, Chamberlain Judd's general's uniform elicited many inquiries about Hawaii's fighting services.

The Japanese Minister of War said to Armstrong, "We hear much of the fighting quality of your men."

Armstrong, highly stimulated by the wine, replied: "We depend upon our diet to win our wars, sir. We feed our men of war a species of banana which stimulates courage. Full of this excretion, commonly known as banana oil, our intrepid warriors do not hesitate to kiss the hot lips of the enemies' guns."

In all seriousness, the Minister of War answered: "I, too, contend that diet is all important. You cannot make fighters out of rice and fish. If only I could persuade the Emperor to control the country's diet for only seven years . . ."

He halted. The dinner was interrupted by the bearer of a dispatch. It was from the Russian Ambassador and was immediately read aloud. The Czar, Alexander II, had just been assassinated. That ended the festivities.

The next afternoon Foreign Minister Count Inouye called and announced over the ceremonial tea that he had come to King Kalakaua upon confidential matters of state.

"Japan," he said, "would like to negotiate a treaty of everlasting friendship with Hawaii, one which will permit us to enter your ports the while observing your laws, while you enter our ports and trade therein in compliance with our laws."

Armstrong, schooled in international law, begged permission to confer in private with the King and Grand Chamberlain Judd. After Inouye withdrew, he explained that Japan's present treaties gave her no sovereignty over her important treaty ports such as Yokohama, but forced her to allow foreign consuls to be supreme judges of matters involving the rights of Japanese. "If we compact such a treaty it may induce other nations to re-negotiate."

"Such a treaty of equality is the least we can do in return for our cordial reception," said King Kalakaua.

When Inouye returned, Armstrong told him that His Majesty, the King of Hawaii, was prepared to compact a treaty of friendship and equality at once, adding: "Any treaty, of course, must be ratified by the Hawaiian Chamber of Nobles."

Inouye, delighted at his easy conquest, bowed repeatedly. "Your Imperial Highness, may I consider the treaty an open state secret—shared by the Imperial family, but withheld from inquisitive foreign officials?" As Kalakaua assented, he hastened to take his important news to the Emperor.

To show Emperor Mutsuhito's instant appreciation, princes and nobles showered the Hawaiian monarch with rare cloisonné vases, rich silks, lacquer boxes, old bronze, heavy embroideries, and even two ancient Japanese steel suits of armor. Robert tried one on. He climbed in quite easily and clanked about with some importance. But once the vizor was drawn, getting out was another matter. As Robert pleaded to be extricated, the King laughed until tears rolled down his cheeks while Judd grimly suggested that they leave the valet liquorless in the canned suit for a week.

More gifts kept arriving from the princes, climaxed with the conferring of the Grand Cross of the Rising Sun upon

King Kalakaua. When the last day of their visit arrived, the King rebuilt his dream of empire. He saw a new Hawaii rising from his seven islands—islands as productive as Emperor Mutsuhito's. He saw Hawaii free of the foreign threats. But he felt the treaty Inouye proposed was not enough to cement the bonds between Hawaii and Japan. Summoning Robert, he sent him to the Minister of the Imperial Household to ask for a private audience with the Emperor.

Within the hour Count Inouye arrived to escort Kalakaua to his Imperial Majesty. The two Hawaiian advisors saw the King's departure. "Our Bird of Paradise is getting delusions of divinity," said Armstrong. "Yesterday he told me that Hawaiian kings were descended from *Akua* (meaning godhood) but that the missionaries denied this origin to promote their own feeble God."

When the supreme rulers were seated, with Inouye between them, King Kalakaua began: "Your Imperial Highness, I am departing from your friendly shores tomorrow but, before going, I have two important proposals. You have suggested a treaty of perpetual friendship between my country and yours. I go further. In times past my people have been threatened by foreign powers, and so are the vast throngs of Polynesians spread through the entire Pacific. We must lock our countries into a firm union against all aggressor nations. Sire, I propose nothing less than a Federation of Oceanic States with Emperor Mutsuhito, yourself, as the nominal head. To cement such a federation, I further propose a direct union between our royal families—Prince Hatsu and my six-year-old niece, Princess Kaiulani of Hawaii, the most beloved of my land and direct heir to my throne."

Mutsuhito wondered how far Kalakaua had divined his thoughts. To make the Pacific secure, Japan must have not only Hawaii and Alaska, but also the Dutch Spice Islands and the Philippines. And here was King Kalakaua offering federation with Hawaii—the last link necessary to his chain of outlying bastions, and Japan lacked the naval strength to take advantage of it! The thought of joining families was quite another matter. "The mixing of our blood symbolizing a union between our great kingdoms is indeed good, but let our dear children Hatsu and Kaiulani first attain their years of discretion so that they themselves can join in the pleasure of choosing each other as life companions." Returning to the first proposal: "In regard to federation, Kalakaua, you are right. We must fortify ourselves behind this wall of union, but the time is not ripe. Let us keep this thought of federation constantly uppermost in our minds. After your trip, inform me as to the weaknesses and strength you find in the armor of the European nations."

It was a wily and cautious speech, and promised nothing. But David Kalakaua left Japan with his heart swelling. A great Emperor had sat with him as an equal, had recognized him as the head of his people; this trip had been no mistake. The time, the Emperor said, was not now. But it was coming. David Kalakaua saw far into the future wherein he was likewise an emperor—of the Polynesian peoples. His ancestors had been worshipped as gods; within himself he carried a divine spark, anything was possible. He would rescue all Polynesians from foreign servitude; his gods were with him.

21 The Fire-Goddess Pele Intervenes

While King Kalakaua was being entertained by Viceroy General Li Hang Chung at Tientsin, the Hawaiian party's next stop after Tokyo, disaster struck his homeland. From a fiery eruption of Mauna Loa, billions of tons of white-hot lava slithered down the snow-capped mountain's massive shoulders and advanced in a broad river of fire upon Hilo, Hawaii's second largest city. Like a giant dragon, the lava flow consumed lehua forests, damned up streams, and coiled across valleys. Roaring filled the air and the ground shook. At night, hundred-foot fountains played fiery jets, making the heavens glow.

The alarmed natives decided: "Our fire goddess Pele is angry at the thousands of Orientals infesting her land." Practically everywhere, pig-tailed Chinese and short-cropped Japanese outnumbered Hawaiians. Maria Alapai, strongest of Oahu's kahunas, prophesied: "This flow presages a disaster even greater than the destruction of Hilo," while the vindictive Kamehamehas asserted: "At last Pele shows her contempt for the Calabash King."

When Maria Alapai spoke, Hawaiians listened. There were many kahunas in the island, gifted men and women who had studied the stars and could read the heavens. They foretold events with uncanny accuracy. They could throw a curse upon an offender which would kill him. If he did not die at once, the feast for the dead would be held for him—he might even attend. His fellows from that time on paid him no attention. He was dead. And after a few days he would literally die, and there would be no mark of any kind upon him. Kahunas were feared and respected.

Recently four ships had dumped two thousand four hundred and ninety coolie laborers, with their quota of pox. A score died on Oahu every day. The death toll mounted; the price of coffin lumber soared. With relatives lying unburied on their mats, stinking in death, the natives shouted their anger. "The whites are not content to displace us with cheap Chinese laborers who give us this death, but dump us into our graves at a profit on each coffin!"

As the stench of death by pox filled the air and the wailing of the land increased, the distraught Princess Regent Liliuo-kalani summoned the Privy Council. Her forehead was drawn in grief and her eyes were dull from sleepless anguish. In a flat voice she said: "Of our former half million we today number but forty thousand, and each day more of us die. Unless God helps us, the end of our people is upon us. But one hope remains. Once before, when David—and you, Ber-nice—and I were children in Mr. Cooke's school, we had such a smallpox epidemic. At that time, Mr. Cooke said that be-fore our country could be spared from the Lord's righteous anger, we must have a moral reform. God helped us then. Today, our sins are greater. We live in wanton debauchery; all too many have sexual diseases; abortions abound. So once again God has visited us with a scourge. To stay it, I have called you leaders of Hawaii together. Let us humbly ask our Heavenly Father to forgive us our lusts, our love of finery and promiscuous living. Shall we kneel?"

For the first time in the history of the Council, the group

of fifteen knelt—all but the oldest, the aged granddaughter of Kamehameha the Great, Princess Ruth Keelikolani, who remained seated, her three hundred and fifty pounds a mountain of protest. At their prayer for divine help her anger increased and when the chastened Privy Council rose, Ruth snorted a contemptuous "Humpf" through her broken nose and lashed out: "Lydia!" She disdained the title of Princess Regent Liliuokalani— "For shame that you should pray to a fanciful haole-God while Pele's lava flow threatens to engulf Hilo. Weakling! Imbecile! You and your profligate brother have brought about this disaster by traveling the white man's disease-strewn road. 'Let us kneel,' " she intoned derisively. "Would you have Pele destroy not only the city of Hilo but our entire nation by kneeling and praying to a foreign god, you cheap haole-loving Aikanaka, when our own gods are so strong!"

As the Council dispersed and its actions became known, the Hawaiians were filled with a sense of guilt. Perhaps, they too, like Kalakaua and his sister Liliuokalani, had gone too far on the white man's road.

Ruth's stand for her own gods added dissension to Honolulu's anguish. "Whose gods are stronger? The white man's or the Hawaiian's? Are we punished for following the white god's ways or for not following them enough?"

Walter Murray Gibson, who had become editor of the *Pacific Commercial Advertiser*, knew that the epidemic would continue until the weak had died and then, like former plagues which had visited Hawaii, abate. Seeing his chance to strengthen his paper against the entrenched *Gazette*, the opportunist decided to take God's side in the Christianized country and forthwith wrote an editorial praising the Princess Regent for calling upon the Power above to take away the pox.

The grateful Liliuokalani sent for Gibson and, once she talked with him, was convinced that he had Hawaii's true interest at heart. The crafty Gibson seized his opportunity. In their frequent consultations, he supported the Princess Regent and then broadcast her views in the *Advertiser*. When she wanted his backing to enlarge the army of police and quarantine Oahu, he went further and declared that she should form a new body of troops to be known as the Princess's Own Volunteers, slyly suggesting that she would need these when she succeeded her brother.

Gibson's motives were mixed. He enjoyed playing any political game, especially with an attractive woman. He had no idea of deserting Kalakaua—but Kalakaua might not return. After a life of risk it might be possible to play safe.

Gradually the relations between Gibson and Liliuokalani took on intimacy. He asked for a small photograph to hang in his home and got a large autographed one. He confessed past sins and when the Princess suggested that prayer might do him good, the excommunicated Mormon leader joined her Congregational church. As a reward for his conversion, the Princess Regent offered him the post of Hawaii's tax assessor. Although protesting his unworthiness, he at once accepted.

Banker Charles Reed Bishop went to Liliuokalani immediately. "Gibson's appointment is impolitic. You know how Gibson and Moreno led the King to the brink of disaster. This man will not hesitate to injure your true friends—the substantial citizens of the government. To obtain political strength he will lower some assessments; to penalize political enemies, he will raise others. I give you fair warning: this time, if Gibson goes, the King goes with him."

She flared: "You are afraid he will make a true tax evaluation of your wife's property. Charlie, you forgive so slowly.

You heard Gibson's confession at last Sunday's prayer meeting. Is it not for us professing Christians to give a weak brother a helping hand?"

"Yes, but I don't want my arm snatched off!"

Liliuokalani did not hear him. "If Gibson goes, the King goes with him," was ringing through her ears. She would have to get her younger sister Likelike's child, Kaiulani, out of the way if she were to succeed to the throne. But first, she resolved to surround herself with strong men like Bishop and Gibson.

As the smallpox mortality rate fell, many Hawaiians said, "God is with our Princess Regent. She was right. Her haole-God is stronger than our gods."

Ruth Keelikolani violently opposed this conclusion. So did the people of Hilo, where the fiery lava flow was approaching ever nearer. Their fear had been increased by the rumor that Liliuokalani's Minister of Interior intended to use dynamite to divert the lava stream. Such profanation, they knew, would aggravate Pele's fury, making Hilo's destruction inevitable. In their terror, the Hiloites sent a vessel to Honolulu and implored Princess Ruth to speed to their aid to assuage Pele's wrath.

Ruth, too, had heard of the plan to use dynamite. At the invitation, she decided to go at once to Hilo. This was her opportunity to prove her gods stronger than the haole importation or their scientific skills. She took along with her twenty of her retainers, including a half-dozen well-hung young men for bed warmers, and for food, two barrels of poi and smoked salmon backs. Accompanied by the Hilo delegation, she was pulled to the wharf in her two-foot-high wagon by eight men, while a ninth shielded her with a huge blue parasol. To get aboard the ship, the ponderous sixty-three-year-old woman was hoisted in a lifeboat. When she arrived off Hilo, thousands of jubilant natives welcomed her, wading out into the water to meet her incoming lighter, and, hoisting it on their shoulders, carried her through the surf. Their fears of Pele were overcome by their joy. At last they had a chieftess who could talk with their goddess. What mattered that the flow was only three miles away?

Days passed and with each twenty-four hours, the thirty-foot lava wall tumbled forward forty or more feet. Yet Ruth refused to budge from her Hilo home. The thousands who had greeted her began to mutter: "The strength has gone out of our chiefs." Even among her own twenty retainers, skepticism set in. When young Oliver Stillman, one of her entourage, suggested that she might step out on the porch and see for herself the mushrooming column of smoke rising from a near-by burning forest, Ruth remained deaf. When the withering hot blasts, blowing over the twenty-five-mile lava furnace, carried the acrid smell and heat into her darkened room, she did nothing, sitting silently, hour after hour.

And while Ruth waited, Princess Liliuokalani decided to prove the power of the Aikanakas by a miracle even greater than the stopping of the smallpox in Honolulu. The same God who had succored her then would halt Hilo's destruction. And with the miracle, Hawaii's throne would eventually be hers. The same fickle thousands who had greeted Ruth now rushed into the sea to welcome Her Royal Highness, the Princess Regent Liliuokalani. Had not her God banished the killing pox? In delight, they hoisted her lighter above their heads, carried her through the surf and up Waianuenue, the avenue of rainbows, singing "Aloha Oe"— which Liliuokalani had herself composed, after witnessing a tender parting of two lovers.

Oliver Stillman, seeing her reception, reported it to Ruth. For the first time, Ruth roused from her lethargy. "The God-loving bitch finally came, did she? Now let her kneel and pray so the pillars of heaven will rattle." She ordered a large meal and went to the porch for the first time since her arrival. When she saw how near the ominous lava wall was to the city she ordered, "Make ready, Oliver, we go to the flow."

The next morning when Princess Liliuokalani, accompanied by eighty equestrians, approached the lava flow, she found Ruth encamped on a slight rise near by. Remembering the haughty chieftess' taunts at the Privy Council meeting, Princess Regent Liliuokalani called: "Ruth! Ruth Keelikolani! You fat ass with your gods, come out!"

For some minutes there was no answer. Then, from another tent, Oliver Stillman appeared.

Liliuokalani recognized him. "What, you he-goat! Aren't you keeping the old one warm? When she wakes, tell her that the Princess Regent Liliuokalani will make a prayer to a real God at the Haile church tonight to stop this flow which threatens the city."

The stinging taunt hit its mark. The old Kamehameha Chieftess, naked except for a cloth about her middle, filled the entrance to the tent. "This for you and your Thurston-God," she said, hawked her throat and spat noisily. "When you are through with your haole-puling, I will talk with Pele."

That night the church was overflowing. Spurred by Ruth's challenge, the Princess Regent did her utmost. She told how the Hawaiian population of Honolulu had been threatened with extinction. She told of the smell of death that pervaded the island, adding, "But it was not until we confessed our sins and prayed to God with cleansed hearts that He heard us and in His infinite mercy lifted the curse from us. Today, Hilo and your homes are threatened. Again, let us search our

hearts, repent our sins, and put our whole trust in Him from
Whom alone comes strength sufficient to take this danger
from us. Shall we kneel?" The congregation prayed.

A week passed and there was no lessening of the flow. It
inched forward irresistibly to within a thousand yards of the
city. Princess Liliuokalani called a second meeting. "The
fault," she said, "lies not with our God but with us. The
hardness of our hearts and the unremittingness of our sins
anger our Lord. Purge yourselves, and if you believe, God
will remove this threat at our doorstep." She prayed again.

The flow continued. As faith dwindled and people began
moving their possessions out of threatened homes, Liliuokalani resolved to rob Ruth of any possible triumph. She ordered the Minister of Interior to have his men use dynamite
to create a barrier which might divert the flow past Hilo and
into the sea.

Ruth heard the dynamite explosions, waited until the following afternoon and then summoned her retainers. She
laughed: "So the Kalakaua bitch has prayed herself out and
used all the science the white devils possess. Now we shall
stop the flow! Oliver, fetch me red lehua blossoms of Pele.
Simon, get me a gourd full of strong awa."

Night fell and the old Chieftess, escorted by twenty of her
faithful, approached the lava front. Within fifty feet, she motioned them to come no closer. The watchers' apprehension
grew to acute anguish. They could not take their eyes off the
molten river pushing ahead, making its own banks as its
sides cooled. On its surface, the stream carried hundred-ton
cakes of partly-cooled lava. As the stream slowly advanced,
there was an awesome grinding as the black, cooled-clinker
lava tumbled to the foot of the moving molten wall.

With the glare and heat of the lava upon her, the
old Chieftess moved majestically, approaching step by step,

slowly and alone, walking up to her goddess. Within the twenty onlookers surged a mighty feeling. This woman, who had been rocked on the knee of Kamehameha the Great, was making her supreme test to prove her gods more potent than the sightless God who lived in a book.

Ruth tossed in a handful of *ohelo* berries. The cauldron of lava consumed them so quickly that even the smoke was not seen.

"Pele took them!" shouted Simon Kaai.

Ruth took the red lehua blossoms and threw several branches into the red hot lava. The little group saw the red flowers of Pele snatched from the air as though a hand had reached out with the flame. Then Ruth took the gourd full of awa, Pele's drink, and threw the gourd into the lava stream. It blazed and where it fell rose a curious cloud, perhaps steam, but it took the shape of a woman with long hair.

"See!" shouted Oliver Stillman above the roar, "Pele rose up from the flames!"

Silence descended.

Then, they heard Ruth chant: *"Mai huhu Pele . . .* Please don't be angry with us, Goddess of Fire. Please don't be angry. . . ." The giant Kamehameha Chieftess was supplicating like a child. "Spare us, O goddess, your people and your lands, O Pele. If we die, who will there be to sing to you? To dance for you? To tell of your wonderful power?" And then her voice slipped back again into the grinding roar of the tumbling lava. ". . . *Mai huhu oe ia makou, Pele.* Please don't be angry with us, Pele."

As she besought her goddess, the twenty felt the presence of the gods of their childhood. And they knew that the flow would be stopped by morning.

That night, as they slept soundly, the ground became silent, and at dawn, Oliver Stillman sped to Hilo to tell the people that their city was safe. In thanksgiving, the people returned with him. They forgot Ruth's huge, homely face, the great jowls and folds, the flattened nose with flaring nostrils, the scraggly eyebrows and deep wrinkles, the warts, the ponderous frame. The woman was beautiful, beautiful as their goddess Pele; and some even whispered: "She is Pele."

22 Kalakaua Continues His World Tour

With no knowledge of the events taking place in Hawaii, King Kalakaua and his suite pursued a rather disappointing way in China. Their arrival went unheralded. The Dowager Empress, aged and infirm, was growing too weak for affairs of state, despite the heroic efforts of three hundred nurses. When Kalakaua arrived at Tientsin, Viceroy Li Hang Chung, general to the Chinese armies, sent a sedan chair to convey the royal party to his palace. No prince or minister appeared to greet them. Through the narrow, stinking streets the sweating coolies labored against a mass of people who moved flat against the walls to permit passage, gazing stolidly at the King without a smile or salute.

When Kalakaua was seated in the sweltering palace and Li Hang Chung arrived, there were practically no formalities. General Li began firing questions.

"How many islands are there in your kingdom? How old are you? Do you have a parliament? How many people are in your kingdom?"

Throughout the questioning, pipe bearers watched the Viceroy and tended the bowl on the floor. When Li opened his hand a bearer instantly placed a pipestem in it. After a few puffs, when the hand relaxed, a second bearer removed it. The questions never stopped.

"You have many Chinese in your country, and you say you treat them well?" His tone indicated that he doubted it. "Are you the son of your predecessor?"

"I come from another dynasty." Kalakaua's tone was icy.

"Well, as a boy, what did you do?"

Kalakaua hesitated. "I went into the army when I was fourteen."

"How large is this army?"

"Few regular troops. I rely on volunteers," said Kalakaua.

"How many troops do you muster, General?"

"Thousands are available, but the number engaged depends upon the work to be done. As European countries offer fees to architects, I offer rewards for duties performed. Public acclaim—this hero-worship—is poor reward and soon forgotten. For killing a commander-in-chief, I offer thirteen thousand dollars and official rank; for killing a French soldier, one hundred and thirty-seven dollars; for capturing a first-class ironclad, one hundred and thirty-seven thousand, and to anyone devising a plan by which the French are defeated in a fight, I give four hundred thousand dollars!" He looked Kalakaua, Judd, and Armstrong straight in the face. "You are all Hawaiians?"

"Yes, straight from Hawaii," replied Kalakaua, slightly nettled.

"But," protested the General, "you are dark brown, he," pointing to Judd, "is half brown, and" pointing to Armstrong, "he is white."

"I was born of Hawaiian nobility," said Kalakaua, "and these are both American missionaries."

General Li directed the coolies to pull faster on the punkahs. "So you have missionaries," he commented. "Do you like the devils?"

"Yes, they are good people," replied the King. He wanted

to end this interrogation so he added: "We have just come from Japan. Emperor Mutsuhito showed us marked courtesy and unending hospitality."

"Mutsuhito, bah!" retorted General Li. "A Jap dog! None of them can be relied on. Would you relish a dish if you suspected death in each bite? Every thought of a Japanese is rooted in deceit. It goes beyond measure. One attempts to put a yardstick to the three visible surfaces of their promises and then he finds that those surfaces are constantly changing."

"Thoughts seldom permit measurement," replied Kalakaua and rose to end the interview.

"I'll wager that Mutsuhito proposed a treaty of free ports before you left his unending hospitality," commented General Li drily.

Kalakaua wanted to get out of China. After some perfunctory sightseeing they left for Siam. The wealth of that country left Kalakaua dizzy. Then they sailed down the hot, muggy Gulf of Siam, headed for the Malay States in the south of the long Peninsula. The Sultan of Johore had sent them an invitation to visit that country.

One day during the exhausting journey while Kalahaua slept, Armstrong and Judd conferred. "We're failing in our mission," declared Armstrong. "We are charged with inculcating democracy into Kalakaua's thick noggin, and we go to Tokyo where he takes on the notion of divine origin; to China where he plans a state religion with himself at its head, and in Siam he decided that he must have a yearly income exceeding three million."

"Yes, I know," responded Judd. "Everywhere we go, even two-by-four princes have annual incomes exceeding ten millions!" He consulted his little black cash book. "We've already used up our sixteen thousand dollars for this trip and we're almost three thousand into the Coronation Fund."

"And three quarters of our trip remain!"

To their plaguing responsibilities were added Robert's unpredictable drunken outbursts. As Kalakaua and his aides were dining with the Sultan of Johore, a court official hurried in and whispered in the host's ears: "Your Excellency, these men are imposters. The real king is on Your Excellency's yacht, dressed in a golden cloak." The Sultan described the "king" to his three guests. When Kalakaua good-humoredly related pot-valiant von Oehlhoffen's escapades in Japan, the Sultan laughed uproariously. "Leave this jewel with me. My entertainment is running dry."

After dinner, Judd and Armstrong separately went in search of the wastrel, and, what was more important, the feather cloak. Armstrong got on Robert's trail first. He learned that four men were bearing Robert from brothel to brothel in the Sultan's own gold and jewel encrusted palanquin. One whorehouse master told Armstrong, with pride, that the Supreme Potentate of Oceania had favored his establishment by taking along one of his females, and as for the cloak, he described in some detail how, upon leaving each house, Robert insisted that an attendant lift the regal feather raiment on high while everyone, including his honor guard of ten, prostrated.

Armstrong found Robert asleep in the golden palanquin in a deserted bar. The Minister of State shook the litter and jabbed his cane through the glass shutter deep into the baron's tender ribs. Robert sat up.

"Where's the feather cloak?" demanded Armstrong.

"Never shaw it!"

A fierce desire to strangle the man possessed the Minister of State. He climbed stiffly into his carriage, motioned the Sultan's palanquin bearers to follow him, and drove off to their hotel to find Judd holding the cloak, which he had found aboard the Sultan's yacht, with an honor guard of ten.

Robert's pranks were entertaining, but they added dollars to the costs mounting in Judd's little black book.

Poor as they were, the world-girdling trip went on in royal splendor. Robert whiled away many a long hour at sea by recounting his sexual adventures to Kalakaua. While they stood looking at the pyramids of Egypt, Robert told of the night just past when he had made a record in conquests in the city of Cairo.

Armstrong tried to elevate the conversation. "Alexander the Great here fixed his empire. Julius Caesar made love to Cleopatra on yonder slow-flowing Nile . . ."

Robert von Oehlhoffen, no mean scholar, added: "And here, Mark Antony, who governed one-third of the known world, 'reeled through the streets at noon,' drunk with the love of a beautiful woman and then fell on his own sword because he had been conquered."

"These Romans," said Kalakaua, "were prime asses. I have yet to find one who could influence me."

From Cairo, Khedive Tewfik Pasha's special railway car brought them to Alexandria. Thick-piled Turkish rugs covered the floor and a silk canopy, with gold tassels, hung overhead. For Kalakaua, there was a cushion of blue velvet with the Hawaiian coat of arms embroidered in gold. As the Hawaiian monarch stepped from the coach, the Khedive grasped both of his hands cordially and drew him over the carpet-covered walk to a carriage in which they drove the three miles to the palace. Across the street, within comfortable distance of the palace's entrance, was a heavily-shuttered building, Tewfik's harem. Several shutters moved slightly, for the women were curious to see the foreign king. "How many women are there in this harem?" Kalakaua asked.

"I make it about three hundred and fifty," said Tewfik. Kalakaua smiled. "And what does the Khedive do the other fifteen long nights of the year?"

It was the time of the Mussulman fête, and a grand ball was held at the palace of Rasel Tin overlooking the lighted harbor of Alexandria. Early in the evening, King Kalakaua selected as a partner a tall Grecian belle with clear pink and white skin, black hair, and blue eyes. After their first waltz, he guided her expertly into the shadows of the grand balcony and put his arm about her. She did not resist. As he was about to kiss her upturned lips, he saw the double-shadow of watchdogs Armstrong and Judd. They were followed in turn by a stuffy British consul, obviously a colonial. As the King disengaged himself, the Britisher, using his half-empty arrack glass as a pointer, directed Kalakaua's glance to an old rusty dismantled coal-receiving hulk lying in the shadows of the bay. "I say, Your Majesty, that vessel is the frigate *Resolution*, the very one in which our intrepid Captain James Cook sailed to your Sandwich Islands some ninety years ago and discovered them for the civilized world."

"Yes, and because of your intrepid Cook," Kalakaua said gallantly, "I am here tonight with this lovely lady." He bowed and brushed her hand with a kiss as the trio, mumbling apologies, left hastily.

The next morning, the Khedive's barge, manned by twenty-four oarsmen in red shirts and fezzes, bore the Hawaiian suite to the Naples-bound *Asia*.

Said Judd, "We part now with the pomposity and extravagance of the decadent East and approach the enlightened West where liberty, equality, and fraternity exist."

To this profundity, Kalakaua retorted, "I found nothing decadent in the East—the Egyptians, like the Japanese, Chinese and Siamese, simply trace their sovereign's origin to divine sources as we Polynesians did before you whites came along. And the common people," he added, "are happiest when they accept it."

Armstrong was considering a more immediate problem. They were approaching Italy and certainly they would meet the glib-tongued schemer, Celso Caesar Moreno. Sure enough, as the *Asia* dropped anchor in the Bay of Naples, Moreno was the first aboard. With him was a group of military and state officials and three Hawaiian cadets in Italian uniforms—Wilcox, Boyd, and Booth. The one-time Hawaiian foreign minister hurried to his former monarch, knelt and kissed his hand.

"Moreno! God, man, it's good to see you," the King said with delight, embracing him.

Moreno, ignoring Armstrong and Judd, introduced the Commandant of the Naples Naval Academy, the Mayor, the Prefect of Police, and other dignitaries. Judd busied himself with the three Hawaiian scholars who had cost the government more than five times the originally estimated three thousand a year each. The trio had changed wonderfully in their six months abroad. Robert Wilcox, the assemblyman who had introduced Moreno's ten-million-dollar loan into the legislature, had married a princess belonging to the ruling house.

Before the aides knew what Moreno was about, the dapper man hurried the King aboard the Commandant's barge, leaving the pair kingless. Commanding Robert to guard the baggage, Judd and Armstrong hurried in pursuit. Four hours later, they came upon them in the salon of the Hôtel Royal des Etrangers.

The irate Armstrong sputtered: "You wished to see us, of course."

"Certainly," the King returned cordially. "Gentilissimo Signore Moreno, you remember these men?"

"I don't remember them in those splendid rags," said Moreno curtly, and bowed his departure, reminding the King of his appointed audience with King Umberto the following afternoon.

Armstrong asked, "What would happen if this story of your running away with that rapscallion were sent to diplomatic corps in Honolulu?"

With some heat the King returned: "Remember your place, Armstrong, or you'll be taking the short route back home."

Next day, as Kalakaua met Queen Margherita, he used his formula for successful conversation: "Your Naples is the loveliest sight I have yet seen." He had returned from Pompeii that morning and added: "It is wonderfully strange to see all the places in your land I have read about in my text books."

"And I, in turn, marvel at your splendid command of English. You even speak it with a British accent. But then, I've found your sons equally gifted."

"My sons!" the King exclaimed.

The Queen smiled indulgently. "In Italy, we are perhaps more frank about our natural offspring."

"Do you mean those kanakas—Wilcox, Booth, and Boyd?"

King Umberto said sharply: "Your Minister Plenipotentiary and Envoy Extraordinary to my court presented them as your natural sons—that is the only reason I permitted them to enroll in my military academies."

Queen Margherita moaned. "Blood of the saints! This Prince Wilcox said he was heir presumptive! He married the eldest daughter of the Princess Victoria Colonna di Stigliano!"

Kalakaua's Minister of State decided it was time to check accounts. "Sire, you said 'Minister Plenipotentiary Moreno'?"

"Certainly!" King Umberto was astonished at the question.

Armstrong bowed to his King: "Your Majesty?"

King Kalakaua tried to extricate himself. "Celso Caesar Moreno was once my Foreign Minister and as such he must have appointed himself."

Armstrong closed in. "Your Most Gracious Majesty, how would you deal with this adventurer?"

"Immediately set my foreign office right on the imposter."

"But nothing must be said of the scholars," hastened the Queen, "the Princess would die a thousand deaths." She hid her face in her hands. "Our royal house will never live down this disgrace."

At the Queen's distress, King Umberto agreed. "Yes, the scholars must finish their education."

Upon their return to the hotel, the Prefect of Police pounced upon them. "Either the decoration or my five hundred lire. Kings are like this to me," he snapped his fingers under Judd's nose. The interpreter translated: "The Prefect says your Equerry-in-Waiting promised him a decoration this morning for 500 lire." At that moment, the unsteady Robert came down the stairs with a woman. The Prefect of Police rounded thumb and forefinger. " 'But for five hundred lire and a signorina, ah, the Grand Cross of Oceania, so big,' " and he joined the forefingers and thumbs of both hands, " 'with a jewel in the center.' " He shook his fist under Robert's nose. "My money, dog, or I will see that you rot in the *prehensio.*"

"Judd," ordered the King, "pay the bastard and give him two hundred extra lire to shut him up." As Judd grudgingly paid out the bonus, Armstrong muttered: "So this is how you've been getting your booze money." Robert ignored him.

In the apartment, Armstrong began reciting a long list of grievances. Robert retorted spiritedly: "You forget yourself, Armstrong. In Europe I have the rank of Baron."

Turning to Kalakaua, Judd said, "Sire, either this fellow parts company with us or I write to Honolulu about Moreno."

The King agreed. "Robert, you have failed in your trust as Hawaii's poet laureate. So far you have produced but one miserable poem. As for your temperance promises in San Francisco, Tokyo, Peking, Tientsin, Singapore, Calcutta, Aden, Cairo—I'll let you judge for yourself. You accompany us on one condition: no more liquor. And for your stay in Italy you are restricted to quarters in this hotel."

However, after they had left Italy for Vienna, the King again welcomed Robert's anecdotes. There was a complete reconciliation. Kalakaua promoted Robert to the status of Adjutant General and presented him with a uniform: Robert knew Vienna. He guided the King around the Shottenring and down Kartnerstrasse. Then they entered the Prater.

Robert ordered wine and the King beer, using the phrase his butler had taught him: *"Bier hier, Bier hier, oder Ich fall 'um."* Katrina, the beermaid, laughed at the King's pleasantry and complied. As they drank, several of the girls studied their royal patron at a distance.

"Ein hübscher Kerl," said Katrina. She admired the King's brown skin, blue-black wavy hair, the high forehead, aquiline nose, and well-shaped lips which parted in a ready smile,

displaying strong white teeth. She told them the King had pinched her leg.

"*Ach,* Kings are like men the world over," responded one of her listeners, "always wanting to feel."

"Does the King dance?" asked another.

"I'll ask him," said Katrina and walking up to Kalakaua curtsied. "Everyone who comes to Wien dances with Katrina, *möchten Sie?*"

The King put aside his cigar and clasped her in a waltz. As he passed the orchestra he requested Strauss's "Tales of the Vienna Woods." All other couples left the floor and when the King and his partner concluded, everyone in the large hall stood and applauded vigorously while the Hawaiian monarch embraced the blushing Katrina and kissed her full on the mouth.

King Kalakaua was wakened the next morning by Judd and Armstrong who marched into his bedroom with a newspaper. "This comes of promoting Oehlhoffen!" charged Armstrong. He slapped the page, with a sketch of a beerhall girl in a dusky man's embrace. "This rag says that Emperor Franz Joseph himself has ordered you to leave the country."

The King laughed. "Fictitious prattle!" Then he became serious. "Isn't there enough piety in Honolulu, that we must carry it wherever we go?"

"Thank fortune," said Judd, as they retired, "there's only Berlin, London, and Belfast left."

Their reception in Germany was satisfactory to Kalakaua, for above all things he wished to see a military demonstration. On their second day in Berlin, the Prince of Prussia (later Kaiser Wilhelm II) called with two carriages in which they were driven to a field about four miles from the city. There the King and his suite witnessed a demonstration not unlike the one they had seen in Japan.

Kalakaua watched, breathless. "Never," he commented, "have I seen such fire-power. Only in Japan did they approach this."

"My officers taught them—the Japanese," replied Wilhelm. "But our German army depends upon speed; power is secondary The English," he added, "still use Percherons to convey field pieces." As he completed the remark, seven thousand cavalry altered their direction and charged right down upon their carriages like an avalanche. The King and his advisors thought it a plot to destroy them and prepared to jump from their carriages when, presto, the charge stopped with the cavalry's noses at their very wheels.

From his carriage the smiling Wilhelm called, "That's Germany's way to keep the peace. Ready for instant war if need be. Patriotism fanned by the hot blast of war burns brighter!" He laughed heartily. A fit of coughing seized him.

On the following day Kalakaua ordered two experimental Krupp guns, one field and one mountain battery. His army was going to be modern.

In England the King and his suite were accorded honor after honor. The King promenaded with the Princess of Wales—the future Queen Alexandra—on his arm at the outstanding social function of the year; he had audiences with Queen Victoria; Her Majesty accepted his Grand Order of Oceania while she, in turn, conferred upon him the Grand Cross of St. Michael and St. George. Late hours, however, were beginning to tell on the King and during the long, last banquet, the Lord Mayor's at Guildhall, he closed his eyes several times. However, enough conversational snatches came his way to let him know that England's most pressing problem was the suppression of the riotous Irish Land Leaguers. When called upon, Kalakaua began: "Your Royal Highness"—bowing to the Prince of Wales—"My Lord Mayor, Gentlemen . . ." He paused. The prepared speech had fled his memory. However, imperturbable as usual, he thanked the Royal Family and the colonial governors for their many kindnesses. Graciously, he added: "No event in my round-the-world tour has given me more pleasure than this London reception. But, Gentlemen, one advantage exists in my own little country. There are no damned Land Leaguers to stir up riots, blow up buildings, and to stone my officers to death. We have a place for them—*j-a-i-l!*" The applause was instant and deafening. The King had played the right chord.

Prime Minister Gladstone's eyes opened a little wider and he whispered to the American Ambassador, James Russell Lowell: "I'm afraid His Majesty will hear from the Irish about this."

The King continued for a few minutes and then, amid loud applause, sat down without Armstrong and Judd hanging on his mental coat-tails.

Great was the resentment in Ireland. A Dublin journal quoted the King's remarks and added: "The Nominal Ruler of Hawaii, a lineal descendent of Hoky Poky, Wunky Wum, must at this distance be given a figurative rap over the knuckles; however, we understand that he will soon visit our Emerald Island, and doubtless many are anxious to make that rap more memorable . . ."

"Irish mud," said Kalakaua. "Let those rebels come to my kingdom and I'll show them." The speech, however, shortened the trip. A heavy guard from Scotland Yard escorted the Hawaiian party to the first vessel bound for the United States. No sooner had they landed in New York than hack drivers descended upon them and one, seeing Kalakaua, removed his cigar and shouted to a driver: "Jim, here's a fat one for you. Better collect your fare first."

The King was back on the plain cobblestones of democracy. "So this is your stinking freedom, eh Judd?" he asked.
"I'll have none of it in Hawaii."

Upon his arrival in San Francisco, ten months since he had
left for Tokyo, he embarked without pause, and that evening, as the wharf faded into the fog and they steered a
course for Hawaii, Robert began covering page after page
with scraps of lines. To make the composition more difficult,
the King frightened away the poetic muse by warning: "Remember, Robert, a good poem must be ready!"

As with all trips, the best part was the homecoming. Gibson's *Advertiser* had carried column after column of foreign
clippings describing the many honors bestowed upon their
Polynesian monarch. After a huge public reception at the
wharf, the travelers entered the gaily festooned palace. Once
there, Robert looked at Kalakaua and got his royal patron's
nod. As the King raised his hand, a hush settled over the
audience. With the great of Hawaii at attention, the poet
laureate cleared his throat and read:

> "O'er land and sea, I've made my way
>   To farthest Ind, and great Cathay;
> Reached Afric's shore and Europe's strand;
>   And met the mighty of every land.
>
> And yet I feel that I may boast,
>   Some good within my sea-girt coast.
> Richer than any of my grander peers
>   That I within my realm need have no fears;
>
> May mingle with my people without dread;
>   No dagger fear for my unguarded head,

And boast a treasure, sent me from above,
That I have indeed, my people's love."

The King, deep in debt, balanced the polite applause against the cost of taking the poetaster around the world. The night before, Robert had thrown overboard a silk top hat, his ninth and last!

23 The Japanese Are Interested

Upon his return, a less determined man than King Kalakaua might have despaired: There was so much to do, so little time, and so precious little understanding. Queen Kapiolani sensed the stirring of greatness within her lord and it filled her with dread. He spoke of "mechanized troops" to "liquidate the interlopers," and "establishing an Empire of Oceania." One evening she tried to warn him in terms of a Kauai proverb of her family: *"Alas, broken are the hands of those who forsake the ways of their fathers."*

But David returned: "Once, Kapiolani, you did not wish me to be King, but I have restored the greatness of Hawaii's rulers; you did not want me to tour the United States, but, single-handed, I got the reciprocity treaty; you quarreled because I wanted to be the first ruling potentate to gird the world, but honor upon honor was rendered me by the world's great. Now that I have seen the world, I am determined to establish a lasting place in it for the millions of our Polynesians yet unborn so that our way of life will not perish."

"But you, yourself, are destroying the Polynesian way," she contended. "What of this Prussian-trained army? This marriage of Kaiulani with a Japanese prince? This proposed coronation?" She held out her arms to him. "Oh, David, won't you come back to me as you once were?"

"God damn it, woman, if my Empire of Oceania fails, it will be because of you and your timidity."

The Queen retorted spiritedly, "choose your own way. If it were not that I love you more than your empire, I wouldn't tolerate that rascal Gibson . . . Forgive me, David," she hurried out of the room so that he should not see a Kauai chieftess in tears.

Kapiolani's fears of Gibson were well-founded. It was the tax assessor who nurtured Kalakaua's ambitions. After a stormy session with his unsympathetic cabinet, during which the ministers refused to endorse his proposed seventy-five-thousand-dollar coronation, the exasperated King demanded their resignations, and sent for Gibson. "Walter," he said, "proclaim your Prime Ministership in tomorrow's *Advertiser*."

Gibson grasped his master's hand. "Sire, I will make your name ring through the ages. When future generations speak of their Caesars, their Napoleons, their Washingtons, they will hail you, Kalakaua, savior of the Polynesians!"

"Come, come, Gibson! Your first official act will be to entertain Michinori S. Nagasaki, Master of Ceremonies of my great and good friend Emperor Mutsuhito."

As Hawaii's first Prime Minister, Gibson immediately consolidated his power and destroyed those who threatened it. When the King remonstrated, he retorted: "Sire, ruthlessness is a concomitant of greatness. Kaiser Wilhelm and Bismarck never hesitate to decapitate weaklings!"

The first head to fall was that of old Parks, Marshal of the Kingdom under four sovereigns. Collector General Allen of the Customs House was followed by Smithies of the Land Office, Registrar Brown, and the Board of Education and even Dr. Arning of the Molokai Leper Settlement, who refused to buy Gibson's sheep at Gibson's prices.

When the firing and hiring was completed, Gibson reported, "Sire, I can now say that you have a loyal body behind you. We can now proceed with our Empire of Oceania."

"And the money?"

"Sire, Spreckels assured me he would loan the kingdom two million providing the government would let him mint a million dollars of coins with your image on the obverse. And he wants to lease more crown lands and get assistance in importing more Japanese laborers. We must have a greater male population to assure us of a large army and still maintain Hawaii's economy."

"A large profit can be made in coinage," commented the King. "But the two million now is more important. Next week Nagasaki of Japan arrives. See that he is well treated and we will have all the labor Spreckels wants."

To entertain Nagasaki, Gibson omitted nothing. His Excellency was greeted at the dock by the government band; troops lined the route to the palace; he was escorted by forty white-uniformed royal guards, whose red busbies accented their six-feet-two, and four heralds proclaimed his arrival at the palace with a fanfare of bugles. The King received the honored guest in the throne room.

Nagasaki presented Orders of the Rising Sun to Princess Liliuokalani and Prime Minister Gibson. For Queen Kapiolani, another order, and there were many gifts, including silk wallpaper. There were kimonos and rare silk rolls for little Princess Kaiulani.

Following the presentations, Nagasaki requested the honor of a private audience with His Gracious Majesty, and His Excellency, Prime Minister Gibson.

Nagasaki was Mutsuhito's chief advisor on foreign affairs. He had been naval attaché in London for two years and had carefully studied Great Britain's naval strength. He had helped the Emperor plan for the Westernization of Japan and it was he who had proposed the treaty of friendship between Japan and Hawaii to break the Great Powers' hold on Japan's treaty ports. Through white agents in Washington he had procured a copy of the ultra-secret Alexander-Schofield report to President Grant approving the desirability of the Pearl River lagoon in Hawaii as a site for a naval coaling and repair station. In addition to his major objective to set up a spy system in Hawaii by means of contract laborers, Nagasaki wanted to determine the truth of the report.

That afternoon, Nagasaki explained that the Great Powers were disturbed over the proposed Hawaii-Japan treaty and as a result, a convention was to be held within six months in Washington to study the question of extraterritoriality. This might happily yield a new set of treaties.

Prime Minister Gibson indiscreetly asked: "But, Sire, I understood this treaty between Hawaii and Japan was to be regarded as ultra-secret. How did the other powers learn?"

Nagasaki bowed in confusion. "I was made to believe the information emanated from Hawaii. If it was our unworthy foreign office the leak will be sealed."

King Kalakaua interrupted. "Tell me, Nagasaki, does the treaty meet with Your Most Excellent Majesty's favor?"

"Certainly Sire. But Emperor Mutsuhito asks your gracious indulgence to postpone its consummation so that the forthcoming negotiations in Washington may not be jeopardized."*

For a moment Kalakaua resented the manner in which he had been exploited. However, anxious to get on, he inquired

---

* The Washington convention, precipitated by this proposed Hawaii-Japan treaty, restored the treaty ports to Japan. But once that was achieved, Emperor Mutsuhito refused to sign the treaty of friendship with Hawaii.

with what delicacy he could muster: "And how is my favorite, Prince Hatsu?"

Nagasaki bowed again. "Well, Sire." With many apologies he said that His Imperial Master, Emperor Mutsuhito, begged King Kalakaua's continued indulgence to hold the idea of marriage in abeyance until the Prince could visit Hawaii.

Swallowing his disappointment, Kalakaua suggested, "Perhaps Prince Hatsu will attend our coronation?"

For a moment Nagasaki was baffled. "Coronation, Sire?"

Prime Minister Gibson explained: "After Polynesian Kings have ruled ten years, their grateful subjects tender them a jeweled crown. It's an age-old custom in Hawaii."

Nagasaki promptly apologized for his ignorance and assured them Japan would send emissaries.

Kalakaua's aplomb restored, he reached the third pressing point. "What about sending more Japanese laborers to Hawaii?"

Again Nagasaki was evasive. "With Your Gracious Majesty's leave, before I commit my Emperor to an answer, may I make a tour of your beautiful islands?"

Kalakaua knew Japanese spies abounded among the contract laborers. But to get the two million from Spreckels and to hasten the establishment of Oceania, he would have to bring in more laborers. "I was about to propose such a tour myself. But before you start, I have arranged entertainment befitting the emissary of my great friend, Emperor Mutsuhito. Tomorrow, a military review will be held in your honor."

By dawn, townspeople were thronging the thoroughfare to Punchbowl Plain to see Hawaii's first military review. Since the arrival of the German uniforms and Krupp artillery a martial spirit had enlivened Hawaii's soldiery. Precisely at nine-fifteen the Royal Guard with towering busbies, the Princess's Own, and the Household Troops, all carrying gleaming bayonets, goose-stepped past the reviewing stand where Kalakaua in a field marshal's white uniform, stood with his guests of honor, Princess Moitea of Tahiti and Nagasaki.

Kalakaua had coached his field commander, Lieut. General John Dominis regarding the mock battle that was to be part of the review. "In the engagement between cavalry and infantry, Our cavalry must win; we want Japan as a military ally. Princess Moitea will be impressed with Our might; and, remember, tomorrow Our legislature is taking up a bill to triple the military appropriation."

In the midst of a bayonet drill, a boy perched in a coconut tree gave away the on-coming cavalry maneuver by shouting, "Here comes Daddy on a white horse!"

Daddy was Lieut. General John Dominis. The crowd roared as forty cavalrymen, led by "Daddy," swept around Punchbowl Crater. Their attack, however, was repulsed by the infantrymen who, thanks to the warning, had been able to deploy in fours, while the main body formed a hollow square bristling with bayonets. As the infantry began firing, some of the men neglected to remove their muzzle stoppers and yelps of astonishment, pain, and rage sounded above the din of battle before Dominis was able to call his dragoons and lead the retreat.

Kalakaua made the best of it. "This test, Nagasaki, proves my contention: the infantry is the queen of battle. Given proper fire-power, infantry can hold any position, regardless."

With the review over, Nagasaki, properly escorted, sailed off on his tour of the islands. On his return Kalakaua invited him to the boathouse to discuss the labor question.

"Your Majesty," evaded Nagasaki, "I have heard that you are an excellent helmsman; before leaving your beautiful land, I should like to get a glimpse of it from a yacht."

Nagasaki, as Kalakaua shrewdly suspected, wanted to see Oahu's windward coastline, and the secret—but famous—Pearl River harbor.

The King replied, "Capital. Let's take our discussion aboard. And we'll take along some cold fowl and wine and make it a day."

Kalakaua more than lived up to his reputation as a helmsman and Nagasaki watched in admiration when they arrived at the narrow Pearl River lagoon entrance and the King guided the yacht over the shallow, dangerous reef. Nagasaki was all compliments while his eyes were busy noting that the protecting reef conformed closely to Schofield's report. After dredging, the lagoon would make one of the best sheltered naval bases in the world. The high surrounding mountains would easily conceal heavy rifles to guard against any approach. Altogether ideal! Outwardly, to Kalakaua's amusement, Nagasaki gave no indication of any thought of the lagoon. They picnicked on Ford Island, within the lagoon itself, and the Japanese directed his conversation to the rich loam. "In Japan, Your Majesty, we would put a high price on fertile soil such as this."

That gave Kalakaua his opening. "Hawaii desires that your people may come quickly to make my country the garden spot of the world."

Nagasaki bowed. "Sire, my recommendation shall be to have my Imperial Master send as many good laborers to Hawaii as you may need."

This was victory, as far as it went; at any rate there was nothing more to be done until the Emperor acted.

After Nagasaki's departure Kalakaua turned his full attention to Gibson. Within the past six months Gibson had, bit by bit, taken control of the Spreckels-financed government. In addition to his duties as Prime Minister and Foreign Minister, he had assumed, *pro tem,* the portfolios of Minister of Finance and Minister of Interior. He was still tax collector, and Chairman of the Boards of Education, Health, and Genealogy. With the legislature in session he and his followers had rammed through a second coronation appropriation for $75,000; a bill to defray the King's additional around-the-world expenses, another doubling the King's yearly stipend, and yet another, tripling the military appropriation. These were only a prelude to a proposed loan of two million dollars labeled "extraordinary expenses." The King, studying the reports, concluded he had every reason to be satisfied with his Prime Minister.

The loan bill was violently opposed but it passed. Spreckels discounted it at eight per cent, but with two added concessions. The legislature doubled his ship subsidy, making it $72,000 a year, and he received permission to mint Hawaii's new coinage at a sixteen per cent profit.

The two concessions resulted in a delegation of business men visiting Gibson formally to protest the giving of so many favors to Spreckels. Gibson rose to the occasion.

"Gentlemen," he said, "within the past fortnight any one of you had the opportunity to advance the government the necessary two million dollars. But it was Spreckels alone who came forward. His Majesty's coronation comes off next month.

"Gifts from King Kalakaua's well-wishers will be received. Spreckels said something about giving a private yacht."

And looking at the stricken faces before him, Gibson smiled. "Gentlemen," he concluded, "good-day."

24 A Belated Coronation

As the heavy *kona* rain thundered on the palace roof, Kalakaua tossed, sleepless, in his canopied bed. In three days he would be crowned. The coronation, his first step toward empire, had to be a success. . . . The Punchbowl batteries must thunder at the exact moment he received the crown. . . . Could Gibson have neglected to send the invitations abroad? Although all the crowned heads of the world, from Queen Victoria to King Nauteiti of Makin Island, were supposed to have received a four-colored invitation, only five Japanese had arrived, headed by Envoy M. Sugi, Vice Minister of the Emperor's Imperial Household, and his wife. . . . Kalakaua thought of the recently erected coronation pavilion. This rain would ruin it. . . . He decided that he would not wear the ermine robes; the Hawaiians would like the feather cloak much better. . . .

As he turned and punched his hot, damp pillow, Queen Kapiolani called, "Can't you sleep, David?"

"No, I'll never endure another coronation as long as I live. This damned rain! The prisoners ought to be out now gathering reeds. Good God, I forgot to prepare my general amnesty!" . . . As the clock struck five, the King dropped into fitful slumber.

At ten the next morning, Queen Emma and Princesses Ruth and Bernice listened avidly to Mrs. John E. Bush's recital of the tribulations at the palace. This Lady-in-Waiting to the Queen had walked out when a rival was given a better position for the ceremony. "You should hear the official announcement." She rose, held her right hand aloft and intoned, " 'David Kalakaua, the King, the great general, the sacred *alii* of the heated *kapu,* the prostrating *kapu,* the *wohi* of the standing *kahili,* the guardian of the whales—' "

Princess Ruth hawked her throat with a roar. Her spittle-bearer ran up with a bowl.

"Why doesn't the guardian of the whales read the newspaper *Paeaina?* Last week it told how David's mother Ane embraced the black man, Blossom, in pahaina prison."

Mrs. Bush nodded. "Kalakaua did read it. Someone asked him why he did not arrest the editor and the King said, 'He is brave—the mixture of blood is always good. Has it not elevated me to the throne above all the Kamehamehas?' "

Business men were already counting coronation costs. In Prince-consort Cleghorn's Dry Goods and Notions Store, Banker Bishop now added,

4	Heralds Uniforms	$80.00
4	Heralds Bosoms	10.00
60	Large Corsets	150.00
40	Bustles	90.00
2	Tins Astonishing Crackers	3.50
40	Black Cloth Twill Suits	800.00
42	Men's Black Paris Hats	164.00
22	Extra Wide Patent Slippers	96.00

Thurston stepped into the doorway to avoid mud flying from the King's carriages hurrying to the wharf to meet the *Alameda* and such foreign dignitaries as might be aboard. Bishop called to him, "Lorrin, the committee women have just ordered one thousand, three hundred and ninety-three dollars worth of goods!"

A moan escaped Thurston. "Add the thirty thousand to entertain foreign princes, five miserable Japs. This coronation is just the beginning of that black bastard's strivings. To run this kanaka sugarcane patch we pay him twice the salary President Cleveland gets to run a Republic of fifty million!"

But despite all protests and sneers Coronation Day arrived and with it, unfortunately, still more rain. Midst the din of nailing a tin waterproof roof on the pavilion rose the voices of two hundred palace servants, scores of maids-of-honor, ladies-in-waiting, chamberlains, marshals and troops practicing German military evolutions to the shouts of commanding officers.

The King, in his bedroom, gulped half a tumbler of gin and water and swore. "I'll be damned if I'll postpone it. Anyway, rain is a good omen." He lifted his diamond studded crown, Hawaii's first, and tried it on. Suddenly he cried, "God Almighty, where's the Bible?" He caught his private secretary a cuff alongside his head. "How the devil can we have a coronation without Judd's big *Ka Baibala Hemolele*? Run, you bastard; tell Judd to fetch it, quick!" He turned to the Queen. "I hear Bishop is wearing his black suit. Does that fathead think coronations come every year?"

"And his wife, Bernice," said Kapiolani, "is holding a reception during the Coronation." That was a slip. She hadn't meant to tell him. "Oh, look! David, don't our dragoons look fine?"

David looked out at the yellow uniformed riders with red busbies and shouted, "Fine! Look at the red run down their faces! Their uniforms will be ruined. See the water running out of their boots."

"Come David," coaxed the Queen, "cheer up. This is your big day."

"Where's my gin?"

The King's valet hurried up with a tumbler.

Kalakaua tossed it off. "Hah, that's better. How many do you suppose will go to Bernice's reception?"

"The Coronation will draw more," Kapiolani tried to reassure him, "if only this rain . . ."

Because of the rumored boycott and the selling of Royal invitations by soldiers sent to deliver them, the King had decreed that official invitations would not be needed at the palace gates. He looked out again at the cold, dripping pavilion and the sodden flags. It was nine o'clock, and not more than a handful were huddled in one corner. He caught sight of the five Japanese sitting forlornly in the area set aside for the guests of honor. "At any rate, the Japanese understand protocol!"

Pretty little Princess Kaiulani, delighted at the dress-up party, ran in and threw her arms about the King's neck, "Look, Uncle David, isn't my dress cute?" She was in light-blue, lace-trimmed corded silk which reached the floor.

"Don't touch him!" hastened the Queen. It was too late. "Goodness, girl, you got lip-dye spots on his trousers and coat!"

Tears rolled down Princess Kaiulani's cheeks. Kalakaua tried to soothe her. "It doesn't make any difference. Come, smile. Here, let me put the crown on your head." The little girl cried all the harder.

"Of all times," Kalakaua said to the Queen, "did you have to shout at her? Never mind, Kaiulani, with this rain your Uncle David wanted to wear blue trousers today. And the spot on the coat I can cover with a medal." He clapped his hands. "Piehu!" As the man came running up, he shouted: "Here, you excrement of a goose, get my Order of the Conception of Portugal." It was his largest.

Turning to his sister, Miriam Likelike, he scolded, "It's your fault, Likelike. You shouldn't have let Kaiulani dye her lips so young."

Governor Dominis, in a seven-button, white waistcoat with a stand-up collar of black velvet, jersey trousers with gold lace stripe, white silk stockings, and white kid gloves, strode in. At his side hung a straight dress sword in a black scabbard and the ensemble was crowned with a black plumed cocked hat. "David, I want to get this straight. Either Liliuokalani and I lead the princesses and consorts of the blood or we don't attend."

Likelike flared. "You shriveled-up incompetent. Isn't my child the only one born to the Kalakaua dynasty, and the heir presumptive?"

Kalakaua sank into a chair exhausted. "I wish to hell I'd never heard of this damned coronation. All right, Dominis. You and Liliuokalani, then Kaiulani, and Likelike, shut up! You're younger."

Pouring his seventh half-tumbler of gin, the King demanded: "What time is it? . . . 'A quarter of eleven?' " He raised his voice above the din. "We've got just fifteen minutes. Where's Cummins? John, line them up on the stairway. Lilio! Liliuokalani! *Where is* that woman now?"

Regal in gold brocade with a front of white satin and a heavy crimson train, Liliuokalani appeared in the doorway. Her headdress, a crown of delicate white feathers, was tipped with tiny, luminous pearls.

Governer Dominis went to her and whispered: "I bluffed him into giving us the lead, all right. Likelike was madder'n a raped duck."

The clouds opened and the sun shone as the kahili-bearers came out of the palace and stationed themselves along the arched Japanese bridge linking the palace with the pavilion. Troops were already posted along the front of the palace walls and on each side of the steps. The dampened audience of three thousand turned expectantly. Tempers were short. Many of the women dressed in newly-purchased Sunday finery had bedraggled petticoats. Four heralds with bright trumpets and stiff bosoms stepped forward and sounded a brisk sennet. Grand Marshal Cummins led the procession, followed by officials of the Royal Household. After a pause, came the Princesses of the Blood. To Liliuokalani's mortification, little Kaiulani got the plaudits of the crowd. Then came official bearers of the sceptre, of the sword of state, of the crown on a purple pillow, of the Etruscan ring, of the feathered cloak, of the ermine robe, of the sacred *pouloulou* sticks and of the sacred kahili of *Pili*.

The King shone in his splendor royal—blue trousers and white Prussian blouse. His white helmet had a plume of red, white, and blue. His dozen orders sparkled. Queen Kapiolani, in white satin, leaned on his arm. The royal pair were followed by bearers of Her Majesty's train, ladies-in-waiting, and maids-of-honor.

Slowly, to Captain Berger's new "Kalakaua's Coronation March," played by the combined Royal Hawaiian and Reform School Bands, the King and Queen walked toward their throne chairs. As they reached them, the seventy-voice choir burst forth:

> "Almighty Father, hear!
> The Isles do wait on Thee!
> That Thy Hand shall lead
> Our chosen chief and King . . .

For the glory of all ages,
Evermore, evermore, amen, amen, amen!"

When everyone was seated, Grand Marshal Cummins
cleared his throat:

"Princes, Visitors, Nobles, Representatives of the People of
Hawaii here assembled!

"I hereby proclaim unto you that David Laamea Kamanakaupuu Mahinulani Nalo'iaehuokalani Lumialani Kalakaua
is the true King, generalissimo, etc., etc., Grand Master of the
Royal Order of Kamehameha, Grand Master of the Order
of Kalakaua, Kapiolani, Order of Hawaii, Order of Oceania,
Knight Order of the Imperial Order of the Chrysanthemum
of Japan, Crown of Siam, etc., etc., Order of the Liberator
of Bolivia, son of Alii Caesar Kapaakea and Alii Ane
Keohokalole, descendant of Alii Aikanaka, rightful occupant
of the Hawaiian throne, sovereign of the Hawaiian Islands . . ."

At the conclusion of Cummins' pronouncement, Chancellor Judd advanced, and standing before his sovereign, asked:
"Sire, is Your Most Excellent Majesty willing to reaffirm
your previous oath?"

"I am willing." The King put his unsteady right hand on
Judd's Hawaiian Bible and repeated slowly: "We, David
Kalakaua, King of the Hawaiian Islands, do hereby sol-
emnly reaffirm to maintain the constitution."

Chancellor Judd placed the sword in the King's hand:
"Receive this kingly sword as the ensign to justice . . ."

The feather cloak was put into the trembling hands of the
perspiring chancellor who, in turn, gave it to the King's
marshal, who dropped it over the King's shoulders. To King
Kalakaua, resplendent in plumage of mamo, Judd then proclaimed: "Receive this ancient royal mantle, ensign of knowledge and wisdom."

As a page advanced with the crowns, the choir broke into song:

> "Almighty Father, we do bring
> Gold and gems for our king . . .
> Amen, amen, amen!"

The King rose and the president of the legislative assembly took the King's crown. He raised it high before the people as a universal sigh of admiration escaped the audience. "I, Godfrey Rhodes, do present this crown to the rightful King of these Islands, approved by the acts of the legislative assembly of the year of the election, 1874, and of additional acts in 1880 and 1882." He handed the crown to the chancellor.

Judd placed the crown in the King's hands, saying: "Sire, receive this crown of gold to adorn the high station wherein thou hast been placed . . ."

The King lifted the crown by the tip-top cross with one hand, and set it on his head. As he took his hand away, the crown slipped and there was a gasp from the crowd. Judd reached quickly, but the King, quicker, caught it with his free hand. Imperturbable, he placed it on his head again.

Kalakaua took up the second crown and placed it on the head of Queen Kapiolani, saying: "I crown thee, Kapiolani, to share the honors of my throne." While the King's chaplain was intoning a prayer, the King swore: "God damn that Gibson. I knew he wouldn't get that salute off when I put the crown on my head."

"Shhh, David, while the chaplain prays," said the Queen gently.

In the midst of the holy invocation, the rain-dampened "astonishing crackers" let go from the palace towers. Salvos of heavy gunfire exploded and re-echoed fearfully. The choir burst forth, *allegro tempo*:

"Cry out, O Isles, with joy . . .
Evermore, amen, amen, amen!"

It was over and the court resigned itself to a fortnight of unadulterated pleasure. Even the rain could not dampen the festive spirit. To the Coronation Ball guests came in oilskins, carrying their clothes and changing them in the palace.

On that stately occasion the King selected diminutive Mrs. Sugi, wife of the Japanese envoy, whose head came medal-high, as his partner. She could barely understand him; however, she never failed to smile brightly as he wheeled and turned her masterfully. In the midst of the quadrille, Mrs. Sugi suddenly slumped out of the King's grasp and slid to the floor. The Japanese males seemed oblivious as the King picked her up, carried her to the adjoining room, and gave her to the ladies-in-waiting.

When the King returned Sugi said: "My wife has disgraced this court. We are sorry. We shall not return to insult you again."

The King laughingly reassured him.

The ladies-in-waiting loosened Mrs. Sugi's clothing and discovered that her corset was overtightly laced, and upside down! The corset properly adjusted, she appeared on the floor again at the King's request, enjoying the evening's fun after a reviving jolt of liquor had warmed her small body.

The many feasts, the hula dances, the cricket matches, the regatta, together with a state dinner with its attendant fuss passed.

There remained but the unveiling of the statue* which

---

* The original was lost on a burning ship and a second was ordered. When the second arrived, the first was restored and brought to Hawaii—hence there are two identical statues—one in Honolulu, the other at Kohala, Hawaii.

Gibson had ordered in Boston four years earlier. A special platform had been erected for the King and his select guests including the five Japanese envoys, supreme court judges, captains of visiting men-of-war, and ministers of the crown. Around the veiled statue milled a large crowd of curious on-lookers. While the dragoons saluted with sabers raised, Captain Berger directed a march dedicated to the newly-crowned King. As the twelve o'clock time-ball dropped atop J. W. Robertson's observation tower to signal the end of the Coronation festivities, four heralds tootled, the Punch-bowl battery fired—this time on the exact downbeat—and at Prime Minister Gibson's curt command, the curtain parted and lifted slowly, inch by inch.

The spectators saw the sandals, the sturdy brass legs, the golden loincloth, the feather cloak of shimmering gold, the outstretched, welcoming hand, the kingly chin—and then, those surrounding the King gasped, while the uncouth roared with laughter.

"There, that's the true symbol of Kalakaua's greatness!" said Thurston.

Hoodlums had inverted a chamber pot over the statue's head.

King Kalakaua said: "You may drop the curtain, Gibson."

25 In the Interest of Empire

Before the coronation was over Spreckels' two-million-dollar loan was spent and again Kalakaua lacked money to launch his Empire of Oceania. As the nucleus of his land army was poised for action in the South Seas, the King set doggedly to work to train a marine force and instructed Gibson to begin negotiations for a second-hand man-of-war. To assist him in training his proposed Polynesian navy, Kalakaua put Lieutenant George E. Gridley Jackson, a former member of the British navy, in charge of the Palama Reform School for boys. Jackson set to work with a will to drill the wayward boys in Britain's naval regulations and procedure.

Learning of the proposed Polynesian empire and the navy in training, Spreckels refused to lend the King another dollar, and threatened to demand payment of his loan, which was now over three million—if the number of Japanese contract laborers was not doubled.

Two months after the coronation, Japan's Undersecretary of Foreign Affairs, Katsunouki Inouye, arrived in Hawaii as the Emperor's special labor commissioner. After a swift island-to-island inspection, Inouye went to the King and bluntly told him that the lot of his 20,000 countrymen in Hawaii was intolerable. He complained of insufficient food, ill-usage, unwarranted and frequent acts of violence, and deductions in wages made by unscrupulous planters.

"Furthermore, my countrymen suffer from the lack of medical attention, the paucity of interpreters, and the absence of labor inspectors."

Hard-pressed Prime Minister Gibson protested: "But who would defray such extraordinary expenses?"

"The planters, who profit," said Inouye. The Japanese commissioner pressed the point, for if trained spies could be brought into Hawaii without cost to his government his stature at court would increase. "Until I am assured that these faults will be rectified, the importation of Japanese labor to Hawaii ceases."

Inouye had talked with Spreckels and knew that Spreckels wanted to double the number of Japanese laborers. "Unless provisions are made whereby one-fourth of every Japanese laborer's wage is withheld and turned over to the Japanese consulate for a Trust Fund, His Imperial Majesty's government stands ready to recall every Japanese already in Hawaii," he warned.

The King replied with equal bluntness, "What you propose would put every Japanese laborer in my land under the direct control of your Japanese consul."

Inouye returned: "Not at all, Sire, His Imperial Majesty merely desires that each of his subjects may someday have sufficient funds to come back to die on the sacred soil of his ancestors. He does not wish this money to leave Hawaii. He is willing to deposit all money collected—upwards of half a million annually—in your government's Postal Savings Bank at two per cent interest."

To the impecunious King and his Prime Minister this was

pure manna from heaven. Gibson hastened: "Off-hand, Your Excellency, there seems no reason why your proposals cannot be arbitrated to our mutual satisfaction."

The agreement, including the importation of "doctors, interpreters and inspectors," to be paid by the planters was completed. Within two months Japanese laborers began arriving and the white community, for once, endorsed King Kalakaua's foreign policy. The first vessel discharged nine hundred and forty-eight scrubbed men including a dozen of the so-called professionals. Within the week, a second shipload of nine hundred and forty-two arrived with nineteen doctors, interpreters, and inspectors.

With the initial fifty-thousand-dollar deposit in the government Postal Savings Bank, Kalakaua and Prime Minister Gibson decided to set a South Sea Federation plan in motion. Before an Empire of Oceania could be achieved it would be necessary to visit all the islands, make friends with their rulers, and propose, when possible, a federation which would later be merged into Empire. The Gilbert and Marshall Islands were chosen for the initial testing-out trip. If results warranted, other islands would be visited and their cooperation enlisted.

The selection of leaders for the expedition presented grave difficulties. Finally, Warden Tripp of Oahu Prison, and Frederick Clarke, young editorial writer from the *Commercial Advertiser*, were summoned to the palace. Tripp, an old sea Captain, had made numerous "blackbirding" expeditions to the Hebrides, Marshalls and Solomons and spoke several Polynesian dialects.

In their audience with King Kalakaua, Premier Gibson painted a picture of Hawaii's coming greatness. Then he announced: "His Majesty has singled out you two to become his envoys extraordinary and ministers plenipotentiary to the Gilbert and Marshall Islands to lay the cornerstone of our Empire of Oceania."

Warden Tripp, whose pay was two months in arrears, asked: "Expenses will be advanced, I hope?"

"Not only that, Captain Tripp," retorted Kalakaua, "but I will lend you one of my own sailing vessels."

The Prime Minister told them the future of millions of Polynesians in the far-flung reaches of the Pacific depended upon the success of their mission and added: "Could I be spared from my high office, I myself, would lead you." He sent for the diplomatic uniforms—the ones Judd and Armstrong had worn on the globe-girdling tour, and with a toast proposed by King Kalakaua: "May the gods of Polynesia attend your great and holy mission among my future peoples!" the pair of envoys departed.

Brisk trade winds billowed their sails, allowing Skipper Tripp to steer a straight course for two thousand miles to Makin Island. As their ship threaded the shallow turquoise-colored lagoon, they were beset by hundreds of canoes filled with natives.

King Nauteiti, a bronzed giant, waited for them ashore, saw their elaborate uniforms from a distance, and hastily wrapped a colored skirt about his sturdy loins. Learning that the envoys wished to make "strong talk" he ordered lauhala mats spread over the dirt floor of the grass-roofed conference hut and commanded his chiefs to squat, while the common-folk congregated outside.

Captain Tripp, who understood the fears of these simple people, reminded the native king of his dangers. "On all sides," he said, "the great nations of the world are devouring your neighbors. How long do you think you and your neighbors will remain free?"

King Nauteiti made no effort to stem the tears which coursed down his cheeks.

With that introduction, Tripp extolled his own powerful leader, King David Kalakaua, and pictured Hawaii's happiness, free from the gnawing fear of foreign encroachment. Tripp said that the King of Hawaii was prepared to offer the people of Makin help against foreign aggressors if they would put themselves under his leadership.

At the unexpected offer, King Nauteiti was transported with joy. He sent runners to summon all his people. Four hours later, when the assemblage was settled, the chief translator bellowed Tripp's message: "We have with us envoys from Talataua*, greatest of all Polynesians. Talataua is mighty. He has thousands of subjects who do nothing but bear arms and are prepared to fight any invader. Of all living rulers, he alone braved the oceans of the world and dined with kings and slept with their daughters. So great is Talataua that he sends white men as messengers."

The translator bowed and begged Clarke for permission to display the autographed letter he carried from King Kalakaua. With great reverence, he held aloft the parchment with its four-inch seal. "This paper which talks says Talataua wants to be our father. Shall it be so?"

Nauteiti spoke briefly. "My children. Night after night I have cried for you because the foreigners are grasping the islands around us and making slaves of our people. But now my tears are gone. My stomach sings. My great brother Talataua has offered me help. I say it shall be so!"

Prolonged shouts of joy rang through the coconut trees. King Nauteiti turned to the two envoys. "Tell Talataua to help us quickly."

Feasting, drinking, and dancing followed, and each night

* Outside of Hawaii, the "K" sound is virtually unknown among Polynesians.

the envoys were presented with new virgins. As a mark of fine distinction on the first night, Captain Tripp was presented with King Nauteiti's own twelve-year-old daughter.

With no little reluctance the ministers plenipotentiary tore themselves away and set sail for the No Noute Islands of King Tim Binoka.

That ruler demanded: "How strong is Talataua in men who fight? How many fire-barking ships has he?" When told that Hawaii's army numbered ten times the total of his thousand people and that King Kalakaua was training a Polynesian navy, he was delighted. "Then tell my great brother to come quickly and help me set matters right at Tarawa and Bikini." His eyes blazed. "When my men put out to sea to catch fish, the white men steal our women. We will cut out their hearts and eat their livers."

The envoys crowded sail for Samoa where, luckily, they intercepted a Honolulu-bound steamer and put aboard the two proposed treaties of confederation.

When Kalakaua received the favorable report from the two Gilbertese kings, he summoned his cabinet and read the letters. "These documents of federation attest to the strong desire inherent in all Polynesian people to put themselves under my rule."

Prime Minister Gibson rose. "You ask, perhaps, what can small Hawaii do in the face of the encroachment in the South Seas by the large powers who are snatching up these islands which belong to us? Gentlemen, when foreign powers threatened South America, President Monroe, representing then a comparatively small country, announced: 'The Americas for Americans!' " Flushed, he took a heavy parchment from his diplomatic portfolio. "Members of the cabinet," he said in a voice that trembled: "I give you Emperor Kalakaua's Manifesto: 'Oceania For The Polynesians.' "

King Kalakaua was conscious of a warm thrill that ran through his entire being. They were launched upon a history-making effort, one that would ring down the years to come. To unite all Polynesians as one people, to preserve and cherish the things they held sacred, to employ the power thus brought into being for the good of the people themselves, Kalakaua felt the weight of the future upon his shoulders. As he raised aloft his brimming glass his hand shook with excitement.

The men who listened became, in that instant, partisans of the great dream for Hawaii's future. They drained their glasses slowly but turned avidly to listen to a manifesto by Foreign Minister Gibson. In this were recited the kindred origin of all Polynesians and Hawaii's responsibility in assuming leadership. The manifesto ended in a solemn warning to all foreign powers to keep "Hands Off Polynesia."

The next outgoing steamer carried King Kalakaua's Manifesto to the chief aggressors in the South Pacific—England, Germany, and the United States. Strange indeed, but gratifying, was its reception. The United States, thinking that England's fine hand was involved, responded through Secretary of State Frederick Theodore Freylinghusen: ". . . *the sympathies of the United States are always in favor of good self-government by independent communities of the world . . .*" and commended King Kalakaua for his action. Great Britain, in turn suspecting the United States of covering up her own aggrandizement in Samoa by letting King Kalakaua act as a front, expressed through the Earl of Granville profound sympathy with the efforts of the Hawaiian government ". . . *to exercise a civilizing influence over the populations of the Polynesians* . . ." But the suspicious Prince Bismarck, suspecting both Great Britain and the United States of collusion against Germany's expansion in the Pacific, dispatched five cruisers to the South Pacific with orders to fight if necessary to protect Germany's newly-gained island possessions.

26 Some Ancient Customs Restored

While Kalakaua's envoys sought treaties of federation in the South Sea Islands, the King turned his attention to the restoration of the Polynesian religion. Carefully coached all through his boyhood by Haaheo, David knew far more of native beliefs than most of the royal children who attended the Cookes' school. In his heart he was unable to reject the faith of his forefathers and he was profoundly affected by the thought that he was a part of that faith, a divine part. Also it was apparent that an Emperor of Oceania, with the Polynesian religion dominating all of the islands of his domain, must at all times be able to justify his divine origin and purpose. Kapiolani, he thought, would approve and aid him.

To his surprise and dismay the Queen heard him with mounting anger. When Kalakaua proposed to rekindle the fire of Hawaii's early culture by reaffirming the divine origin of its rulers, Kapiolani's eyes flashed.

"How dare you use our gods for your own purposes?" she interrupted. "You want to rule an Empire of Oceania because you claim to be divine. For this sacrilege our gods will surely destroy you."

Kalakaua smiled tolerantly. His visits with the rulers of Japan, China, and Egypt, all of whom believed themselves divine, had convinced him that no ill effects need follow a claim to divinity. "Every man has godhood within him, Kapiolani, and he who acts and lives like a god, the gods embrace and the people adore."

Since he could not convince the Queen, Kalakaua sent his state carriage to bring Maria Alapai, the noted *Kahuna,* or priestess, to him. Maria came but she was uneasy at the palace and asked Kalakaua to go with her to her home. The King agreed and in the evening, with the small illumination of a single *Kukuinut*-oil lamp the King laid before her his plans to make the Polynesian religion a vital part of the life of the islands.

"Maria Alapai, you know that we Hawaiians alone possess the power of death of all people. We can pray others to death, or die when we choose." She nodded and listened while Kalakaua explained that they would begin with a small group of skilled diviners, and gradually draw into it the leaders of the Hawaiian people. Kalakaua looked forward to a powerful religion to which every Hawaiian would belong.

"But the Christians, they have made many converts among our people—what of them?" Maria asked shrewdly.

Kalakaua was ready. "We can reconvert some of the important Christians, a man like the Reverend William Kanui of the Congregational Church; have him renounce his Christianity. I have talked with Kanui and I want you two to be our leaders. Our cult and our practices will be secret and only the heads will know when we act. Together we will seek out and reconsecrate the five hundred altars of Old Hawaii. Who today remembers the great altar of Lono within our city? Haaheo took me to the consecrated stones before I was old enough to use my Halala. Beginning here, our religion will sweep the Pacific and gather all Polynesians into the fold of their true gods."

After Maria Alapai and the former minister of the gospel, William Kanui, were inducted into the secret cult, King Kalakaua summoned all Hawaiians versed in the mystic arts of the kahuna. Almost overnight the palace yard was filled with the sounds of drums, chanting, the blowing of conches, and the recitals of prayers. But it was not until the night when King Kalakaua invoked the prayer-to-death ritual for Queen Emma that fear entered into the hearts of the novitiates. And when, within three days, the "crooked spirit of *Uli*" entered Queen Emma's body and brought out her living spirit, fear of the King mounted. Those who attended Queen Emma's convulsive death admitted that she foamed at the mouth, as do all victims of Uli.* Belief in Kalakaua's mystic powers grew, and thereafter when the King's carriage passed Hawaiians fell prostrate.

At this resurgence of paganism, Honolulu's white Christian population took alarm. A number of families quietly sold their household goods and sailed for San Francisco. Lorrin Thurston railed: "This nigger sorcerer revives voodooism to subjugate the native population. That done, he will exterminate every white."

Could Thurston have witnessed the Sunday evening sexual rites at the palace he would have been more alarmed. Fifteen Hawaiian men, and thirty-six women, sat on the ground in a double circle under the tree where, forty-five years before, Caesar Kapaakea, Ane Keohokalole's boy husband, had buried the placenta. Before each woman was a small stone male idol; before each man, a female idol of fertility. A conch shell sounded, announcing the arrival of the King. The nose-flutes began to play softly and the assemblage prostrated. Kalakaua strode majestically to the altar on

* Some authorities in Hawaii assert that Queen Emma was poisoned by King Kalakaua.

which burned the eternal flame. Over it floated a banner, a field of yellow edged with red on which was a figure of the sun mounted on a cross with the religious society's new name, HALE NAUA, beneath. The King stopped before the altar. The kahuna Maria Alapai, official annointer, waited while the King dropped his robe, then sprinkled his naked body with the waters of Kane. Kanui wrapped the hereditary loincloth of Aikanaka about the King's hips, then fastened the feather cloak about his shoulders. The King adjusted the feather helmet and then sat upon a throne. Loosely encircling the group lay a braided golden floral strand, while on the ground beside the King lay six balls of olona twine. With Maria Alapai's and Kanui's aid the floral strand was raised and tightened so that it encircled the group and bound them together. Maria Alapai was distributing the sacred mats for the novitiates to sit upon, and the torches were lighted. All were silent.

Kalakaua began:

"O, Members of the Hale Naua! Tonight I will divulge to you the origin of love as it was revealed to me through my Polynesian god ancestors.

"Man's desire is seated in the eye. It is the cause of man's erection of the penis and woman's yearning. This desire is carried from the eye to the brain from whence it spreads to the belly, the arms, the legs, and finally it concentrates in the testicles and the ovaries. But our gods distinguish between love and lust. The seat of lust is in the skin of the belly and of the arms and only to a lesser degree in those springs of passion, the eyes. This lesser degree of love makes us merely want to look upon those we are fond of, instead of having coition with them—such as our children, our friends, or our parents."

The novitiates chanted in unison:

> "Great is our *Kilo-Kilo Kahuna Nui!**
> Divine is the origin of our Kalakaua!"

The men left the circle, withdrawing to the shadow of the palace wall. The women watched intently. If King Kalakaua rolled the ball of twine so that it stopped in front of a woman, she would be goddess for the night. Without apparent choice, the King rolled the ball of twine. It stopped in front of the youngest, Mele, scarcely seventeen. Dutifully, Mele rolled up the olono string, approaching Kalakaua until she was in his clasp, then followed her divine lord into the palace, while the thirty-five women remaining sat waiting until the men who had withdrawn returned to the circle, and the ceremony was repeated.

The King led the way to a bedroom, removed Mele's ceremonial clothes and lifted the naked girl to his bed. Mele trembled.

"Here, Mele, remove my loincloth of Aikanaka," the King ordered, irked at her slowness. "Now listen, quietly."

At first the song of the chanters, accompanied by the sweet piping of nose-flutes, came softly, gradually increasing in power:

> "This body is sacred to thee,
> This way and that I'm turning . . .
>
> Your fragrant two buds of the mountain,
> Are scarlet lehua to me . . .
>
> Quick! Quick!
> Yield the nectar sought by the birds . . ."

* Very great diviner of the stars.

Mele's involuntary shaking lessened as she relaxed in the King's arms and, her emotions deeply aroused, she drew close to him.

When it was over she whispered: "Lord Divine, I must remain with you always. Love Eternal, why does the Queen sleep alone when she might have this?"

At the mention of Kapiolani the King roused. He said, "Why do you ask? Tonight I love only you."

"One woman is like another to your rapacious Halala," she chided. "Did you not order the men away at our second meeting and have your Halala enter ten women before the night was through?"

Sleepily Kalakaua replied: "My divinity must not be too closely associated with my physical endowments. Now sleep."

The King was awakened by the chanters:

> "Morning climbs the sky,
>   The heavens awake with joy
>   Lo, day is come."

He turned to Mele. Her eyes were red from long, silent crying.

"What is it, Mele?"

"Why cannot we sleep on together, Flame Eternal? Dissolve these senseless old rituals. I know you are more man than god."

Kalakaua was stern. "The ceremony of Hale Naua must not be mistaken for mere physical gratification."

As the girl's tears wet her cheeks afresh, he relented: "I will roll the olona ball to you next time, Mele."

27 Exit Mr. Spreckels

It was a Hawaiian spring morning, brilliantly clear, except in the jagged green-clad Koolaus, behind Honolulu, where thunderclouds tumbled into the valleys, trailing veils of mist in which rainbows arched.

"Of peuty it in Hawaii so much gives, Claus," said Mrs. Spreckels. They were standing on the bridge of Spreckels' *Mariposa* rounding Diamond Point crater.

Spreckels, in his late fifties, was making the financial fight of his life. The Eastern sugar refiners, second largest trust in the United States, had concentrated their fifty-five million dollars upon Spreckels, to drive him out of his rich Western preserves. They had invited him to sell out at their figure. That failing, they raised the monopoly cry in Congress, hoping to restore the duty and cut off Spreckels' cheap Hawaiian-grown sugar. Their spokesman, Senator Merrill, told his senatorial colleagues: "The reciprocity treaty with Hawaii is losing the United States four million dollars annually, while only one man profits thereby—Claus Spreckels, who holds King Kalakaua in the hollow of his hand." Failing to break the treaty, the combine glutted Spreckels' California market with cheap Eastern sugar, and to starve Spreckels'

251

refinery, sent to Hawaii to buy all the independent growers' raw sugar, at any cost.

As soon as the *Mariposa* docked at his pier, where Berger's Band had come to greet him, the Spreckels drove to their new Punahou home. Claus proudly led his wife through the glass doors, etched with homeland scenes of the Black Forest, into a conservatory filled with her favorite plants, up the broad, sweeping stairs to the glassed-in observatory in the tower from which there was a magnificent sweep of the sea. Mrs. Spreckels saw the flower-filled vases. Her eyes filled with tears.

"Momma, don't you liking it?" he demanded.

She nodded happily, blowing her nose. "*Dumkopf,* but of course." The roly-poly pair kissed.

Spreckels sighed, "Now it is Gibson and the King I must see."

In the seven years that Kalakaua had known Spreckels, he had run up his personal debt to six hundred thousand dollars. And as Spreckels became more indispensable to the King, so much more intolerable became Spreckels' monopoly to others. His agents controlled the greater part of the Hawaiian plantations and he dictated to them the amount of sugarcane to plant; only his vessels carried full cargoes in and out of Honolulu; and, through his control of the cabinet he dictated the importation of Japanese labor.

Spreckels sought out Gibson. Without hedging, he confided that he had come to Hawaii to scrape together enough money to go into the Eastern refiners' territory and build the world's greatest refinery in Philadelphia, forcing the Eastern men to accept his terms. To finance this, the Hawaiian government would have to meet part of its obligation.

When Gibson replied that the government had not been

able to meet its employees' payroll for the past two months and that he had already drawn seven hundred and fifty thousand dollars against the Japanese Laborer's Fund, the well-informed Spreckels roared: "*Gott im Himmel!* Dot is two hundred tousand more than it holds! Vell, von chance I am giving. I my six hundred tousand personal note to Kalakaua renewing, if control of the city wharves, waterworks and the lighting franchise, you give me."

For once Gibson stood up to the man. "Your vessels already have a large subsidy for touching at our port, Claus, to say nothing of getting free water and wharfage, which your competitors must pay."

Flustered, Spreckels shouted, "Py Gott! I wanting these rights so I can freeze Eastern capital out from Hawaii so they their sugar can't shipping. If it not gives this, I my six hundred tousand wanting immejutly. Maybe you understand when I foreclose your *Advertiser* paper until the thirty-seven tousand owing you give me. I your Calabash King want to see. Eder he gives Claus's terms or I make your sugar patch kapoot!" With that ultimatum he stomped out.

When Gibson told the King of Spreckels' demands, Kalakaua stated flatly: "I am ready for a showdown. Our legislative following is strong enough now, Gibson."

The influence of the Hale Naua had brought every Hawaiian member of the legislature into the King's camp. They believed in Kalakaua's divinity; he had only to ask for votes, and the votes were cast as he wished. When Spreckels called that afternoon he came directly to the point: "Rex, of expenses in this government it gives too many."

Kalakaua smiled, "Apparently, Claus, you know nothing of foreign policies."

"You've made a pretty fair return on all money invested

in Hawaii, Mr. Spreckels," said Gibson. "Princess Ruth's Maui claims, for which you paid thirty-five thousand, are now worth in excess of five million dollars. And the coinage has netted you something!"

"Of chicken food it gives ein little. Put why send this Iaukea for twenty tousand around the world mitt medals? And Gibson, why you buy a gud-for-nudding warship in England?"

Fed up with the man's inquisition, King Kalakaua said calmly, "Mr. Spreckels, there is such a thing as national prestige. My kingdom cannot operate on grocery store principles."

This reference to the multimillionaire's past enraged him. "You yourself not making even a good delivery boy, Rex. Of financial affairs you know nudding. You spend two hundred tousand more of Japanese money in the Postal Savings Bank than is there. When Japan for it calls, what you do then?"

With perfect equanimity King Kalakaua replied: "Spreckels, your financial demands will be met within two months. Gibson, you might explain."

Gibson was delighted. "Mr. Spreckels, the Government of Hawaii is now negotiating with Mr. Henry Armstrong of Skinner and Company, Ltd., London, for a ten-million-dollar loan which will meet all outstanding commitments!"

Spreckels, caught, repeated incredulously: "Ten millions! What security you offer? All dis Gott-damn spending by your kanaka-nigger King has got to stop."

King Kalakaua paled. "Spreckels," he said, "this is my country. Get out of Hawaii before I throw you out!"

Spreckels nodded. "I getting out. I will to California go and sugar peets grow. Grass grows in the streets of Honolulu when Claus is through mitt you." He flung down his Order of the Star of Oceania and crunched the jeweled medal under his heel.

As Spreckels stomped out, the King turned to his Prime Minister. "Gibson, go tell the legislature what Spreckels said. Instruct them to pass the ten-million-dollar loan instantly."

28 The Gods Demand A Sacrifice

The ousting of Spreckels was a distinct triumph for King Kalakaua. A new and stronger sense of power was growing within him as his subjects obeyed his will in the legislature and through the disciples of the Hale Naua spread belief in his divinity. He had prayed Queen Emma to death, a death well merited since she was a leader of those who opposed him and his gods. He, David Kalakaua, had brought those gods back into the life of the Hawaiians and because of this the gods had given him powers beyond those of men.

Into this mood of exaltation came disturbing news. Mauna Loa on Hawaii Island, the largest active volcano in the world, erupted. Down the sides of the mountain poured the greatest flow of lava within any living Hawaiian's memory. By night, the ruddy light from the lava fountains could be seen from Kalakaua's palace, one hundred and eighty miles away. The earth trembled; three hundred and eighty-three distinct shocks were felt within twenty-four hours. Kalakaua watched in terror. The fear he had instilled into his disciples turned upon him. Pele, goddess of fire, intended this eruption for him. She might destroy him.

Natives fleeing from Hawaii Island told how the molten

256

lava was crossing mountain roads, cascading in a thirty-mile stream down to the sea, where it sent up tremendous clouds of steam, accompanied by explosions which sent huge clouds of lava thousands of feet high.

Worse omen of disaster, a large school of red *akule* fish was sighted off Kau, David's ancestral grounds. To David and every Hawaiian this school of fish was a direct sign from the gods that some great wrong had been done. The gods must be appeased, and throughout seventy generations appeasement had meant the death of a member of the ruling dynasty, sacrificed to atone for the wrong done. Only thus could the gods be conciliated and won back to their people.

Kalakaua was shaken by fear. He sent for Maria Alapai but she refused to come to him. Again he sought her in her home.

Incensed and terrified the King shook her roughly. "Do you think my powers have left me?" he demanded. "Are you planning to pray me to death?"

She shook her head.

"Then what do these signs foretell?"

"Sire, the gods demand a member of your royal clan."

His fears confirmed, the King hurried to Liliuokalani and repeated Maria's portent. "Who will it be?" he asked.

"You were so god-potent the night you prayed Emma to death," she taunted, "why don't you tell me?" She looked hard at her brother, who was sweating profusely, and trembling. The throne won't be his much longer, she thought; but between her and the throne was the Princess Kaiulani. "What of Kaiulani?"

Despite his fright, the King revolted. "How can you consign an innocent child?"

Liliuokalani laughed. "I see you are still a weakling, my divine brother. What of her mother, Likelike? Before she left for Hilo she told me that this lava flow was meant for her."

"When does she come back from Hilo? I tell you, one of us three must die."

She studied him coldly. "I am meant to outlive you, David."

After a three day wait Likelike returned with Kaiulani, and Kalakaua went to her at once.

"What is the flow doing? And is it true, did the akule wash ashore near your birthplace?"

Likelike burst into tears. He waited for the paroxysm to pass.

"How many akule were washed ashore?"

In a whisper she replied, "Thousands."

"Are you ready to die?"

"Yes, David. I went to the firepit at Halemaumau and offered my chants. I want to die."

"Have you told Liliuokalani?"

"Lydia is an evil spirit!" flared Likelike. "She knows everything I do; what I feel, everything. She hates me because my daughter Kaiulani stands between her and the throne. David, you alone can save me!" She leaped upright, crazed with fright and, coming at him with her fingers curled like claws, she cried, "You too, are sending me to death."

He ordered, "Sit down!" As she obeyed, a feeling of cruel exultation swept over the King. It was Likelike who would die, not he. If he prayed her to death he would be greater with his people than any Kamehameha, *even greater than Aikanaka*. As for the whites, where was there a white man with the courage to pray his sister to death? The gods demanded this sacrifice of him, David Kalakaua. They would not find him wanting.

Likelike read her doom in his exultation. Submissively she

listened as he told her that he would return after midnight to assist in her final rites. Then he hurried back to the palace and sent for Junius Kaae, secretary of Hale Naua.

"Kaae," he announced, "our gods are valiant within me. There will be a midnight meeting of the Hale Naua. Those who come will behold the greatest supernatural act ever witnessed in Hawaii. Our gods will speak through me, their divine agent."

Kaae looked at the King with awe. Kalakaua seemed taller, mightier. Well might he be a god who had come to earth! The secretary turned and fled to carry the news of the meeting.

The disciples of the Hale Naua were at the palace grounds early. They feared Mauna Loa and Pele, and the King. When Kalakaua appeared, they were aware that some great change had come over him; the gods must be with him. Their fear was mixed with a curious sense of spiritual exhilaration—a god was with them!

With Maria Alapai carrying the shark's consecrated ashes, another a sacred stone knife, and a third the Everlasting Fire, the assemblage left the palace grounds quietly as the clock struck two. Fear and awe dominated them; even Maria Alapai was afraid. When the hushed group of more than a hundred reached Waikiki, the King strode to the spot just left of a banyan tree, where Haaheo had told him had stood the altar of Lono. With the proper invocations he instructed four men to shovel sand aside. Soon a spade rang against a rock.

One of the aged Kahunas cried out: "Kneel, this is holy ground. It is Lono's *heiau*."

As he spoke Kalakaua resolved that this meeting should never be forgotten. Each disciple present would make a sacrificial offering of blood so that he would be branded and never after question the King's divinity. Taking the sacred stone knife from Kanui, he commanded each member to disrobe and as they passed before him, singly, and bent over the altar of Lono, he passed the stone blade through the Everlasting Flame and slashed their breasts so that their blood spilled on the altar.

Maria Alapai ordered everyone to prostrate as Kalakaua prayed:

"Ancestral god! We prostrate ourselves before thine altar, humbly beseeching forgiveness for leaving the altar untended. Great is our sin, O Lono.

"For atonement tonight, I offer you the highborn Chieftess Likelike, my sister, descendant of Aikanaka!"

A wail from the Hale Naua members, which seemed to rise without effort, filled the night. As the cry increased in tempo, Kalakaua intoned the strongest of death chants:

> "O Uli, and thou, image of nameless god
> Bite her throat where it is slender;
> Destroy it and wrench out the jawbone!"

The prayer was repeated three times. Then the members of the Hale Naua entered the home of Likelike, where they found the royal princess composing her song of death.

They listened as her voice rose, clear and steady; Likelike was resigned to the role she was called upon to play. She took leave of the great mountains, of her favorite island, of the king wave and queen wave at Kona, of the misty falls of Akaka, of her home, of the mate to whom she had come a virgin, of her daughter, Kaiulani. And then, while the hushed assembly marvelled, her voice grew strong and triumphant. Her death song burst into a pæan as she rejoiced at going into the abode of her gods.

The voice ended abruptly on a note of victory; the subdued Hale Naua assembled before the altar, and King Kalakaua invoked the final curse. Round and sonorous his voice seemed to fill the night and his disciples trembled at the dread words:

"Uli descend!
Descend!
Wrench out her jawbone!

The hunt is ended.

Like a shaft of light, so fast
Her spirit rejoins its mate with Pele."

There was silence. The acolytes lay prostrate before their almighty ruler. They knew Likelike was dead. As, slowly, they raised their heads, they saw in the sky above them that the glow of Mauna Loa's eruption had lessened. Slowly the rose faded until the blackness of night swallowed the last vestige of Pele's anger. And they knew Kalakaua was god!

29 The Opium Traffic Gets the Royal Nod

The day following his sister's burial, King Kalakaua asked Kaae, "What do the people say about Likelike's death?"

"Sire, we tremble because the gods are so strong within you, but I rejoice that our *Kilo-Kilo Kahuna Nui* can instill fear even into the haoles." This was balm.

"So the white bastards are at last aware of my powers!" Abruptly he turned to affairs of state.

"Kaae, I need one hundred thousand dollars." Kalakaua knew that the London loan had soured and before the British and Germans entrenched themselves in Samoa, he must establish a consulate and a government there. Besides, the boys from the reform school who had been training for months under Admiral George E. Gridley Jackson were almost ready to serve upon a man-of-war.

Kaae hastened: "After Likelike's death demonstration your subjects are more than ready to contribute tokens of appreciation."

Kalakaua shook his head. "I need one hundred thousand dollars! Kaae, a profitable source of revenue is slipping through our hands. If I were to have the legislature license the handling of opium in Hawaii, how much do you suppose Afong or that rice planter at Ewa—Aki—would be willing to pay for the privilege?"

For Kalakaua only one issue was involved. Between failure of empire and greatness stood the lack of money.

"Won't the missionaries howl?" began Kaae.

"Didn't you just tell me that even the whites are frightened of my power over death?" retorted Kalakaua. "Tomorrow morning I intend to introduce the measure into the legislature. Today, you must conclude your arrangement with Aki."

When the opium licensing bill was presented to the legislature, consternation ruled. During a recess, Lorrin Thurston conferred with Sanford Dole. "If the opium traffic in Hawaii is given the legislature's stamp of approval, civilized people the world over will accuse us of endorsing this vile drug. We must swallow our pride, go to Gibson and ask him to influence the King to withdraw the bill."

"We'll have to be cautious," urged Dole. "We'll get nowhere with Gibson by criticizing the King."

"You do the talking," said Thurston.

When they entered Gibson's office, Dole came to the point at once.

"We are here about this measure endorsing the entry of opium into Hawaii."

"I know nothing about it," replied Gibson, "it's straight from the palace."

"As man to man, Gibson," Thurston broke in, "please influence the King. This goes beyond politics."

Gibson raised his hand. "As long as these dope-sodden Chinese are in the country, laws won't stop opium importation. Yesterday the *City of New York* brought in two chests with false bottoms filled with opium and our own police helped them ashore! We discovered two hundred ounces in ship's firewood split open, hollowed, and glued together. They bring it in in heels of boots, in broom handles, in butter tubs—last month in one ship each fourth tub of butter held ninety-one tins."

Meanwhile, Register of Deeds Junius Kaae followed Kalakaua's orders by contacting Chinese agents and getting bids on the opium trade. He reported to the King. "Sire, Aki offers forty-five thousand and the Kwong Sam Lee group forty thousand."

"And if pressure were applied?"

"Aki might go to fifty-five thousand."

"Sixty thousand is a better figure," the King said blandly. He did not tell Kaae that another Chinese had already given him seventy thousand dollars with a percentage of the opium trade which should yield an added hundred thousand dollars yearly.

Kaae returned to the Ewa rice fields that afternoon. "Aki, the opium license bill is passing. You still like opium business?"

"Me likee too much."

"You got money ready?" demanded Kaae. "Number One Guy wants sixty-thousand dollars cumshaw quick."

"Sixty tlousand?" repeated the Chinese. "Me give floty-flive tlousan."

Kaae told him that they had a bid of sixty thousand. The unsuspecting Aki hastened: "Me play. Me pling sixty tlousan dolla."

"Tonight! Savvy? All hard money?"

That evening King Kalakaua entertained Captain Burwell and guests from the U.S.S. *Pensacola* at the palace. Aki, wandering about in search of the King, came into the room carrying a heavy basket.

Kalakaua hastily excused himself and went to greet the Chinese. "Good evening, Mr. Aki; my registrar of deeds has been expecting you. He's in the library now. Go right in."

Aki, bowing, said, "Glacious Numba One Kling, me so solly. Me pling mis'lable twenlee tlousan dolla. Too much tlouble fechum so much clash quick. Me pling plenty tomollow making sixly tlousan."

Junius Kaae walked up quickly and hurried the indiscreet Aki into the library. After putting the twenty thousand into the King's private table drawer, he returned with Aki to the entertainment, the pair standing apart. As they drank a glass of port, Kaae suggested: "Aki, perhaps you bring little present to the King tomorrow morning. Numba One Guy very fond little suckling pig for breakfast."

"Me all-time savvy," Aki said, bowing happily. Even with sixty thousand to the King, the opium license should net him and his tong two hundred thousand dollars a year. "How does Gracious Numba One Guy wishing his pig cooked?"

Kaae said that the King preferred the pig cooked in the ground with bananas, taro, yams, chicken *luau, lomi* salmon, and *lau-lau* s.

After Aki had gone, Kalakaua took the gourds and began chanting for his select little audience. The champagne party continued in the palace grounds until four, when guests and King transferred to the *Pensacola*. There the party went on until dawn. Adept at reading cards, the King told the fortunes of the ladies until sunrise when he drove to Waikiki for a plunge and returned to the palace shortly before eight, ravenously hungry.

Aki, who had cooked, and gathered money all night, was waiting. The Chinese bowed profoundly as the King entered. "O Lold of Heaven, a small offling, a small li'l sucklin' pig flo bleakfast."

The King picked up a joint of suckling pig. "This numba one fine, Mr. Aki!"

Aki bobbed again. Then, bringing forward the graft money, he said, "My Glacious Kling, please to accept li'l blasket with flew ten-cent plieces."

"Here," said the King, calling to Kaae. "You know what this is about, you take it."

Kaae took the basket away but Aki stood near the King smiling blandly. "Floty tlousan dolla, making sixly tlousan . . ." he repeated.

Smacking over the goodness of the chilled raw *lomi* salmon, shredded with chopped onions and tomatoes, the King turned to Aki. "Kwong Sam Lee offers me seventy-five thousand dollars cumshaw." Aki, his happiness evaporated, began to wail: "O, Numba One Kling, me so solly. All-time, too much, no money can get."

Kalakaua wiped his fingers on a napkin and threw it to a retainer. "It would be too bad to lose the opium contract when you already have invested sixty thousand." He added craftily: "You understand, Aki, you don't even have a signed note."

The Chinese saw that all he possessed and had borrowed was at stake. He hastened: "Me pling tomollow evening."

The King neatly lipped off two fingers of poi and added: "Mmmm. And two suckling pigs for tomorrow morning's breakfast."

"Me pling, me pling," the harassed Aki hastened and departed. Standing around had cost him fifteen thousand dollars.

Aki spent Sunday scouring the countryside for money. The night, again, he spent cooking. Sharply at eight Monday morning, he drove into the mauka gate of the palace and found the King surrounded by a group of his Hawaiian friends, among them Junius Kaae. There had been a Hale Naua session the night before and, after their night's exploits, the guests were hungry. Kalakaua called to him, "My appetite is waiting, Aki. You're late."

Overwhelmed with confusion, the Chinese bowed. "Me too much solly. Me pling 'leven tlousan cash dolla!"

The King waved his hand. "Forget the four thousand, Aki. That's a trifle. Besides, your little porkers are delicious. Leave what money you have with Kaae. In a few days," he added to the Chinese rice grower, "you should get the final news of the disposition of the opium license. Good day, and good luck."

. . . Three days later the duped Aki learned in the newspapers that the opium license had been awarded to his rival, Chung Lung.

30 The King's Nav-ee

The Christmas holidays of 1886 were in full swing. King Kalakaua, Prime Minister Gibson, Registrar Junius Kaae, and other well-wishers of Hawaii's new South Seas legation arrived at the wharf to drink to the representatives sailing on the S.S. *Zealandia*. Financed by the $141,000 opium bribes, the legation was headed by John E. Bush, one time printer's devil and former Governor of Kauai. A half hour before the "All ashore" signal, Grand Chamberlain Iaukea handed King Kalakaua a tortoise-shell box containing six jeweled orders.

The King asked Bush to kneel. As champagne glasses were held aloft, Kalakaua intoned, "John E. Bush, Minister Plenipotentiary and Envoy Extraordinary to the court of our good friend King Malietoa of Samoa, we hereby invest you Grand Officer of the Star of Oceania." Taking from Iaukea a jeweled-studded sword, the King slapped Bush smartly on the back. As the Ambassador staggered upright, Kalakaua pinned the jeweled order on his breast and embraced him.

"This box contains five more orders. Present them to the Polynesian kings who join our federation. But always, Bush,

268

tell them that this jewel makes them members of the great Empire of Oceania."

Turning to the Legation Secretary, Henry French Poor, he said: "Henry, study well Samoa's economic and social background." To Joseph D. Strong, the court artist, "Catch the spirit of the Samoan chiefs on your canvas! One picture, well executed, is worth ten thousand adjectives." Concluding, the King addressed Bush. "As Our Minister Plenipotentiary, be circumspect lest the governments of Great Britain, Germany, and the United States learn of your power to make treaties of federation. When you leave Samoa, proceed to Tonga, thence to the other islands, tendering advice and assistance." He then shared his big secret. "To provide you with the necessary diplomatic éclat, I am buying a warship to convoy you from island to island . . ."

The *Zealandia's* whistle blew. As the lines were cast off, Bush, at the rail, raised a brimming cup: "Sire, Disraeli got India for Queen Victoria. Bush will get you Oceania!"

Word that King Kalakaua was in the market for a man-of-war spread quickly. Bright and early the next day, Foreign Minister Gibson was offered a vessel of one hundred and seventy-one tons, combining both steam and sail, which would make a splendid training ship for the Hawaiian navy. Her owner boasted, "She's sound of teak and oak. Scrape her bottom, brighten her up with paint, and she'll be a credit to any country. And for twenty thousand dollars."

Gibson recognized the bargain and sought Kalakaua to persuade him that Lieutenant Jackson needed the *Explorer*. The King was far from convinced. He accompanied Gibson to the waterfront with reluctance. Gibson reassured him: "Sire, once our ten-million-dollar loan is concluded, and the money from our South Seas Empire rolls in, I will get you a real navy. Properly overhauled, the *Explorer* will surpass anything the United States Navy now has for a training ship."

"Remember, the Samoans have seen German and British men-of-war, Gibson. This fertilizer hauler, regardless of how much paint you slap on, will not add dignity to Bush's mission."

Gibson, never niggardly, had been forced into a pinch-penny role. Without Spreckels' loans, government salaries were three months in arrears. "But Sire, Bush needs a ship immediately. Everyone will understand that the *Explorer* is just a beginning."

At a hastily convened cabinet meeting, the bargain was closed for twenty thousand—ten thousand in cash from the Japanese Postal Savings account and the remainder in government notes. Before nightfall the *Explorer* was in drydock, with shipwrights, riggers, sailmakers, painters swarming over her. Six artillery pieces, taken from the Punchbowl battery, were mounted fore and aft, together with U. S. Army Gatling guns which could fire six hundred rounds per minute.

As the warship gradually emerged from the former guano hauler, criticism abounded. Thurston branded the ship, which had been re-christened *Kaimiloa,* "another hair-brained bust," but the training ship set Honolulu a-bustle. There was silverware to be purchased at the Pacific Hardware store; sea clothing for the schoolboys and band; ship's crockery; brass work; flags and pennants to sew; rope, canvas, paint, and the usual supplies.

While the *Kaimiloa* was still in drydock, Jackson brought his reform-school boys aboard to familiarize them with sea and battle routines. Finally, the big day dawned for the lads. Before their King and the Secretary of War and Navy—Gibson's new title—the salts swore to "serve loyally and true" aboard the *Kaimiloa* or on any other ships of His Hawaiian

Majesty's Navy for two years, and to engage and fight the King's enemies.

That evening the ship's officers in their new uniforms went to the official *Kaimiloa* ball at the palace for the investiture. Jackson was weighted down with gold braid. The ladies were in Paris gowns fully in keeping with Hawaii's gala social event.

In the course of the evening, Gibson presented the officers to His Majesty, King Kalakaua of Hawaii, Emperor of Oceania. As each man knelt, the King presented him with a commission. Dancing followed; then a midnight repast. In happy mood the King lifted his glass to Gibson.

"I congratulate you, Mr. Secretary, upon the splendid appearance of the officers of Our Navy. I hope they will give as good an account of themselves under fire, as they do under the barrage of the ladies."

There was a burst of laughter.

Gibson turned the compliment nicely. He lifted his glass to the naval officers and addressed Jackson: "And I, in turn, am proud of your officers, Admiral Jackson. I have no doubt they will prove themselves loyal subjects and brave."

In that fine spirit the company proceeded, by the light of the full moon, to the *Kaimiloa* for the commissioning. It was two hours past midnight, but the ratings were routed out and ordered to dress for field inspection. As they were drawn up before the merry celebrants, Admiral Jackson formally declared: "By virtue of the power invested in me, I, George E. Gridley Jackson, Admiral in His Majesty's Royal Hawaiian Navy, do hereby pronounce His Majesty's Training Ship *Kaimiloa* in commission!"

Later that morning, the shake-down cruise was scheduled —a short run through the choppy Molokai channel. As the King came aboard, the twenty-boy band played "Hawaii

Ponoi." Taking no chance of subjecting himself to ridicule before a large audience on shore, Jackson had the ship towed out to the roadstead. Difficulty was encountered when the newly trained officers failed to give the commands to hoist sails; and when it came to bracing the yards' round, smartly, they were at a complete loss. Admiral Jackson, furious at his officers' incompetence, ordered the braided gentlemen below and commanded the warrant officers to take over, which they did, promptly and well.

King Kalakaua put his hand on Admiral Jackson's sleeve and said good-naturedly: "Jackson, once your officers get their sea legs, these minor ills will evaporate. Don't be too hard on them." Turning to the paymaster, he added, "See that the band boys get a bonus."

As the ship glided past Koko Head, the King called to Jackson, "Admiral, let's see how fast you can overhaul yon enemy ship!"

Jackson had the word passed to the marines to don their coaling suits, ordered his men to battle stations, crowded on sail, and called for full speed ahead.

As soon as the pistons began to drive, soap bubbles floated out of every joint and fitting. Some shoreside wight had poured soft soap into the boiler manhole! As the yellow warship blew soap bubbles, the enraged Admiral stomped to his cabin and proceeded to get roaring drunk.

The King turned to his Navy Secretary. "Gibson, get your bubbling birdshit tub out of Hawaii. Send her to bush, at once."

But before the *Kaimiloa* cleared Honolulu harbor there was a gin-inspired mutiny, and four commissioned officers, including the navigator, were put ashore. When Jackson called for steam, there was no response; the cylinders were full of water. At the end of the first day the *Kaimiloa* still wallowed in sight of Oahu. Finally, she got under way; Hawaii's first training ship was embarked upon her maiden voyage looking toward the beginning of the Empire of Oceania. Her orders were to meet Bush at Apia Harbor in Samoa.

31 Bismarck Issues An Ultimatum

In the eight months since leaving Honolulu, Ambassador Bush had suffered. The Samoan mission had begun well enough. King Malietoa, forty-five, and a splendid specimen— six feet two in his bare feet—invited the representative of his brother sovereign Kalakaua for a ceremonial *kava* drink. Undying friendship was pledged; speeches followed, and feasting lasted until midnight.

Returning the honors, Bush dined Malietoa and his sixty chiefs. Capitalizing on the convivial spirit of the diplomatic gathering, Ambassador Bush presented Malietoa with the Grand Cross of the Star of Oceania, after which he read the twelve articles which prescribed: "The official dress is knee breeches, black dress coat with cuffs and lapels trimmed with green and gold cord, a white satin vest similarly trimmed, black silk stockings, patent leather slippers, court rapier, and a court chapeau without plume." To Malietoa's vast relief, Bush decreed that the *lava-lava*—Samoa's official court dress —would suffice in Samoa for the Order of Oceania.

Investiture concluded, Great Brother Kalakaua's health was drunk again and again while different chiefs oiled themselves and danced their *Siva* for the Hawaiian delegation.

Then Malietoa's daughter donned a swishing grass skirt*
and danced a lascivious eye-filling number.

At two, Malietoa took his leave. Wine was brought for the
twenty chiefs remaining upright, who insisted that their generous host take a separate glass with each one. Bush humored
them and held his ground until dawn, when the party broke
up with good feelings all around.

To German Consul Eugen Beeker's mind, Hawaiian Envoy Bush's activities didn't make heads or tails. What made
sense was that the Hawaiians were hitting it off entirely too
well with the American Consul, Colonel A. B. Steinberger.
Following the usual German pattern of conquest in the Pacific, advance agents had entered Samoa as clerks of the trading company, the *Deutschen Handels und Plantagen Gesell-
schaft der Sudsee Inseln zu Hamburg,* more familiarly known
in the South Seas as the "Long-Handled Company," in which
Imperial Chancellor Bismarck had considerable stock. These
army- and navy-trained "colonizers" squatted at strategic military sites. All land disputes were settled under the rifles of
warships by German Consul Beeker, who was also the president of the Long-Handled Company. King Malietoa, who
had dared to remonstrate, had been deposed, and a rival
chief, Tamassee, friendly to the Germans, was given the
rulership. And now, the Hawaiians were courting this deposed Malietoa! Even more threatening to Consul Eugen
Beeker was the latest diplomatic message from his foreign
minister; it brought word of Kalakaua's "Little Monroe Doctrine"—The Pacific for Polynesians—and warned Beeker to
beware of the United States' consul in Apia.

Bush did not plumb the depth of German intrigue until

---

* Artist Joseph Strong brought the grass skirt back to Hawaii—virtually the
only contribution made by Kalakaua's expensive mission. The grass skirt
was enthusiastically adopted in Hawaii, and it soon became known the world
around as the Hawaiian hula skirt.

Tamassee's eldest daughter came to him and said that her father was a prisoner in German hands and did not want the kingship, which rightfully belonged to Malietoa. Bush called Malietoa and his chiefs to a secret midnight session. He told them that Hawaii's might, including a navy, was ready to help them gain independence. "Crook just one little finger to King Kalakaua and say: 'Be our big brother', and federation with Hawaii is yours."

King Malietoa waited for the shouting of his chiefs to subside. Deeply impressed by this overture, which he had vainly sought from France, England, and the United States, he said simply: "Your words, Ambassador Bush, are like a sun rising over Samoa, dispelling darkness. In behalf of my people, I hasten to accept the outreached hand."

The victory caught Bush without the necessary documents of federation. An opportunist, he commanded Malietoa to raise his right hand and repeat:

"I, King Malietoa of Samoa, before my chiefs in holy council assembled, do hereby agree to enter a political confederation with his Imperial Majesty, King Kalakaua of the Empire of Oceania . . . and to maintain what articles of confederation may be deemed proper, now and forever, so help me God."

Bush outlined the new government for Samoa as King Kalakaua, Gibson, and he had worked it out. The next day he wrote to King Kalakaua: "Sire, you can have everything your own way here. And I think, with some careful diplomacy, we can bluff out old John Bull, expose Germany's perfidy, and bind Samoa to Hawaii with hoops of steel." Ambassadorial duties completed, Bush settled down to relaxation and entertainment at Apia's International Hotel.

For the Fourth of July, Bush's American consular friends

invited him, the ranking diplomat in the islands, to their Independence Day dinner. In the midst of the patriotic celebration, a group of German "clerks," with side arms, entered
and toasted the German Emperor: *"Hoch! Hoch! Unser
Kaiser!"*

Bush held his temper until they began to sing *"Deutsch-
land Über Alles"*, whereupon he jumped to his host's defense, raised his glass high and shouted: "I drink to the
eternal damnation of the German Emperor!" The Germans
rushed for him, but the Hawaiian Envoy plunged through
the window into darkness.

A friendly chief found Bush the next day, thrashing about
in the jungle, and offered him his secluded grass hut. There,
in a dense grove of oranges, limes, breadfruit, and bananas,
Kalakaua's Minister Plenipotentiary remained in close hiding for three days. The small grass structure soon became
the continuously open gin-resort of chiefs from near and
far.

The depressed Malietoa was in despair. News of the federation had leaked to the Germans and a price was put on his
head. Like Bush, he had to go into hiding; there was no news
from his great friend, Kalakaua; and Bush, drunk most of
the time, was undermining the morality of the loyal chiefs
by taking up with Tamassee's daughter. Alarmed, Malietoa
secretly dispatched a letter to King Kalakaua saying:

> *Great & Worthy Brother:*
> . . . *Mr. Bush's condition during his residence here is of
> a most disreputable kind. His habits are very bad and dan-
> gerous to my people. He appears to be addicted to the use
> of ardent spirits. I have attempted to break him of the
> habit with no avail. He is an immoral man and my chief's
> wives have forsaken their mates for him. He has associated
> here with the lowest kind of people of half castes and*

*whites, and as a result, I beseech you, My Brother, to take
away this man.*

> *I have the honor to be,*
> *Your most obedient servant, etc., etc.,*
> (Sgnd) King Malietoa.

Scarcely was the letter off when the German cruisers *Olga*
and *Adler* steamed into Apia harbor. With the political situation in this tense state, His Hawaiian Majesty's Training
Ship arrived at Apia and failed to give an answer when the
German flagship *Adler* saluted. Promptly the *Adler* fired a
warning shot across the bow of the strange man-of-war. When
still no reply was forthcoming, Admiral von Schmier sent a
boarding party to demand instant redress. The ranking officer on the bridge explained that no insult was intended,
but that the training ship had no saluting batteries, and that
the only officer who understood navy protocol, Admiral
George E. Gridley Jackson, had not been topside for days.

For eleven days Jackson had remained in his cabin. When
he came topside, discipline was in shambles. Ratings were
swearing at commissioned officers; marines refused to holy-
stone the deck. Jackson's temper centered upon a twelve-year-
old midshipman who refused to salute him on the bridge. In
a towering rage he had the lad lashed twelve strokes and
clapped him in irons. Discipline somewhat restored, he
again retired. It would be time enough to come out again
when Bush came.

News of the *Kaimiloa*'s safe arrival reached Bush, and he
pulled himself together and paid her a visit. Disappointed
at the appearance of the converted guano carrier, Bush
nevertheless complimented the ship's personnel on their
splendid appearance. "I wish to impress upon each one of
you the importance of your presence in these dangerous waters." Addressing the young midshipmen—half of the crew

were under fourteen—he added, "Never, never forget, boys, that the Samoans will look upon each of you as brothers." Turning to Admiral Jackson: "You, sir, are giving my embassy a high degree of éclat." After several rounds, they departed on the Admiral's gig for the beach and the hospitality of the American Consul, Steinberger.

The *Kaimiloa's* three junior officers found them there the next day. The officers reported that the twenty band-boys who went ashore the night before had not returned; sailors and marines had broken their one-in-four liberty by swimming ashore; marines ordered to coal the man-of-war had refused until promised a raise in pay; the senior officers were missing; and someone had broken into the Admiral's liquor stores. Their report made, the three officers presented their resignations, effective immediately.

Bush, nursing an angry head, so far forgot himself that he scolded the skipper before his junior officers, saying: "Admiral Jackson, your crew is a disgrace."

Jackson retorted, "Why in hell don't you try sailing that floating dung-tub yourself!"

Colonel Steinberger interceded: "Gentlemen, gentlemen . . ."

Bush was not to be headed off. He called his legation secretary and ordered him to board the *Kaimiloa* and settle the disgraceful condition. "Take these three officers along." At their insistence on resigning, he shouted: "Shut up. You're in the navy. You can't resign."

Aboard the training ship there was mutiny. A group of drunken lads seized a sailor climbing the *Kaimiloa's* Jacob's ladder, tied, bound him, and chained him to the deck. Then with a wild laugh another drunk yelled, "Now everybody off. I'm going to blow this son-of-a-bitching tub sky high!"

Fortunately, Admiral von Schmier on the near-by *Adler*

had stationed a close lookout on the unpredictable *Kaimiloa.* Apprized of the mutiny, he dispatched a boarding party. They found a gunner actually fixing the fuse to a keg of black powder. He was put in irons on the bridge for the night, tried the following morning, and dishonorably discharged. That left but one man, Bo's'n James F. Hilbus, capable of handling the deck. Hilbus received a spot promotion to Lieutenant Commander, second in command under Admiral Jackson.

Meanwhile German Consul Beeker's code messages reached his foreign minister, who went directly to Bismarck and informed him of the Hawaiian proposal of federation with Samoa; the failure of the *Kaimiloa* to salute the German flag; and the monstrous indignity done to the German Kaiser by envoy Bush. The Americans might be involved, because the Hawaiian minister to the United States, Henry A. P. Carter, had just been appointed to represent King Malietoa in Washington.

Bismarck was not to be bluffed. In anger, he commanded: "Cable Beeker to declare war on Samoa! Dispatch the *Sophie,* the *Bismarck,* the *Gneisenau* to Apia. Keep the *Adler* and *Olga* there. Order von Schmier to bring that ape Malietoa to Berlin to stand trial in our courts. Instruct Ambassador Hatzfeldt in Washington to inform President Cleveland that if Hawaii does not recall the Samoan embassy immediately and continues to interfere in favor of Malietoa, Hawaii will automatically enter into a state of war with Germany! I'll blast that *Gott verdammter Neger* into the next world."

32 Kalakaua Runs Into Trouble

Unknown to David Kalakaua, on the very night the *Kaimiloa* sailed for Samoa, seven determined white men met to decide the King's fate and Hawaii's future. Lorrin Thurston had arranged the secret rendezvous, with Dole, Waterhouse, Castle, Editor Atkinson of the *Hawaiian Gazette*, Dr. Martin, and the newly arrived Colonel Volney V. Ashford of Ottawa, Canada.

Thurston stated the issue bluntly. "We meet to plan the destruction of King David Kalakaua and to make the country safe for ourselves and our children."

Although there had been no outbreaks or attacks by the Hawaiians, the fear engendered by the Hale Naua and the horror of the story of the praying to death of Likelike had so increased that more than six hundred white families had left the islands. Thurston, like the remaining whites, was hiring guards to patrol his home grounds and protect his family. Grandson of Asa Thurston, one of the first missionaries to arrive at the islands in 1820, Lorrin Thurston was fighting for the preservation of his own rights as a native-born white Hawaiian, and for the work of three generations of the missionaries of the Christian religion. Because of the inherent danger, he went armed everywhere. But he was no coward. Tall, wide-shouldered, with a square face and a heavy black beard, deep-set brown eyes, Thurston was an impressive figure. He was prepared at this meeting to plan a campaign that would rid him and Hawaii of Kalakaua, forever.

For this purpose he had enlisted Ashford, because of the man's knowledge of military tactics and his record with the New York Volunteers, which he had joined as a private rising, within a short time, to the command of a cavalry unit.

"Colonel," said Thurston, "tell us your plan."

Ashford, a tall man in his forties, with heavy moustache and beard, rose. "Outnumbered as we are, we must rely on surprise. A strong military organization enlisting every fit white man must train in secret. On the pretext of organizing clubs, I believe that we can start Volunteer Rifle Corps throughout Oahu. Secrecy is our only hope and our prime weapon. To begin with, only this group should know our true purpose."

The idea was received with enthusiasm, particularly when Ashford suggested Prime Minister Gibson as a charter member! For protection, every man solemnly pledged, on his sacred oath, not to divulge anything of the plan, of the membership, or of any contemplated action.

These men were desperate. They saw not only themselves, but their families and fellows deprived of everything they had worked for. And, as one, they hated Kalakaua. The secret was kept, so well kept that the *Kaimiloa* had been away three months before the King stumbled upon it by pure chance.

Kalakaua had decided to go deer hunting on Molokai and sent for a light-weight carbine at a gun store which had just received a shipment. The clerk, in confusion, admitted that the entire shipment had been sold to the Volunteer Rifle Corps. Kalakaua sent for Gibson.

"So, Gibson, ammunition and rifles are arriving in Honolulu and going into the hands of my sworn enemies!" At Gibson's bewilderment the King snarled, "I tell you this Ashford is training an insurrection army right under your nose."

Gibson pushed aside the King's onset. "Sire, those rifle clubs are for sporting purposes. I, myself, am a charter member. We drink beer, eat pretzels, and break clay pigeons. But I have a communication here, Sire, from Secretary Bayard, which is really important. . . ."

Angered, Kalakaua replied, "A charter member are you? Smart, very smart, Gibson. And you sent my only warship with my army officers and my Punchbowl battery off to chase butterflies for Bush in Samoa. Gibson, as Minister of War you are responsible for the state of my home defenses." The King stopped. "Forgive me Walter, we have seen too much together to quarrel now . . . What is this message you were bringing to me?"

"Bismarck has informed President Cleveland that unless we get out of Samoa he will declare war on Hawaii!"

"Declare war!" repeated the King.

As if fate had conspired to pile bad news atop bad, the Grand Chamberlain entered with the letter from King Malietoa. As Kalakaua read it, his color drained. "Great God—" he read aloud in snatches, " 'Ambassador Bush, immoral man associated with the lowest half caste women . . . I beseech you to take this man away' . . . That God damned ingrate! Elevated to my juiciest post, spent thirty-five thousand of my own money—and what? Booze and whores! Get him here, Gibson. Order him to come back and I'll horsewhip him myself!"

The heart went out of Gibson. The Empire of Oceania was going a-glimmering. And yet, he must cheer the King.

"Sire, despite our temporary reverses . . ."

Kalakaua stared into space. The future, the real future, stretched before him.

"Empire is dead, Gibson. The *Zealandia* leaves for Samoa at midnight. Get instructions on her to close the embassy. But be careful. People must not learn that Bismarck has threatened war." His personal danger smote him afresh. "Gibson, how strong are these rifle clubs?"

The meaning of Ashford's ingenious ruse at last came home to Gibson. Alarmed, he blurted out: "By God, Sire, we *are* stripped naked of arms. I, myself, authorized them to use government arms and ammunition. Ashford must have five hundred armed men!"

"Holy Jesus, Gibson! You sanctioned the use of government rifles and ammunition against my express orders!" Another danger flashed through the king's mind. "I saw that scoundrel George Ryan in uniform yesterday. How did that mongrel spawn get inside my army unless you yourself are treasonable? You approve the lists!"

Gibson looked into Kalakaua's dark eyes unwaveringly.

Kalakaua, ashamed, said slowly, "Perhaps I am wrong. But get rid of Ryan. Weed out every unreliable man. Gibson, if those insurrectionists should storm the palace, there is no escape. If I am killed, Liliuokalani will snatch the throne. Perhaps Liliuokalani is scheming with Thurston. Get the Queen and Liliuokalani out of the country until this blows over." He went to the drawer which held the remainder of the opium bribe money. "Here, take this." It was the last roll of ten thousand dollars. "There's a Jubilee celebration in London for Queen Victoria's fiftieth year on the throne. Wangle invitations from Wodehouse. But get Liliuokalani out of the country, at once."

As Gibson started for the door the King called, "Wait. Find out how strong they are. We outnumber these whites forty to one, and the Hawaiians are loyal to me. Send Major Baker to Hawaii to get fresh enlistments for my regular army—all Hawaiians. I want men I can trust."

"Sire, the treasury is empty."

The King thought a moment. "To hell with money; this is my kingdom. Give Baker an official order authorizing him to remit the taxes of those who enlist. Get the Hilo police to organize a regiment! I'll make this palace impregnable, loopholes in the front steps for sharpshooters, iron shutters on the powder magazine. Double the guard, Gibson, never less than one hundred and fifty. Get me four watchdogs, one for each palace gate. I'll make them so bloodthirsty they'll go mad at the smell of a white man."

"Tomorrow," he said more quietly, "I'll instruct my troops myself in their bayonet drill. I'll have the Elite Guard, the Queen's Own, and the Regulars parade in battle dress. Thurston and his whites will know that I can deal with them. And Gibson, dispatch Major Sam Nowlein to see President Cleveland and get United States warships . . ."

"What reason can you give, Sire, for such drastic action?"

"Reason? Say Bismarck is sending his fleet to Honolulu. While Nowlein is in the United States, have him buy arms. And order the *Kaimiloa* to come back at once; I want her guns and ammunition. I am still King."

The day that Queen Kapiolani was being received by Queen Victoria at Buckingham Palace, the *Kaimiloa* entered Honolulu's roadstead. A tremendous crowd had gathered at the waterfront. As the ship skirted the coral reef, Captain Jackson, on the bridge with Hilbus, detected something wrong. "Mr. Hilbus, those men on the dock are armed!"

"They're unpacking cases, sir, and the men are being issued arms. All white men. There's a new man-of-war too, sir, the U.S.S. *Oregon*. And there's the old *Adams*. Looks as if they're stripped for action."

As the *Kaimiloa* secured her moorings, a detachment of white men boarded her. Within the hour, the Honolulu Rifle Club had thrown off all pretense, and was massed in strength at the Oceania dock. A ship had just arrived from the mainland with arms for the palace. The whites, forming a cordon, held back the native police, boarded the ship, broke open the cases, and issued rifles, revolvers, and fifty rounds to each man on the spot. A second boarding party, headed by Colonel Ashford and Thurston, took command on the *Kaimiloa*.

"What's on here belongs to us," Thurston informed the bewildered Jackson.

Ashford, annoyed by Thurston's lack of military procedure, barked: "Jackson, you are under arrest, and I want no further conversation with my prisoner, Mr. Thurston!"

Secretary of War and Navy Gibson had watched the insurrection from the Opera House and hurried across to see the King. "Rex, the Honolulu Rifle Club is in action! Thurston's gang boarded the *Kaimiloa* and confiscated the arms. There are five or six hundred armed men. They seized the shipment of arms Nowlein bought in Connecticut."

In cold fury, the King demanded: "As Minister of War how could you let my shipment of arms be seized?"

"Sire, your person would have been in mortal danger if I had taken enough troops out of the palace to handle that crowd."

The King paced the floor. "Do you mean that Admiral Jackson turned over my entire battery? Without a fight?"

Gibson nodded.

"Good God, now they've got artillery!" He shook his fist in

Gibson's face. "Go down there and recapture the ship." As angry street shouts came to the palace he changed his mind. "No, by God, keep our guard here at the palace! That traitorous bastard. Surrender without a fight. I'll sack him."

"We could organize government workers," began Gibson.

"Half of them must be traitors!" snapped the King. But Gibson's suggestion had merit, so he ordered: "Mobilize every native in government employ! Get them here in the palace grounds. Issue them weapons. We must be prepared to stand off an assault tonight."

Curtis Piehu Iaukea hurried in with a *Gazette* extra. As the King scanned the first page, Gibson hurried to his side. Headlined were sworn statements by Aki, telling in detail of the opium bribe, even to the suckling-pig breakfasts.

"It's a lie," said the King in a hollow tone. "Gibson, arrest Atkinson! Read that statement!" He pointed to an editorial:

Article twenty-five of our Constitution says plainly that no person shall ever sit upon the throne who has been convicted of an infamous crime. . . . The principle involved is that the throne shall be occupied by one who is uncontaminated by a seventy-one-thousand-dollar bribe!

Gibson stood irresolute. "Sire, it would stir up a hornet's nest."

"I said arrest Atkinson!" shouted the King, "And thank your lucky stars that I had the foresight to send Nowlein to Washington to demand warships. What would we do without the *Oregon?*"

As night approached, the King became more uneasy although the palace grounds were jam-packed with three thousand troops alerted to repel attack. The Aki article plagued him. He reasoned: Without Kaae, it would not have happened. I must dismiss him. He sent Iaukea to summon Kaae. After Iaukea had gone the King debated. Kaae had a strong

following, particularly among the Hale Naua. Supporting
Kaae might keep the Hawaiians strong and united behind
him.

Kaae, who had read Atkinson's exposé before Iaukea arrived, refused to return to the palace. "He wants me to
shoulder his bribe." He went to a desk and picked up a pen.
"Here's my resignation, dated and signed. I'll be damned if
I'll go into his rat trap."

When Iaukea reported Kaae's refusal, the King snarled.
"The God-damned ingrate. Afraid to set foot in the palace!"
He thought: If Kaae, who knows my kahuna power, deserts
me, on whom can I depend?

As the night advanced, sleep evaded the worried King. At
last he got up and dressed, moving faster and faster in his
urgency. His one thought was to get away. He raced down
the steps. "Where's the commanding officer?" he demanded
of his sentry. When the officer appeared, the King ordered a
heavy guard to escort him. Thus protected, he moved
through the streets and down to the *Oregon*. Identified, he
was permitted aboard.

A marine, preceding him, wakened Captain Burwell as the
King entered the cabin.

"Burwell," the King blurted, "they are going to kill me.
I had to come to you myself."

"Who in hell is going to kill you at this ungodly hour?"

"Dole, Thurston, Ashford—all the whites. They're after
my crown."

"Only one person can kill you at a time," Captain Burwell
responded irritably.

"You don't understand, Captain. It isn't just the whites.
It's all these Chinese. They're dopeheads, full of opium. One
of them even accused me of accepting a bribe. Burwell,
you've got to help me."

"Rex, for God sakes, let me pour you a drink. A hot brandy?"

"No, I've sworn off. I'm drilling my troops."

"A gin?"

"All right, gin. But just one."

He grasped the gin bottle and poured his tumbler half full. He gulped the liquor and wiped his lips with the back of his hand. Kalakaua downed the second half-tumbler, and began again: "Burwell, I don't even trust my Prime Minister."

The Captain looked Kalakaua over with some anxiety. This was not the debonair, affable, pleasure-loving King who had remained until dawn on his ship telling the ladies' fortunes with cards. This man was greasy with sweat, his hair unkempt, his red-rimmed eyes sunken in a grey unshaven face, and his loose lips trembling.

Burwell humored him. "I'll have a secret, emergency telephone line installed direct from my cabin to your palace office the first thing tomorrow morning. Should the occasion warrant, I'll land marines to supplement your own guard, depend upon it."

When the King returned to the palace at dawn, he found his Minister of War awaiting him. "Rex, a leader of the Honolulu Rifles is willing to throw in with us. One of their principals would like to have a position as ambassador to Canada and work for a treaty of reciprocity with that country!"

"And endanger our treaty with the United States and lose the *Oregon* and the *Adams*? Not by a hatful of dung!" At last he was thoroughly convinced that Gibson was a triple-dealing blackguard. "And whom do you have in mind? That drunken friend of yours, Bush? Or maybe you want to skip out with a whole hide and leave me sitting here reaping the benefit of your military mistakes?"

For a moment Gibson's loyalty wavered. But without the King, he himself had everything to lose. "Volney Ashford wants the post . . . He's fed up with Thurston. His price is five thousand dollars and the ambassadorship."

For the first time in two months the King smiled. "Gibson, this is a stroke of genius." He clapped him on the shoulder. "With Ashford out, the Honolulu Rifles will collapse. And when the time comes I'll show Thurston how his own trusted man double-crossed him. How do you intend to use this Ashford?"

"Let him continue to work quietly for Thurston. Perhaps counsel the Honolulu Rifles to call a public indignation meeting to blow off their steam. Resolutions, Rex, never dethroned a King. Then, when things simmer down, we'll send Ashford to Ottawa."

33 The Reformers' Revolution

Seven thousand, the largest white crowd ever assembled in Honolulu, crowded the armory for the Hawaiian League's first public meeting. It was hot and muggy, but the weather was a matter of no moment. Among the people, pressed tightly against each other, there was a sense of unity, not of peaceful unity, but of active, growing animosity. Within the hall they were all friends; the enemy lurked without. Those who did not wear uniforms bulged where pistols and revolvers were concealed, and those without firearms carried thick, heavy clubs, clubs which when swung could bash a man's head in. As the League's leaders entered there was prolonged cheering.

"Get 'im Lorrin," shouted a club holder. "Get that knucklehead's crown!" This was followed by browls, hoots, and boos—all of them fraught with menace; these men were ready for action. The noise grew at the slightest reference to the King; and when one speaker concluded his short address, "Men of Hawaii, that rotten stench that assails our nostrils comes from the palace where our royal dung-collector sits and accepts opium bribes," pandemonium broke loose. Men took out their arms and handled them, eyes wild and threatening.

Lorrin Thurston was scheduled for the main address. He was in uniform. There was wild cheering as he put his loaded rifle across the speaker's table.

Unnoticed, Volney Ashford quietly walked out of the armory and went to the palace.

Kalakaua greeted him cordially. "Good morning, Colonel. I understand you are going to take over the command of my troops during the present crisis? After which you will be my representative in Ottawa to negotiate a treaty of reciprocity."

Ashford asked bluntly: "What assurance have I that this commission will materialize after the danger of today's Citizens Meeting subsides?"

The King bridled. "The commission, Ashford, is written and sealed."

Ashford pulled out his watch. "In exactly fifteen minutes I want four thousand cash, and the other thousand I'll take a month from today when I leave for Canada as Ambassador."

Nettled at the man's effrontery, Gibson interposed: "And if not?"

Ashford's eyes narrowed. "Your second shipment of arms from Connecticut is due on tomorrow's *Mariposa*. How long do you think the pair of you would last if those men at the meeting knew that?"

The King said hastily: "Gibson, I have twelve hundred dollars here. Borrow the remainder from the Japanese Postal Bank fund." He went to his desk and brought out the twelve hundred left from the opium bribes and thrust it into Ashford's hands. While Ashford was counting the money, Gibson returned with the remainder.

"Good," said Ashford, "and I'll take over command of the palace troops. . . . There is, however, still the special diplomatic paper to Ottawa. I want it in writing, Your Majesty."

When it was given to him, he left for the meeting.

Ashford had just gone when a runner arrived, panting. "Thurston demands Gibson's instant resignation, a new cabinet, Aki's bribe paid, and now they're talking of a new constitution."

The King looked at his Prime Minister. "Gibson, they mean business. I must confound them by anticipating them."

"Sire," replied Gibson, "to preserve the crown, I am willing to resign. We might have gained our Empire, Rex, but for those Jesus shouters who smother the sweet breath of life from your people."

Both men started at a loud thunder of clubs against the armory floor and a roar of angry cries across the palace grounds. Kalakaua knew he had to get Gibson out of the palace before the resolutions committee arrived. He took Gibson's hand, pressed it and thanked him. "Better put your resignation in writing, Gibson, and pre-date it a day."

Gibson went to a table, wrote his resignation and handed it to Kalakaua. There was a knock at the door. The King whirled. It was his Grand Chamberlain Piehu Iaukea.

"Sire, His Excellency Japanese Consul Taro Ando is here."

"And what does that fawning Jap bastard want now?" Kalakaua remembered that Gibson was still with him. He held out his hand. "It's good-by, Gibson." As the man walked to the door Kalakaua regretted his curt dismissal. Gibson had been with him for a long time. But—Gibson himself had taught the King: "Ruthlessness is greatness, Sire." He hesitated and Gibson had gone.

"Consul Ando, Sire," repeated Iaukea.

"Bring him in, quickly."

Consul Ando entered, bowed, and wished the King good
health and long life, and requested the pleasure of an audience with the King and Prime Minister.

"Premier Gibson has been requested to submit his resignation," Kalakaua said sharply.

The Consul bowed again. "Sire, four months ago I requested Premier Gibson in writing that the laborer's fund
money be made available to me within sixty days. May I
request that the deposits be turned over to the Japanese
Consulate immediately?"

The King hedged. "As soon as my new cabinet is
formed . . ."

The Japanese selected his next words carefully. "His Imperial Majesty Mutsuhito's servant found two thousand eight
hundred dollars checked out today and was afraid that he
might have to summon warships from Japan . . ."

The threat infuriated Kalakaua. Abruptly he said: "Good
day!" and turned his back upon him.

The delegation headed by Thurston came to the palace
within five minutes. After a fifteen-minute wait, commensu-
rate with regal dignity, the King appeared in formal attire.
"To what can I ascribe the pleasure of this call?"

Thurston replied that the Citizens League had some demands which they wished filled, and read them. At the
conclusion the King smiled blandly. "Gentlemen, in ac-
knowledging the receipt of these resolutions, We are extremely gratified that Our loyal subjects took this consti-
tutional step in presenting their grievances." Without looking
at the sizzling Thurston, he continued, "In regard to your
so-called grievances,"—he lifted the document from the
marble-topped table and held it some distance from his nose
—" 'Gibson must resign his position.' " He walked to the desk

and brought back Gibson's pre-dated resignation. Kalakaua referred to the resolution document. " 'The cabinet must resign'. Gentlemen, we have already ordered the formation of a new one. To the third charge, we do not know what secret dealings Mr. Aki may have had with Our Registrar of Deeds. However, we will gladly submit the subject to Our new cabinet and act according to its advice. Does that meet with the approval of this committee?"

Thurston, outmarshalled at every turn, jumped to his feet. "No, not by a damned sight! Junius Kaae must go, and now!"

"We were coming to that," said the King. Thurston had walked straight into his trap. "As soon as we read the *Gazette*'s account, We demanded Mr. Kaae's instant resignation. However, in all fairness, We gave Kaae the assurance that he would be reinstated with full pay if the charge proved false." He held Kaae's resignation in front of Thurston's face. "The date, you will observe, is two days back."

"We want that no-count Robert Wilcox called back from Italy!" shouted Thurston, "and we want this army out of the palace grounds, and that Austrian battery disabled, the *Kaimiloa* sold, and Jackson tried for stealing government funds . . ."

The imperturbable Kalakaua picked out the least bothersome item: "Yes, Lorrin," he agreed, "Our students have had ample education to be of service to Our country."

"And those whores parading in your Hale Naua society must be thrown out of the palace!" Thurston finished.

The King paced silently for a moment and halted suddenly at a window. What he saw there made his hands go to his throat involuntarily. The strength went out of his knees and he sank into a chair. Hoping that he had not betrayed his fright to the committee, he said: "Gentlemen, I concur. And

you may be interested in knowing that I turned my palace
troops over to Colonel Ashford of your own Citizens
League. I want no bloodshed. Thank you for calling."

The bewildered committee walked out, Thurston leading.
"That unregenerate spawn of a Jamaica quadroon outma-
neuvered us on every score! Made idiots of us. Even turned
his troops over to Ashford." Then, suddenly, as they stepped
out of the palace doorway, they saw what had so badly frightened the King. "My God, look!" shouted the tallest one:
"They're hanging Gibson!"

When Walter Murray Gibson had left the palace, alone,
one of the men guarding a street leading to the armory saw
the Premier and called across the street to another: "There's
the white-haired son of a bitch who brought all this on!"

Gibson began to run.

Like a scattered pack of bloodhounds, men joined the
chase, shouting: "Get him!" As the cry grew, more came running and shouted: "String him up!"

Gibson reached his own front doorsteps just ahead of the
pack, slammed the door, bolted it, and fell into a chair.

"Up with the white-haired baboon!" shouted the men at
the front door.

"Hang him at the palace grounds!"

A dozen hurled their combined weights against the door,
breaking it down. Another group clustered around a soldier
who had used his bayonet to hack a Manila clothesline into
lengths and was braiding these into heavy rope. Before he
was through, six compatriots pushed the struggling Gibson
through the broken door while others restrained his daughter Tallulah.

Despite his danger, the six-foot-one Gibson pulled back his
shoulders and, standing erect on the porch, laughed in their

faces. "You're yellow, the pack of you. Send one up here who's a match for me!"

Someone cheered the sixty-three-year-old man's courage. Then a half dozen rushed him and he crashed on the porch. While men were lifting him, the noose was slipped over his head, and as the rope was yanked by a score of grasping hands, he stumbled and fell down the steps.

At least fifty grasped the rope as they hurried Gibson down the street and through the mauka or mountainward gate of the palace where Ashford's guard had taken over, to the kamani* under which the King held his Ball-of-Twine meetings. One man climbed into the tree and tossed the rope's free end over a heavy limb. Gibson lurched forward, his face in contortions. Two men pinioned his arms and another slapped his face and spat on his white beard.

Hearing the mob's roar, British Consul Wodehouse rushed out of his near-by Miller Street office. He saw the rope dangling over the limb. He ran, and as the crowd parted, he saw the other end around Gibson's neck. His eyes met Gibson's. Gibson tried to speak, but no sound came. He had had a paralytic stroke.

"Remove that rope!" Wodehouse ordered. "Regardless of our differences with Gibson, the man has always stood by his King, courageously and loyally. Bad as his rule may have been, Gibson never resorted to this! Such action will make tyranny in Hawaii a hundred times worse than today."

As the Consul was speaking, Thurston and the other committee members, who had just left the King, arrived. Almost simultaneously, Colonel Ashford ran up. The military

---

* kamani: is an indigenous tree and looks a little like our American magnolia. There are quite a number of varieties in Hawaii but the one on the Palace grounds has colorful heavy leaves and never sheds all at one time.

leader lifted his sword. "Silence!" he shouted, "take your hands off Gibson!"

As they let go, the old man slumped to the ground with the hangman's halter still about his neck. The right side of his face pulled up and his right leg jack-knifed under him. Thurston approached the stricken man and brutally pushed him with his toe.

"Still acting, eh, Gibson?"

Part **Four**

Alas! Broken Are My Hands! *(Auwe! Mo ' ku'u Lima!)*
1887–1891

34 A Young Chief Returns

Leaning over the ship's rail, Cadet Robert Wilcox pointed out to his Italian wife, Gina, oldest daughter of the Princess Victoria Colonna di Stigliano, the far away dome of massive-shouldered Mauna Loa, the earth's largest single mountain mass, arching above a swirl of dawn-pinked clouds. Obeying an imperative order from Foreign Minister William Lothian Green, Robert was returning to Hawaii. In San Francisco, Hawaiian Consul Daniel McKinley advanced the Wilcox's return passage and warned Robert that Gibson had been nearly lynched; that a Reform Cabinet, with Lorrin Thurston at its head, had forced a new constitution upon King Kalakaua; white legislators had taken over the Assembly; the Supreme Court had been packed with Thurston men; and the King's troops—which Robert hoped to command—had been reduced to seventy-five.

As he stood beside his young wife, with the early morning headwind flattening her loose dress against strong breasts and pregnant figure, Robert determined that, no matter what changes had come, nothing would halt his plans to restore the dignity of the crown. He was a tall, handsome man with a dignified carriage. He had large brown eyes and wore a smart, upturned moustache. To look at Robert was to trust him; Gina had felt that from the first time they met. **Gina** was worried, and Robert, sensing her anxiety, drew **her** close.

His years of study in Europe had intensified his love for his native islands; news of the King's humiliation at the hands of the whites strengthened his devotion to Kalakaua. Now that Wilcox saw the beauty of the islands rising from the ocean before him, any hesitation he might have felt at returning gave way to pride and excitement. As their ship rounded Diamond Point, Robert saw a commercialized Waikiki. Where waves had broken on clean, white sand and men had surfed, there now stood a thirty-foot unpainted tower with a slide running down into the water. Above the piercing scream of a girl shooting the chute on a wooden sled, he heard his first steam piano playing "The Girl I Left Behind Me."

Mrs. Wilcox paid scant heed to these cheap devices. Through Robert's binoculars she studied the Waikiki homes, counting twenty-three with sweeping lawns and coconut palms slanting over the turquoise water. Along the waterfront were scores of riders, mostly women, sitting astride clothespin fashion, galloping their mounts madly and outdistancing a curious assortment of mule hacks, basket-phaetons, surreys, carryalls, expresses, and tricycle riders, all streaming toward the dock. On the wharf, Gina saw the stubby little bandleader, Henri Berger, with giant, protruding ears beyond which stuck the waxed ends of an enormous moustachio, jerking with every wave of his baton. Everybody seemed to be laughing and there was a profusion of flowers; women wore them in their hair and men had woven floral strands as hatbands.

As their ship got off a monkeyfist, Gina became aware that of the faces upturned toward them there were only a dozen whites, and not one paid any attention to her uniformed husband. He was finally recognized by a black menial who solicited them for fares and turned to the crowd calling, "Look folks! Mista Bob Wilcox!"

While other passengers were burdened with sweet-smelling leis Robert and his wife stood alone, ignored. At last, two white men shouldered their way to them.

"Wilcox," said the taller, curtly, "I'm glad you followed our instructions to return."

"*Your* instructions?"

"Certainly. We whites run this country now."

Both pointedly ignored the princess until Robert introduced them to his wife as his former assembly colleagues, Sanford Dole, and Lorrin Thurston.

"You're returning her passage money, I trust," said Dole. "Hawaii's running on a business footing now. We've even appointed a committee to take care of the King's finances— to keep him within his six thousand dollars of salary! Not the hundred thousand you kanakas voted him."

"I'm heading the Cabinet now," offered Thurston.

Gina Wilcox, bewildered, turned in appeal to her husband. Robert smiled down at her. She became aware that the man with the bald spot, and the big black beard, Thurston, was still talking, and that the colored hack driver who had brought up their luggage was being mentioned.

"John Blossom here will supply you with further information." Thurston bowed low to Mrs. Wilcox. "And your husband can tell you about your driver. He's King Kalakaua's half-brother. Good day."

Robert looked after Thurston, who soon disappeared in the milling crowd and confusion at the dock. He resented the man's arrogant manner and thought bitterly how Thurston, after long opposition to the King, was at last in a position of power. He was clearly a man who would press his advantage hard.

"What a disagreeable person," commented Gina to Robert when they were settled and Blossom had mounted to the driver's seat. "And what did he mean?"

In low tones Robert replied, "It's an old scandal, never proved, that the father of our driver was the unacknowledged father of King David Kalakaua. Blossom's a decent man. I want to talk with him."

Within fifteen minutes Robert was alive to the current situation. Prime Minister Gibson, Robert's closest friend, after barely escaping hanging, had been sent to San Francisco, where he had died within a few days. Nearly all of the King's friends, and Robert's, had been arrested and imprisoned, and during a special election only a few Hawaiians who owned property had been allowed to vote, with the result that the legislature was now packed with white men.

As they were passing Iolani Palace Robert recognized a man in uniform. He shouted, "Stop! . . . Baker, Baker, how are you?" It was Robert Hoapili Baker, commander of the King's forces and a former assembly colleague. As they chatted, Baker reported that Robert's fellow student in Italy, William Boyd, was back and working in the Customs office for thirty dollars a month. Robert asked to be admitted to pay his respects to the King, but Baker shook his head. "Thurston was just here and gave orders that you are not to see the King."

"Who in hell is running this country?" stormed Wilcox.

"Come to Nowlein's tomorrow night," said Baker in a low tone. "Those of us who are loyal are meeting in secret. We've got to work fast. The Reform Cabinet has given the United States absolute rights to Pearl Harbor and their next move is

annexation." Upon the approach of a white man Baker hurriedly strode off to the palace.

Gina fought to suppress her tears. "Please Roberto, take me
to our hotel."

At the Arlington, the clerk, who had been warned by the
owner, Charles R. Bishop, demanded a week's rental in advance. The twenty-four dollars left Robert less than that in
cash.

During the week Robert learned that Thurston's rude
wharf reception typified the entire business community's
feeling toward him and all Hawaiians. His money ran out
and Gina, beside herself with worry, hounded him into going to Bishop for a loan.

Bishop greeted him effusively, but when Robert asked for
a hundred dollars until he could get on his feet, raised in-
quiring eyebrows.

"A hundred dollars is a lot of money in Hawaii these days,
Wilcox. And you owe the Arlington only forty-two dollars."

"My wife must have medical attention."

"Yes, I know. Pregnancy is an expensive luxury, particularly with an Italian princess. Robert, you should move out
of the Arlington at once. It's too expensive. I'd suggest,
Robert, that you forget what you once were. If you do, the
white community will adopt you as a son, even overlooking
your Hawaiian background."

"You mean my mother's noble Polynesian blood is a hand-
icap?"

Bishop sized up the young man carefully. Then with a note
of condescension in his voice he said, "Robert, to save you
future pain I must be honest. I love Hawaiians, but they
must not be pampered. Times have changed. Don't forget
the King does what we tell him. We even write his speeches.

Those six years of yours in Italy, at our expense, were a flight from reality! Now you must live within your income—"

"Mr. Bishop, I'd like nothing better than to make a living."

"H'm, I understand you turned down a government position in the surveying department."

That was true, the job paid twenty dollars a month.

"You taught once—well, as President of the Board of Education I'll give you twenty-five dollars a month with two months off for vacation—" He stopped as Wilcox rose and faced him.

"I know what you white bastards want, Bishop. You want me to kiss your tight ass like the King does, but I'll see you in hell first."

"Shut up!" roared Bishop. "A kanaka like you can't say that to a white man in this country."

None too gently, Wilcox forced the banker back into a chair. Loud enough for all the clerks to hear, he cried, "You, Bishop, came to this country broke, but with the help of Judd and Cooke you hallelujah'd your way up from the bottom rung. You degraded son-of-a-bitching skinflint! Write the King's speech for the next legislature and you'd better make it good. It will be your last, so help me God!"

35 A Rally Round the King

King Kalakaua wakened from his troubled sleep as a key turned, ever so softly, in the lock of his bedroom door. His heart pounded as he reached for the loaded pistol under his pillow. With the palace gates torn down, his watchdogs killed, his army of ten thousand reduced to less than a hundred, palace noises threw the King into a cold panic. Because he suspected his sister Liliuokalani of complicity with the Reformers, Kalakaua had sent his one remaining bed companion, Mele, to spy on her. He tried to reassure himself that only Mele and Major Baker, his commandant, had keys to his bedroom door.

As the door opened Baker's voice came to him, "Sire, I come with friends."

The King's terror was converted into a rage. "You prowling sons of bitches! How dare you steal into my bedroom in the night? You're fired, Baker. Get out!"

"But Sire, we come to liberate you!"

"Liberate me! Are you making sport of me?"

The King ordered Baker to take the unlighted candle from his bedside table and light it in the middle of the room, so that the intruders could be identified. Baker complied and Kalakaua recognized William Boyd and Robert Wilcox, both in Italian uniforms. "Get out of here before you are found in those clothes!" shouted the King.

Wilcox saw with a shock how Kalakaua had aged. His skin had lost its rich brown and was overcast with grey. Beneath his nightgown his belly sagged; his shoulders drooped forward. His lower lip trembled.

"Sire," he ventured, "Thurston has made you a captive in your own palace and we have come to set you free."

"Why didn't you send a message through my chamberlain?"

"Sire, our messages were intercepted. Only by persuading Major Baker did we finally gain this audience."

The King turned to Baker. "Is that true?"

At Baker's nod of assent, Kalakaua became somewhat composed. He reached into his commode and brought out a bottle of gin.

Wilcox tried again. "Sire, wherever we Hawaiians turn, the whites block us. At your command we are ready to break out of these bonds."

The King, remembering his former "liberators," Celso Caesar Moreno and Walter Murray Gibson, shook his head. He took a large draught and wiped his lips with the back of his hand. "No, Wilcox, I have no defense. My troops are gone."

"You have your people to call on, Sire. Thurston's arbitrary acts have driven even whites to your standard. We suffer with you, Sire. We cry when we pass your ruined gates."

"How could I train troops, much less pay for them?" demanded the King. "Thurston has drained me dry."

"Patriotism has no price tags, Sire! You have but to tell

me: 'Wilcox, lead my people!' and as God above lives, I will collect men sworn to the death to restore the crown to its former greatness."

Kalakaua's response was brutal. "What do you want out of this, Wilcox? A premiership? Has my sister offered to make you her Prime Minister?"

Wilcox raised his right hand. "I swear, Sire, I want only to restore the dignity of our race so that we need not slink down the alley at the sight of a white man. I want to restore the electoral franchise to our people; I want to break this damned Thurston treaty with the United States; I want to see these Reformers run out of the country."

For an instant King Kalakaua seemed to waver. "No, Wilcox, once before when I offered my people an empire they were not great enough to rise to my leadership." He reached for the bottle. "They have gone too far on the white man's way." He was quoting Kapiolani. "No nation has ever met the white man and withstood his spirit-killing diseases." The King looked pointedly at William Boyd: "There's another. At my expense he's been trained to be a soldier in the Italian military academy and what has he done? Sold himself to the whites at thirty dollars a month!"

Wilcox would not be dissuaded. "I do not say, Sire: 'Go back to the old ways.' It is for us Hawaiians to add that of the white man's culture which befits our Polynesian civilization and then to go on to build a new Hawaii, a new people, a new nation . . .'"

The liquor was beginning to take hold of Kalakaua and, momentarily, he had courage. He went to the closet and fetched a second bottle. "Here, have a drink."

Wilcox refused. "Sire, the homage you received from the world's great awaits you today as soon as you cast off this damnable Reformer's yoke which Thurston, Dole, Bishop, and Ashford . . ."

The King interrupted. "Not Volney Ashford. He, of all the whites, is with me."

Wilcox went on: "Give me permission and I'll train a handpicked group of four hundred, no more. We'll establish headquarters in the palace."

"No, Wilcox, it is too late. These whites are strong. If you fail they will hang us."

"Hanging," retorted Wilcox, "is better than kneeling to these haole bastard Reformers."

The intensity of Wilcox's manner, his persistence and proud bearing impressed the King, but he still could not overcome his suspicions that Wilcox was in reality working for his sister.

"Perhaps you are right, Wilcox. Where can you train these patriots? Perhaps Liliuokalani can give you some help. Why did my sister take you into her home?"

"Bishop threw us out of the Arlington Hotel. Liliuokalani and John Dominis, my wife's fellow countryman, took us in. We are destitute. I have tried to get a job, but every white man is against me because I am loyal to you."

Kalakaua knew this to be true and recognized the sincerity of the voice. "Well then, Wilcox, go ahead. Organize your men. We'll see about things when the time comes." But the response was too vague for Robert.

"Sire, I must have proof that I represent King Kalakaua."

"What do you want?"

"The legislature meets in a week. Thurston is telling everyone that he has made a split-tongued mynah* out of you.

---

* The mynah was brought from India to Hawaii. The bird can be taught to speak.

And he says that if you do not read his speech, he'll pull you off your throne! Sire, he is determined to make you kiss his posterior publicly . . ."

That had effect. With the help of the second bottle of gin, the King pledged, giving Wilcox his hand, "I will not read Thurston's speech!"

Hatred was reflected from the tightly knit groups gathered in the Assembly Hall to hear King Kalakaua's opening address. Thurston had collected a large number of whites to witness David Kalakaua's final humiliation, while Wilcox had persuaded his followers to come and hear the King reestablish the dignity of the crown.

Resident Minister Merrill of the United States, and British Commissioner Wodehouse were seated together, interested observers. Studying the men knotted around Wilcox, Wodehouse cautioned: "If some hothead like Wilcox organizes the Hawaiians, it will endanger every white. Better keep your *Adams* in these waters."

Merrill assented. "Wodehouse, something is boiling right now." He pointed out that practically every man in Wilcox's group had been driven out of office by the Reform Party.

"At his worst," Wodehouse sighed, "Walter Gibson was never as absolute as these stiff-necked reformers. They're driving even their own supporters into the enemy's camp."

It was true. During the preceding special legislative session, the reformers had prohibited the sale of liquor. Elections had been rigged. White juries alone were allowed to judge whites. Americans were allowed to practice dual citizenship while the Japanese were forbidden to vote. Reform laws restricted the Chinese to agricultural pursuits and those already in business were ordered to keep their accounts in

European language! The laws passed despite bribery; two Reform legislators were caught red-handed accepting fifty-dollar bribes from Chinese merchants.

Applause greeted cabinet members as they entered—Thurston, Austin, Green, and Ashford, who for the first time, at Thurston's behest, were wearing official dress uniforms. Members of the Supreme Court came next and took their places near the diplomatic corps. Thurston scowled as they filed in. The day before, the Court had upheld by a three to two decision the King's right to appoint his own ambassador to the Court of St. James's. Turning to Austin, Thurston said: "If those legal luminaries refuse to decide correctly, I'm for stopping their salaries."

"You'd only hurt your own friends Dole and Judd and they already decide everything your way," said Attorney General Ashford dryly. Making no pretense of masking his sarcasm, he suggested: "Why not raise the number to seven? Then you could never miss!"

Thurston pretended not to hear the remark but the growing tension between himself and Ashford was clear to those around them.

Across the hall, the Supreme Court judges were commenting upon the cabinet, which was forcing them into making unpopular legal decisions. "Dole, the King is forcing the cabinet to make these decisions to alienate even the whites from our Reform Party," said Chief Justice Albert Francis Judd. "He is a master of trickery. Should this cabinet fall, our whole Reform structure will collapse."

Thurston looked at his watch. He remembered how the King had kept them waiting after the mass meeting in which he had presented his ultimatums.

"What if our fine feathered bird refuses to appear?" Green asked.

"Frankly," said Ashford, "I think it is absurd to make the King advocate publicly measures which he has already vetoed."

Again Thurston ignored him and pulled out his watch. "Our presumptuous lackey is exactly fourteen minutes late now. Let's convene the legislature ourselves, Green. You read the speech . . ."

Saluting batteries halted that proposal. At the tenth salute, the King's six kahili-bearers entered the Assembly. Two took up their positions at the entrance, and the others, two to a side, stood next to the throne. Before the King entered everyone rose. The King sat first, then Queen Kapiolani, Princess Liliuokalani with Consort John Dominis, Princess Kaiulani with her father Archibald Cleghorn. After a roll of muffled drums, Grand Chamberlain Iaukea opened the royal portfolio.

Robert Wilcox wiped his forehead. He had not seen the King since the midnight session a week ago and he was worried. The King always spoke extemporaneously: the written speech on the lectern did not augur well.

King Kalakaua began by saying that it was "a rare pleasure" upon this, "My thirteenth year's rule, to address the loyal representatives of My people." To make his position absolutely clear, he read the address.

Before the second paragraph ended Thurston raged: "Damn his black hide." Not only was the King omitting sections of the speech but he was also inserting his own opinions. "By the great living God," swore Thurston, "this will be his last speech!"

King Kalakaua had scarcely returned to his palace before Thurston followed with the three other cabinet members in tow. Without being announced, the quartet stalked the King to his library. After His Majesty offered them chairs and seated himself in the largest, Thurston strode toward the King. "Listen, Kalakaua! Either you knuckle down to our terms or we'll jerk the crown off your black head!"

King Kalakaua smiled. Driven to the wall by Thurston's humiliations and buoyed by Wilcox's promise, the King waxed stubborn.

Infuriated, Thurston shouted: "Do you understand that you exist merely to voice the opinion of this Cabinet?"

Before making his reply, the King calmly lighted a cigar. After his first exhalation, he said: "Thurston, you can reduce Our household expenses, cut Our salary, dismiss Our army, but there is one thing which you cannot take away—Our self-respect!" In the resultant hush, King Kalakaua, master of himself, continued: "We have resolved that We are never going to make a speech telling Our subjects things which We do not believe."

Purpling with anger, Thurston threatened: "Have you forgotten your narrow escape from hanging with Gibson?"

Ashford interrupted. "Constitutionally, Thurston, the King is in his right to refuse."

Thurston's resentment against Ashford boiled over. "Ashford, I helped quash the charge made against you of accepting the King's five-thousand-dollar bribe and of the adultery you were caught in."

The King sat back, imperturbable, letting Ashford destroy the Cabinet.

"But now," continued Thurston, "I say it publicly: If any man wants to know what hell is like on earth, without waiting for eternity, let him be in this divided cabinet with you, knowing that every word and every act is being misconstrued by a traitor . . ."

Ashford looked at him coolly, "Thurston, if I knew myself

to be so heartily despised, I would have resigned my ministerial seat long ago."

"Gentlemen, you forget yourselves," said Kalakaua.

Thurston ignored the King and returned hotly: "To your face, Ashford, I accuse you of being in Kalakaua's camp and an enemy of our Reform Party!"

"I believe that defines the issue," said Ashford, calmly. "From this hour on, Thurston, I serve my King and Hawaii!"

36 Treachery and Terror

That evening Wilcox found King Kalakaua at cribbage with Captain Woodard of the *Adams,* and spoke to him privately.

"Sire, there will be four hundred Hawaiians at the palace gates at 3 A.M. We are prepared to lay down our lives to restore your crown."

At once the King asked Woodard to excuse him and joined Wilcox. Together they went to the palace and on the way Wilcox went over the final plans. Wilcox had organized his men into three groups. He himself would lead one force from Princess Liliuokalani's house, and under the cover of early morning darkness they would all meet at the palace gates. The King agreed to await them there.

As the two men separated Wilcox said, "Sire, tonight we succeed or go down in glorious failure. If we die, it will be with the knowledge that at least for a few hours we have lived as God's noblemen." He turned and disappeared into the night.

Kalakaua looked after him for a minute and then hurried through the palace grounds.

A great elation possessed the King—he was the Kalakaua of old. In the shadows he could see groups of men working to

316

ready the grounds for action. His arrival fired them as they built gates to fill the holes in the coral stone walls.

Major Baker approached the King, saluting smartly. "Sire, the transfer of ammunition and arms from Iolani Barracks to your palace grounds has been completed and every man is accounted for."

The King nodded and went into the palace. Everything was going well. He knew that Thurston's economy and Ashford's planning had left the whites with little ammunition. For the moment there was nothing for him to do but wait—wait and hope that Wilcox would not fail him. But could Wilcox be trusted? Why had he *really* chosen Liliuokalani's home? As Kalakaua walked through the dim corridors of the silent palace, the excitement he had experienced a short while ago left him and he felt suddenly the loneliness and danger of his position. If this attempt failed, what new humiliations would the Reformers heap upon him? He had tried for so long to lead his people, and now he was tired. So many bitter memories goaded him to make a last stand against the white man. He recalled with horror his grandfather's body hanging by a rope, the head bent to one side; the ravaged beauty of Victoria, and his hatred for Monsarrat. But now, weariness was stronger than a desire for revenge. There was one way of escape. A month ago the American Resident Minister had proposed to buy Hawaii for twenty-five millions. That would give him more than enough to go to California and buy an orange plantation. Mele would go with him—but where was she tonight? He had sent her to spy on his sister, but she should have returned by now. Why tonight of all nights had she not come? He went to his bedroom, hoping to find her, but she was not there.

Wilcox, meanwhile, was organizing his followers at the home of Princess Liliuokalani. He telephoned his crony of

Italian days, William Boyd, using his prearranged code *Restoriamo la Corona* as a signal for Boyd to join him.

As Lieutenant Boyd made his way through the city, he kept a sharp lookout. The streets were dark and empty. The economical Reformers had ordered the lights dimmed at eleven. Boyd also noticed some of the extra police Thurston had had posted, but he arrived safely at Princess Liliuokalani's house. There he found one hundred and fifty men gathered in the dining-room. The atmosphere was tense; every eye was on Wilcox, and no one heard the light footfall of a beautiful Hawaiian girl as she slipped out of the house.

Wilcox, dressed in green Italian field uniform with sword and revolver, was saying: "Tonight, we fight for our liberty and freedom. A privilege few men enjoy . . ."

"You talk bold with our lives," muttered Junius Kaae, a habitual malcontent since the King had made him the scapegoat of the Aki opium bribe. "What if the King's forces fail us? We'll be cooped in the palace grounds like chickens."

"I left the King less than two hours ago," replied Wilcox. "Ammunition was being transferred into the grounds; secret gates erected."

Boyd spoke up. "This is no time for debate. This hour is for action!"

Five minutes remained. Wilcox gave his last instruction. "Proceed quietly. Remember, our strength lies in surprise. I have men stationed along our way of march. Two other forces, as large as our own, will join us at the palace gates. Now, then, load your weapons for liberation!"

Former Congregational Minister Kanui kissed the ball before he rammed it home in his old Springfield. "I load mine for the guts of Lorrin Thurston." His was but one of a strange assortment of weapons—Parrot rifles, .45/70 Winchesters, .44 revolvers, Swamp Angel pistols, Colt .38s and .22s. With Kanui well in advance carrying a lantern, the group stole out of the Princess's home for the two-mile trek to the palace.

Unexpectedly, Kanui met three of Thurston's specially-delegated police who demanded to know his mission. Upon being told, two of them, natives, joined; but the third, a white man, escaped before Wilcox's men could capture him, to spread the alarm.

"He will wake the city. We must hurry," whispered Lieutenant Boyd. Wilcox was not disturbed. "Before the whites can be aroused we will be in command."

Mele had been held in Princess Liliuokalani's room with the princess long after she had completed her spying mission. It was after one o'clock when, taking advantage of the princess's temporary absence, she managed to slip out. She was lucky; not one of the men assembled saw her. It was two miles to the palace and she trudged them resolutely—she was the bearer of great news. She found the King talking to Captain Robert Waipa Parker under the trees where the Hale Naua had once held its meetings. Breathless, she dropped at Kalakaua's feet.

He picked her up and shook her. "Speak up, girl, what is it?"

"Six hours ago Castle . . . visited Liliuokalani. He offered her the throne. Wilcox sat behind a screen and heard it all."

Certain now that Wilcox had betrayed him, Kalakaua slapped her twice. "Where have you been all this time, why didn't you come sooner?"

It never occurred to the King that although Wilcox had

overheard this conversation, he had remained loyal, knowing full well that it was a shrewd move on the part of the whites to set Hawaiian upon Hawaiian. Kalakaua thrust Mele away from him and she fell to the ground.

The King kicked her out of his way and turned to Parker. "We have just twenty minutes. Under no circumstances turn your men over to Wilcox. Get them into the palace and make your stand against him there." Despite his urgency, his cunning did not leave him. "Be loyal, Parker, and I'll make you my Prime Minister." He wrote out an order on a card, commissioning Parker a full colonel and placing him in command of the palace troops.

"All Hawaiians, Parker; they will be loyal." Kalakaua forgot that Parker, like Wilcox, was part-Hawaiian—his mind was on his escape.

"Colonel Parker, I will establish my headquarters at the boathouse. Hold fast. I will send relief soon." Afraid to go alone, he called for his Grand Chamberlain. "Iaukea, where are you?"

Iaukea hurried in and Kalakaua took him by the arm. "To the boathouse and let no one stop us. Good-by, Parker."

Meanwhile the white policeman who had escaped when the two natives joined Wilcox's men reported to the night officer, Captain Larsen, that an armed mob was converging upon the palace. Larsen mounted a horse, galloped madly to the home of General Soper, the Marshal of the Kingdom, and rattled at the front door. The marshal appeared in a long nightgown. "General Soper, Wilcox is heading for the Iolani Palace with over a thousand troops."

Soper, sleep-befuddled, sputtered, "A thousand! My God! We're lost. Get back to the office. Leave your horse here." He ran upstairs and back, puffing, with Thurston's list of thirty loyal whites. "Telephone these men to come to the police station. We've got to take the King prisoner. A thousand! Hurry!"

Wilcox, in the van, had arrived at the *makai* or seaward entrance with his troops. The gate was up. Everything, apparently, was according to plan. It lacked ten minutes of the prearranged hour of three. In view of the escape of the white policeman, he decided to make his entrance then and there. "In the name of King Kalakaua of Hawaii," he cried. "Open the gate!"

"What's your password?" called a guard in voice strong enough to be heard by Colonel Parker, who had set up his command headquarters in the second floor of the palace. The whole procedure seemed crazy to the sentry. A few hours before, he had worked furiously with others to prepare the palace grounds and to join Wilcox's forces. Twenty minutes ago, a woman had come in and the King himself had just hurried out of the gate with Iaukea and had directed, "Under no circumstances let anyone enter these gates!"

"My password?" repeated the astonished Wilcox. "It is I, Robert Wilcox! Come to restore the King's crown!"

"Let us in!" shouted Lieutenant Boyd. "Let us in or we'll shoot."

Several trigger-anxious men opened the bolts of their rifles, convinced they had been betrayed.

Kanui hurried up. "Hawaiians must not shoot Hawaiians." He proposed that men be dropped over the wall to overpower the guard. Willing hands hoisted them and within a short time Wilcox's troops were admitted.

Punctually, Wilcox's other two forces had converged upon the gate. When Parker approached he found Wilcox's men already swarming over the grounds. Then he heard Wilcox himself demand: "Where is the commanding officer of the guard?"

Parker walked up. "I, Colonel Parker, am in command here."

"Colonel in command? Are you off your nut, man? You're wearing captain's bars."

Parker handed him the King's card and demanded: "Why do you come into the palace grounds armed?"

Wilcox thought the world had turned crazy. "We're here to restore the King to power!"

To this, Colonel Parker returned: "Wilcox, the King knows your plans to proclaim his sister ruler of Hawaii."

Wilcox shouted: "It's a lie! The whites made the offer to divide our ranks. I demand to see the King."

Parker refused. "If you attempt to enter the palace, Wilcox, my men will shoot."

At the magnitude of the King's deceit, Wilcox shouted: "Our Judas-King sacrifices four hundred of us because he believes a lie! Parker, if we do not overthrow the white man's yoke tonight, we Hawaiians are lost forever."

"Fight me and you fight the King," said Parker.

"King or no King," cried Wilcox, "we Hawaiians fight tonight for our country's liberation!"

Junius Kaae grumbled, "Where's our mighty union of forces, Wilcox?"

The patriot knocked him down with the butt of his revolver. The ugly situation was saved by a detachment of the Prince's Own which arrived from Iolani Barracks with twenty-five armed men. Their captain saluted Wilcox. "What is your wish, Commander?"

Wilcox pounced upon this unexpected help. "Where are the cannon?" Informed that they were in the palace grounds at the Waikiki entrance, Wilcox commanded: "Detail groups of eight to drag one to each corner of the palace and shoot them!"

By this time Captain Larsen had returned from Marshal Soper's residence to the police station and sent two men to the telephone switchboards with Thurston's list of faithfuls. He dispatched a Sergeant with eight men to take possession of the legislative building overlooking the palace. "Put our best shots in the front windows."

As the Sergeant went off, Marshal Soper arrived. Told that most of his Hawaiian police had turned to the King, he railed, "God damn it, I told Thurston I needed more white police. But no, our Minister of War says: 'Economize. Use kanakas, they come a dime a dozen.'"

As he was speaking, Thurston arrived with a six-shot Colt. A son of the British Commissioner came with a Scott shotgun and Jim Dowsett carried an S&N revolver.

"Thurston, what in hell are we going to do with your cheap home-made ammunition?" demanded Captain Larsen.

"We're lost before we begin," mournfully added the Marshal, "and you're to blame, Thurston. You wouldn't let me get any new arms." As Soper was spluttering helplessly, word came that Wilcox's armed men were already in command of the government building outside of the palace grounds.

"What'll we do?" demanded the Marshal.

Thurston gave the weakling a withering look. "We must confine the rebels to the palace yard and the administration building. We must take Kalakaua prisoner."

At that moment Monsarrat entered and, seeing him, Thurston said, "Monie, there is a bare chance that the King is at the boathouse. Wouldn't you like to guard his royal person?"

Monsarrat responded grimly: "I'd like nothing better." To the runner, Thurston commanded: "Tell the Sergeant to man the Opera House if the insurgents aren't in there. We'll send reënforcements by daylight."

"We tried the door. It's locked!"

"Break down the God-damned door!" ordered Thurston. Turning to Larsen, "Go to Mrs. Sack's Gun Store. Break into it, if necessary, but get all her guns and ammunition."

As the city wakened, news of the insurrection spread. Windows were hastily boarded, doors barricaded. Men moved their families to the comparative safety of the Punchboard Crater. Two of the dismantled *Kaimiloa*'s gatling guns were manned behind sand-bags at the police station. A corps of marines from the *Adams* was stationed at the American Consulate. Honolulu, at last, was prepared to see the struggle between whites and Hawaiians settled in blood.

37 The U. S. Passes the Ammunition

Scourged by terrifying fears, Kalakaua sat imprisoned in his
boathouse. Every forty-five seconds the disturbing shadow of
his guard, Monie Monsarrat, fell athwart his window. Suddenly Kalakaua sat bolt upright, remembering that he had
not countermanded the orders for the Prince's Own Guards.
With their aid, Robert Wilcox might be in a position to overthrow the whites. If that happened, Kalakaua realized, he
would be in as much danger from the betrayed Hawaiians as
he was now from the embattled whites. Unable to think of
a way to escape, he vacillated between remorse and self-
justification. He was certain his sister was plotting to get the
throne, and yet, if he had questioned Mele more carefully
. . . Monsarrat's shadow crossed the clubroom's walls. The
pounding of the King's heart shot needle-stabs through his
chest. He gasped for air. His cold right hand reached for his
constricted throat. An overwhelming terror, such as he had
never experienced before, possessed him. Afraid to be alone,
the King tried to call for his Grand Chamberlain Piehu
Iaukea, but his voice would not come.

He was filled with longing for Kapiolani. He remembered
how she had said that the offended gods would some day
corkscrew their way into his body and leave him paralyzed.

He knew that she alone could drive off these gods. He tried to go to the door, but fell heavily.

For the third time Kalakaua tried to call and this time his voice responded. The stroke was over. He cried, "Piehu, please come. I need you!" Tears streamed down his sweaty cheeks. When Iaukea stood before him with a lamp, Kalakaua was furious that the man had seen him crying. He swore: "Dung of a rutting bitch! Don't you know your duty is to guard my person?"

"Sire, I was in the adjoining room all the while," Iaukea replied. "All this was too much for your heart. I gave you a drink. You fell asleep and I turned out the light."

"Go to the palace and get the Queen, Iaukea. I am a sick man."

The Grand Chamberlain looked at the King closely. "Sire, she sleeps at Waikiki. You sent her there after Wilcox reported that his forces would go into action tonight."

"Yes, yes," he mumbled. "Wilcox, you say? I didn't see him." He listened intently. Curiously, for the first time in years he recognized the *iiwi's* pre-dawn song. The bird always began singing fifteen minutes before sun-up. He thought of the fate of Wilcox's four hundred patriots. "I must save these men who pledged their lives to restore my crown. They must not die."

A gun barked sharply. The night's scene tumbled back into Kalakaua's fear-strained mind. Concern for the insurrectionists would endanger his own life. A new plan hit him. "Piehu, telephone the captain of the *Adams*."

"Sire, it is impossible to talk over a cut telephone wire," replied Iaukea. He wondered if the King had forgotten that Monsarrat had cut the line before his very eyes. "Fetch him then!" Kalakaua ordered. "And summon the diplomatic corps." He paused for a moment and then said, "No, just

Merrill and Miller." Iaukea reminded the King that General William Miller had been dead for twenty years. Kalakaua looked up and put his hand to his brow wearily. "Of course, I know. Summon the Cabinet, and Ashford. And the judges. All of the important whites. I, myself, will show them how to put down this insurrection."

A heavy rifle shot was heard, followed by a volley. The King cried to Iaukea: "Hurry, hurry before it is too late. And remember, I know nothing of Wilcox—if the whites are still in power."

A few minutes after Iaukea's departure, the harassed King heard the approach of marching feet. After Monsarrat's challenge there seemed to be an altercation. "My God," he thought, "Wilcox is coming to kill me." In his desperation, Kalakaua grabbed up an old stone poi-pounder. He crouched behind the door, prepared to kill the first man to enter. Fear overpowered him and, panic-stricken, he looked about the room for a place to hide.

The door opened. "Your Majesty! I'm Woodard, Captain Woodard of the U.S.S. *Adams*." The King tried to control his shaking knees and lurched into the dawn-lighted room.

"Nice little revolution before breakfast," Woodard began pleasantly. "I was on my way here with a marine guard when I met Iaukea. He told me you wished to see me at once."

Kalakaua took Woodard's hand into his wet palm. "Woodard," he pleaded, "will you protect me?"

Woodard told him that Monsarrat had allowed him to enter only upon the understanding that the King was not to be released. "But," he added, "I'll see that no harm befalls you."

"Thank God!" said Kalakaua fervently. "This is a serious uprising, Woodard. It means bloodshed."

The captain agreed. "These mutinous bastards must be

shot down before their treason infects the entire native populace."

"Shot down in cold blood?" asked Kalakaua. "No, no. You do not understand. They did it because they wished to help me. I told Wilcox. . . ."

As the King stopped, Woodard grasped his duplicity. "You sold their lives for your own advancement and then abandoned them?"

They were interrupted by American Minister Merrill and British Commissioner Wodehouse. Word that Kalakaua was at the boathouse had spread and anxiety was keen. A dozen chairs were brought and Ashford, Soper, and Thurston entered. Thurston was speaking: "Every minute's delay gives Wilcox and his cutthroats a better chance."

Colonel Ashford faced Thurston. "Do you recall, six months ago, that I proposed getting a well-equipped white army for Hawaii? This insurrection was planned, Thurston, while you, our Minister of War, were tilting with saloon-keepers and whorehouse masters."

Thurston thundered: "You're damned right it was planned. And you are as much to blame for this bloody uprising as Wilcox or this octoroon sitting on the throne."

As Ashford made for Thurston, several men interposed. Wodehouse mounted a chair and implored: "For Christ's sake, men, think of our common danger. If these savages break out of their confines they'll fire the whole city!"

Captain Woodard agreed. "If they are not dislodged by nightfall, the other Hawaiians will sack the city. Put a professional soldier in command."

"Colonel Ashford, will you take command?" asked Charles Bishop.

Ashford retorted: "Perhaps someone else here would like

to scale that eight-foot wall in the face of Wilcox's fire with only six rounds of ammunition available!"

American Minister Merrill offered: "With a written request from King Kalakaua I will provide ten thousand rounds of ammunition from the *Adams*." He looked to Captain Woodard for confirmation. At that instant, however, the commander of the second battalion of Government forces hurried in from Iolani Barracks. He saluted the Minister of War, Thurston, and reported to Kalakaua, "Sire, most of my troops have joined Wilcox and the handful remaining loyal have no arms. The situation is hopeless."

Colonel Ashford bowed to Thurston. "Do I get a *permanent* appointment as colonel of the troops if I put down this bloody insurrection?"

Kalakaua saw through Ashford's duplicity. After having accepted his bribe, Ashford was now turning back to the Reformers for a sinecure. His last hope gone, the King slumped into his chair helplessly.

Ashford at once issued orders to the Iolani Barracks' commander. "Throw a cordon around the palace and the legislative building. Use as much protective cover as you can. Detail crack shots to advantageous positions." Then turning to Marshal Soper, "Post an order that every able-bodied government male employee, without exception, must report for duty forthwith. Send fifty more men into the Opera House. We must hold it at all costs. If anyone dares approach a cannon, shoot to kill."

38 "They Were Stupid, Not Heroic . . ."

Blood was shed before the boathouse meeting with Kalakaua ended. Firing began shortly after Police Sergeant George Ryan detected a movement of shutters in Healani, the Queen's residence in the palace grounds, where Wilcox had established his command headquarters. The sergeant whispered to three companions, "Those damned kanakas are getting set. Keep a sharp lookout. And keep the cannon covered." He put down his binoculars and raised his second-story window. He eased the end of his loaded .45/70 over the sill and, inch by inch, got into sighting position.

Two Hawaiian volunteers, Lieutenant William Boyd and George Markham, with heads well down, dashed out of Healani headquarters, sped across the lawn and, before the fumbling whites could draw a bead, dropped into the comparative safety of the sand-bagged Austrian field piece emplacement facing the Opera House, where Ryan and his men were stationed.

The alert Wilcox had caught Ryan's action with his artillery glasses and barked a field order to his lieutenant. In Boyd's hurry to get the first shot off, he flipped the primer out of the gun and it fell to the ground. Reaching for it beyond the protecting cover of the gun shield, he exposed himself. One of Ryan's men took aim and fired. The slug's

330

impact, as it hit Boyd in the right thigh, rolled him over into the open and clear of the protecting sand-bags. To prevent Ryan from finishing off the wounded man, his Hawaiian comrades poured a heavy fusillade into the windows of the Opera House. During this fire, Wilcox and William Kanui ran to Boyd's aid. Tufts of grass flew around them as whites saw their chance to get two of the ringleaders, but both Hawaiians dropped behind the sandbags unhurt, bringing Boyd with them.

"Are you hit bad?" asked Wilcox.

The wounded man bit his lip. "All of us will die like dogs for nothing!"

Kanui applied a tourniquet to the bloodied, mangled leg. "Your broken leg will always be a badge of honor for us Hawaiians. Wilcox," Kanui demanded, "why don't we shoot this cannon?" Then, ignoring the bullets, Kanui and Wilcox fixed the primer and got a shell off. To their mortification it carried over the Opera House, exploding in the navy dock near the King's waterfront clubhouse.

Wilcox's second shell struck the Opera House, filling the air with bricks and mortar. The third carried away the window from which the man had shot Boyd.

Armed Hawaiians crouching behind the parapet atop the palace roof—some of Parker's men who had joined Wilcox—waved their arms, exposing themselves needlessly and added to the savage acclaim which filled the palace yard. Anger pent up for generations was being loosed against the white men.

Ashford, meanwhile, had established his headquarters in a private home within a stone's throw of the palace. During the cannonading, Thurston arrived hatless. In the common danger his enmity against Ashford was forgotten. "Volney, what can we do? We have no cannon."

Colonel Ashford looked at his watch. "In five minutes we are storming the Assembly Hall. You'll get your money's worth, have no fear." A series of shots rang out from the upper floor of their headquarters accompanied by a glad shout: "We nailed him!" Thurston ran upstairs and as he saw Ernest Wodehouse, son of the British Commissioner, open his shotgun and blow out acrid smoke, he asked: "Did you get Wilcox?"

"No, Kanui, the preacher!" He pointed out the corpse.

Across at Wilcox's headquarters, a soldier dashed out to a brass field piece. Rifles rang out, and he fell headlong. He struggled upright and was knocked down again by a heavy charge of buckshot. Then despite his wounds he struggled to his knees and crawled forward on all fours. The Hawaiians cheered. He got to the shotted gun and grabbed the lanyard. At that instant he received a hit in the back of the head which opened his skull.

By this time, the whites' armed patrols had stormed the Assembly building. After a flurry of shooting, the hundred or more whites brought out a dozen Hawaiian prisoners. Using them as a living shield, they advanced toward the front gate of the palace. When one of the Hawaiians lagged, he was shot through the back of his head. The wanton murder, seen by Colonel Parker's men on the second floor of the palace, enraged them. A corporal shouted: "To hell with Kalakaua's orders. If we Hawaiians don't gain freedom today, we're slaves forever." He ran down the steps and at the palace entrance called back to his fellow Hawaiians: "Come on! These son-of-a-bitching whites can't hit the broad side of a barn." He sprinted off to a three-inch battery and, while bullets whizzed about him, got off a shot. Before he could get off a second, he fell, lifeless.

In the Opera House, Sergeant Ryan ordered his sharpshooters's fire concentrated upon the gun position where he knew Wilcox was in hiding. A ricocheting bullet, intended for Wilcox, struck the wounded Boyd again, plowing a deep furrow along the right side of his skull and laying his scalp open. As Wilcox stanched the flow of blood with his shirt, Boyd gasped: "By God . . . if I ever get out alive, I'll murder Kalakaua."

Ryan saw Wilcox suddenly emerge from the sand-bagged gun position, with William Boyd slung over his shoulder, and run in a half waddle to Healani. As Ryan fired once, twice, and a third time and missed, he swore: "God damn my bloody eyes. Why can't I nail him?" From every available gun that could be brought to bear on Wilcox, men were shooting. Wilcox, stripped to the waist, was a perfect target, and yet not a shot hit him.

Unscathed, Wilcox gained Healani headquarters with his heavy burden and passed safely within.

Three hours had gone since the first shot. The firing fell off as the Hawaiians remained under cover, husbanding what little ammunition remained. Wilcox counted his dead—nine, and a score of wounded.

"Why do we continue our fight?" reasoned Schoolmaster Kamai of Waipio, one of the wounded. "Had we taken the ministers prisoner before daylight, we might have won the day."

Angry that his generalship should be questioned, Wilcox retorted: "Now that Hawaiians know that they can shoot back at whites, we'll get thousands to join us after darkness sets in." He went to the door. "Look at those dead who died honorably on the field of battle."

"They were stupid, not heroic," a soldier said. "What is there to fight for? Our Judas-King has deserted us."

Emboldened by this unexpected concurrence, Kamai held

up his mangled right hand, through which a ball had passed, carrying away a thumb and three fingers. He looked about him. "Who's for surrender?"

"Who surrenders will be shot!" warned Wilcox.

"We're almost out of ammunition," reminded another. "Why don't we storm the palace and force Parker to join us?"

Before Wilcox realized what was happening, six Hawaiians with Kamai, the schoolmaster, in the lead reached the palace wall, thirty feet away. As the six hoisted their wounded comrade over the coral wall, Wilcox took deliberate aim. The shot tore through the schoolmaster's thigh, but despite the added injury, he scrambled over, while the others, trapped, sheepishly returned to Wilcox's headquarters.

Once over the wall, the schoolmaster yelled to the whites: "I am wounded. *Pau! Pau!* I surrender, I surrender!" White men carried him to Ashford's headquarters and questioned him. He reported that Wilcox was almost out of ammunition because most of it was stored in the palace which Parker was still holding.

"Parker still holds the palace?" asked the baffled Colonel Ashford. In all his secret dealings with Wilcox before the revolution, he had not heard of Parker's command. "What do you mean? Why isn't he with Wilcox?"

"The King betrayed us!" the schoolmaster shouted. He told them how, at the last minute, Kalakaua had promoted Parker to the rank of Colonel and ordered him to resist Wilcox.

The main body of Wilcox's men, however, were far from surrendering. The day wore on, until four o'clock, with little action. The whites, sensing that with approaching darkness their hour of victory was slipping, became desperate. With Kamai the schoolmaster's information, they decided to blow up Wilcox's headquarters. They capped and fused thirty heavy demolition charges to which they attached spikes so that, when thrown atop the building, the bombs would stick to the shingled roof. At five, they hurled the first bomb. It landed atop the two-story building. There was a tremendous report, and shingles, pieces of broken rafters, and shattered windowpanes filled the air. This explosion was followed by another and another. But, although the upper floor of their headquarters was torn to pieces and the Hawaiians were out of ammunition, there was no surrender.

The imprisoned Kalakaua, hearing the giant explosions, shouted: "Piehu, we must get out of this boathouse!" He jerked open the door and announced curtly to Monsarrat: "We are going to Waikiki to join the Queen!"

"In a pig's A -- hole!" retorted Monsarrat. He lowered his bayoneted rifle. "You're staying here, Kalakaua, and if Wilcox wins, my orders are to put a bullet through your God-damned brains."

Kalakaua went back, dreading the fast-approaching night.

At Ashford's headquarters, Wodehouse voiced the fear of the whites. "If we don't dislodge them in another hour, Ashford, our goose is cooked."

Thurston, too, demanded with irony: "General, what do you suggest now?"

"As a last resort, hand grenades!" Ashford replied. "But I am trying to save some lives." He ordered: "Get volunteers and pitch these grenades in through the windows as fast as you can." After a three-minute bombardment, a Hawaiian came out from Wilcox's headquarters waving a white bed sheet and shouting: "Surrender, *pau, pau!*"

At the cessation of hostilities, Minister of War Thurston called: "Command your men to leave their weapons in the building! Come out of the front gate with your hands up. Move on the run across the street to the Assembly Hall. Any false move and we'll exterminate the lot of you."

Although Wilcox counted more than twenty dead and more than eight seriously wounded, he refused to give up with the others. To protect the wounded in Healani headquarters, he sprinted to the brick ammunition building to fight it out to the last alone. Within seconds, the ammunition building shook with the explosion of hand grenades thrown by the whites, who miraculously had suffered no casualties.

Colonel Ashford hurried up and ordered his men to cease firing. "The man isn't fighting!" he shouted. "I'll see that he surrenders!" He approached the wrecked building and called: "This is Colonel Ashford. I come for your surrender, Wilcox!" As he walked in, he said to his former compatriot: "I'm sorry, Robert. When the King turned against you there was no point in my fighting with you." Then, as the noisy mob neared, Ashford promised: "Never fear, I'll see that you get proper legal defense. Your sword, Wilcox!"

Wilcox surrendered his sword, revolver, and empty cartridge belt. As Ashford took them, Sergeant Ryan rushed in, prepared to finish off the Hawaiian patriot. Colonel Ashford knocked the man down with the heavy cartridge belt Wilcox had surrendered. "I am in command!" he declared. "Wilcox is my personal prisoner."

The colonel's action, however just, met the instant disapproval of the whites. "Hang Wilcox!" yelled one while another shouted: "Shoot the son of a bitch now, along with Kalakaua!"

39 Death In San Francisco

Following Wilcox's surrender, Thurston hastened to the boathouse. Without knocking, he and Monsarrat strode into the reception room. Kalakaua was lying down on a wide couch. No one had told the King how the battle was going and, seeing Thurston's pistol, Kalakaua concluded he was to be shot.

Thurston taunted him. "Sire, I come as your liberator, to free you. Your own beloved Hawaiians wait to give you the warm reception due you. They cannot begin to express their deep-felt gratitude for the creation of the Empire of Oceania, the Hale Naua, the *Kaimiloa*, the opium license. . . ."

Kalakaua turned his back upon Thurston, but the Reformer reached down and brought the dazed King upright. "On your feet, you divine son of Pele! Monsarrat and I are escorting you to the palace."

Returning to the palace through hostile crowds, hatless and sandwiched between his armed guards, was the most humiliating act in Kalakaua's life. For the bystanders' benefit, Thurston taunted: "So you lost your nerve, Kalakaua, at the last moment. Turned against the very Hawaiians who intended to restore your greatness. Had you been brave, you might have been leading *us* by the nose now."

337

The widow of a Hawaiian who was killed that afternoon ran across the street to spit at the King's feet. "You killed my man! The gods will devour you, Kalakaua! You will not last long!"

Thurston marched the King past a group of Wilcox's late cohorts who, under armed guards, were tearing down the eight-foot palace walls. Then, in the gathering gloom of nightfall, the trio entered the broken palace. It was a shambles. Even the throne had been used by Parker's men to barricade the doors against Wilcox. Every windowpane was broken. A newel post had been ripped out and one koa balustrade was hanging askew. From the lower floor, which had been converted into a morgue, came the sounds of grief as relatives claimed their dead. Midst this rubble of battle, Thurston and Monsarrat wished their fallen monarch an uninterrupted night's rest and left.

Seeking protection, Kalakaua stole up the broken stairway. Taking a few steps in the semi-darkness of the third floor, his foot slipped and he crashed to the floor in a pool of thickened blood. He swallowed hard to avoid retching. On hands and knees he made for the flag room, the smallest room in the palace. He locked the door behind him. But far away as he was, he could neither shut out the lamentation of the Hawaiians below him nor the noise of prison laborers outside tearing down his palace walls. He opened the door slowly, quietly gained a side entrance and sneaked to the Fashion Stables, determined to get to Waikiki and see Queen Kapiolani. She, he felt certain, could save him.

In the stables he came upon the dozing caretaker, John Blossom, and shook him awake. "Quick, John," he said, "take me to Waikiki!" The man told him that every driver had been killed, injured or jailed that afternoon. Kalakaua offered to drive himself.

As Blossom harnessed the span, he warned Kalakaua: "An order is out that any Hawaiian caught on the streets after dark will be shot. I hear tell Thurston has paroled some of Wilcox's gang to kill you."

Once in the carriage, King Kalakaua followed the unfrequented roads near the waterfront. Vaguely, he descried a Spreckels ship loading for a midnight sailing and skirted the Oceania wharf. At Kapiolani's residence he stumbled to her bedroom. Kapiolani had lighted a candle and when he opened the door she was sitting on the edge of her bed.

At the sight of his composed wife, Kalakaua cried: "Piolani, I want you to have my crown. A ship is waiting to take me to San Francisco. I must go. They will kill me."

Kapiolani looked at her fear-crazed mate without feeling. She saw the clotted blood on his soiled clothing. "Take your bloodied crown? No, David, I won't preside at the funeral of our Polynesian race which you brought to an untimely end."

He retorted spiritedly: "If you will not take the crown, I will make Liliuokalani Princess Regent. But I am going. I will do some work in Washington about our trade treaty and when this Wilcox trouble blows over, I will return!"

"Go, and don't come back, Kalakaua!" she said shortly, but she could not stop crying. He attempted to put his arm about her, wanting to caress her just once more.

"Don't touch me!" she cried. She rang for a servant and when the man came she ordered: "Take him to his carriage."

Kalakaua knew that his only hope was to escape on Spreckels' ship. Worried about money, he decided first to go back to the palace for his jeweled crown. As he approached the Chamberlain's room, he unbuttoned his shirt and took out the gold key, suspended from a fine chain about his neck, to open the crown's leather trunk. The sound of mourners, temporarily forgotten, brought him up sharp. To stay there, he reasoned, would be foolhardy. Instead, he decided to borrow the money on the mainland. Keeping in the shadows, he got to the wharf and on board before the *John D. Spreckels* cast off.

Before the King reached San Francisco, Wilcox and seventy-one compatriots came to trial. Ably counseled by Volney Ashford, the Hawaiians demanded their rights under Thurston's own constitution which provided that white juries alone could try whites, and Hawaiian juries Hawaiians. As a result, the only man in the insurrection judged "guilty of treason" was an obscure white man, a Belgian named Albert Loomens, and he was sentenced to be "hanged by the neck until dead within the walls of Oahu prison"; the others, all Hawaiians, went scotfree. "For the safety of the white community," the Cabinet negotiated a new treaty whereby Pearl Harbor was ceded to the United States in exchange for military protection.

Kalakaua on his way to San Francisco knew nothing of these arrangements. With his usual resilience he had cast from him the dejection of his defeat. Just what his status was he could not determine, but it was better to act as if nothing whatever had happened. As his ship neared the Golden Gate, he requested its captain to stand in the roadstead overnight to give San Francisco ample time to prepare a reception. As a result, next morning, when the ship steamed into the Bay, powder smoke rolled from saluting batteries; factory whistles were tied down, crowds lined the waterfront, and Presidio troops lined the entire Market Street course to the new Palace Hotel, the world's largest.

While honored guests sampled the frappéed wine—on the city—a sharp-faced *Examiner* reporter asked the King: "Sire, were the Hawaiian Islands peaceful when you left Honolulu?" Ugly reports of the Wilcox uprising had arrived. In congenial surroundings a good measure of King Kalakaua's assurance had returned. He smiled, "Perfectly peaceful, of course. As I remember, the sun was shining and my band played 'Home Sweet Home.' But I know you newspaper boys have to write something. Just report: 'His Majesty, King Kalakaua of the Hawaiian Islands, has come to San Francisco for his health.' "

The arrival of his old friend, Claus Spreckels, saved him from further embarrassment. "Claus, I am indeed happy to see you." Forgotten was their last bitter scene, in which the sugar baron had trampled underfoot the King's royal Order of Oceania. The pair embraced. "Claus, I'm afraid that I'll have to confess that I commandeered one of your vessels. Your favorite, too, the *John D.*"

"*Ach, Herr Gott!* I am coming to you, Rex, to make friendship. Of mistakes I have making, the greatest was in leaving you in anger."

At the apology, Kalakaua grasped the stubby German's hand. They clinked glasses happily. "Claus, I need your help again. I'm planning to buy an orange grove and retire in California. I have to slow down—my heart is bothering me . . ."

"Mit an eight per cent loan, perhaps, yes?" said the ever shrewd Claus, laughing. In the intervening years he had become one of America's richest men. Then, as the old cronies talked on, Governor Watson of California, Admiral Brown of the U. S. Navy, and Mayor Pond of San Francisco called to pay their respects. But for the king what once had been pleasure was now duty. An outcast from his own people, each day's rounds of calls, receptions, balls, and dinners merely postponed the inevitable day of reckoning. The King's fifty-four years weighed heavily. Tired as he was, the pleasure of a good night's rest was denied him. Adding to his uneasiness, disquieting political news arrived from home. The Reformers' "Cede and Protect" treaty with the United States had brought threatening protests from London, Paris, Berlin, and Tokyo. His Great and Good Friend, Emperor Mutsuhito dispatched a warship to Honolulu to protest the "cession," saying that Japan would not countenance having the United States occupy a kingdom within her own sphere of influence. Further, Foreign Minister Count Okuma threatened to withdraw his thousands of plantation laborers.

But worse than these diplomatic complications, the revered kahuna, Maria Alapai, sent news that the fiery fountains of Pele in Halemaumau, within Kilauea Crater, were boiling furiously and that red fish had been washed ashore in Kau, the ancestral home of Kalakaua.

At that news the King could not close his eyes for two nights. Even the solace of alcohol was denied him; he only sickened. Despite his distance from Hawaii, he had not outrun his gods. The worried King left for Tiajuana, Mexico. Before retiring in his private railway coach—provided by the Southern Pacific—he instructed his liaison officer to call him at half past seven; he wished to investigate some orange lands near Los Angeles.

Promptly at that hour the lieutenant entered the coach. "Good morning, Your Majesty," he called cheerily. Then he stopped. Kalakaua was sitting on his bed, slack-jawed, glassy-eyed, clad in his underwear.

The lieutenant thought that King Kalakaua was drunk. Knowing that he relished a pre-breakfast cigar, the lieutenant handed him one, which Kalakaua put in his mouth. But after it had been lighted the King could not keep it going. Alarmed, the officer tried to walk the King up and down, holding tightly to Kalakaua's left arm. But the monarch's weight was too much to bear; he sagged and dragged his right foot. The lieutenant settled the King in a chair and, tucking a blanket about him, hurried to the conductor, who ordered the King's coach detached and sent back to San Francisco.

In a semi-coma the stricken King was carried to the Palace Hotel. As he floated in a vague sea of consciousness, voices began to penetrate. A woman near by was pleading: "Please, I must see my King before he dies."

A man's deep tone broke in, "Hell, why not let the old bag take a gander at His Nibs. She's been going on about dancing at his christening, and seeing rivers of boiling lava . . ." It was the *Examiner* reporter assigned to the King's death watch. With him was Louis Glass, of the Edison Phonograph Company. Before starting for Tiajuana the King had promised Glass to make a wax recording to endorse the Edison Phonograph.

For a moment the woman was silent, and Kalakaua recognized Claus Spreckels, Charles Bishop, and Admiral Brown. Bishop had arrived the day before. From his bed the King followed a chant, the Litany of the dying, intoned by the Reverend J. Saunders Reed of the Protestant Episcopal Church.

. . . "from all evil, from all sin, from all tribulation, Good Lord deliver him!"

The woman's cry broke out anew, "I must see my King. There are red fish in the harbor . . ."

"Bring her to me," gasped Kalakaua. Bishop opened the

door and she ran to the King's bed and slipped to her knees. She was old and toothless, but although her clothes were shabby she had a fresh, yellow lei, for royalty, entwined in her scant grey hair.

"Aloha," welcomed the King, putting a hand, clammy with perspiration, on her head.

She began to sob.

As his vision cleared Kalakaua recognized her and whispered, "Leilani!" He had seen her last forty years before, leaving for the "Kaliponi" gold fields. She was "Cape Horn."

"Leilani," said the King feebly, "I greet you with love . . ."

"I want to go back to my land, my native land," she sobbed. . . .

"may it please Thee, mercifully, to pardon all his sins,"

chanted the Rev. Reed.

Kalakaua beckoned to Bishop. "Give her my purse." He fumbled with his left hand for the key suspended on a chain tight about his swollen neck. "For Kapiolani—for my crown . . . I—will never go back. But I can send my voice. Where is the machine that talks?"

Bishop hurried to bring in Louis Glass. As Glass held the mouthpiece in position Bishop and Leilani gently supported the King.

"Aloha kaua!" the King spoke with great effort . . . "we greet each other . . . *ke hoi nei no paha* . . . now go to Hawaii, to Honolulu and tell my people what you heard me say here . . ." His lips moved—"tell my people I tried to restore our gods, our way of life . . ." his voice failed and he fell back. He beckoned Cape Horn to come nearer. She stretched out beside him, giving the King the warmth of her body, while the visitors, embarrassed, turned away. Aware

that he was dying, Kalakaua tried to turn still closer to Leilani, to give her his *mana*, so that his spirit might not wander
but live on in a Hawaiian. But it was too late, he had no
strength and, sighing, with his spirit unreleased, King David
Kalakaua sank back and died.

EPILOGUE

Within a short time Princess Regent Liliuokalani became
Queen of Hawaii. But there was no peace in the Islands
and in less than two years she was driven from the throne.
Hawaii became a Republic. In 1898 it ceded its sovereignty
to the United States and in 1900 became a U.S. Territory.

In the hectic days that followed King Kalakaua's death his
crown was stolen and the jewels removed. But, recovered and
restored, the crown rests today in the Museum at Honolulu,
together with the wax recording made on his deathbed . . .
"Tell my people I tried. . . ."